Sour-Gas Design Considerations

Bruce D. Craig
Senior Consultant
Metallurgical Consultants Inc.

First Printing
Henry L. Doherty Memorial Fund of AIME
Society of Petroleum Engineers

Richardson, TX
1993

Dedication

To my friends and the men under my command in the Republic of Vietnam, 1971:
Life is never again so sweet or so terrible.

ISBN 1-55563-044-8

Acknowledgments

Many people deserve recognition for their assistance and encouragement during the preparation of this monograph. First, the original idea for this monograph was from Glenn A. Taylor Jr. of Exxon Co. U.S.A. who, along with my wife and the SPE Continuing Education Committee, asked that I prepare an SPE course on sour-gas design considerations. Preston L. Meeks of Conoco Inc. continued in Glenn's place and encouraged the course development until it came to fruition. The Sour-Gas Design—Material and Corrosion Considerations course has been presented several times in the Middle East and the U.S., and the notes for this course and students' input formed the basis for this monograph. I express my gratitude to my wife, Deann; Glenn Taylor; Preston Meeks; and the numerous students who made this monograph possible.

The Monograph Review Committee for this manuscript gave invaluable input and it is with appreciation that I recognize the effort of each member: Glenn M. Armstrong, Engineering Design & Testing Corp., Houston; Richard A. Dawe, Dept. of Mineral Resources Engineering, Imperial C., London; Michael R. Milligan, Shell Canada Resources Ltd., Calgary; David Patrick, Arco Oil & Gas Co., Crane, TX; Morris C. Place, Shell Offshore Inc., New Orleans; and K. Van Gelder, Koninklijke/Shell E&P Laboratorium, Amsterdam. I also greatly appreciate the assistance of Sandra Lee who diligently prepared the manuscript, revision after revision after revision, and the tireless work of editing by Kim Herrick and Janice Leslie of SPE.

Last, but of course never least, the editor of this monograph, Glenn P. Coker of Amoco Corp., has been the moderator, friend, and wise counsel who kept this monograph on track.

Bruce D. Craig

SPE Monograph Series

The Monograph Series of the Society of Petroleum Engineers was established in 1965 by action of the SPE Board of Directors. The series is intended to provide authoritative, up-to-date treatment of the fundamental principles and state of the art in selected fields of technology. The Series is directed by the Society's Monograph Committee. A committee member designated as Monograph Editor provides technical evaluation with the aid of the Review Committee. Below is a listing of those who have been most closely involved with the preparation of this monograph.

Monograph Review Committee

Glenn P. Coker, Amoco Corp., Monograph Editor
Glenn M. Armstrong, Engineering Design & Testing Corp.
Richard A. Dawe, Imperial C.
Michael R. Milligan, Shell Canada Resources Ltd.
David Patrick, Arco Oil & Gas Co.
Morris C. Place, Shell Offshore Inc.
K. Van Gelder, Koninklijke/Shell E&P Laboratorium

Monograph Committee (1992)

David R. Underdown, Arco Oil & Gas Co., Chairman
Peter G. Christman, Shell Development Co.
Satish K. Kalra, BJ Services
Medhat M. Kamal, Arco Oil & Gas Co.
Charles E. Konen, Consultant
Sammi H. Raza, Saudi Arabian Oil Co.

Contents

Chapter 1
Introduction

From the hydrogen sulfide (H_2S) evolved from decaying matter (e.g., rotten eggs) to the tarnish on silverware, the presence of sour gas has been a nuisance for centuries. However, it was not until the early 1950's that sour gas became a significant safety hazard. At that time, the petroleum industry began to explore and develop the Pincher Creek and Jumping Pound fields in Alberta, Canada, the McKamie-Patton field in Arkansas, and the Lacq Supérieur field in France,[1] all of which contained significant quantities of H_2S. Premature failures resulting from sulfide stress cracking (SSC) of downhole tubulars in wells in these fields caused concern in the petroleum industry. This concern led to the Natl. Assn. of Corrosion Engineers (NACE) Symposium on Sulfide Stress Corrosion in 1952.[2] SSC is a special case of hydrogen stress cracking that is referred to by many names in the literature (e.g., hydrogen embrittlement, delayed cracking, static fatigue, H_2S stress corrosion cracking, and sulfide stress corrosion cracking). In this monograph, the term SSC will be used for consistency.

As the 1950's progressed, additional exploration resulted in materials problems in sour environments encountered in the Brown-Bassett field in Texas and the Smackover formation of Texas, Louisiana, Mississippi, Alabama, and Florida.

In 1974, Tuttle[3] presented a list of documented failures resulting from SSC. The list is not all-inclusive and more failures have occurred since 1974; however, this list (**Table 1.1**) does describe the scope of the problem and the wide range of alloys that are susceptible to SSC.

In 1966, NACE published a work[4] specific to the selection of materials for oil and gas valves in production and pipeline service that were resistant to SSC. In 1975, this and a second publication[5] were combined to produce NACE *Standard MR-01-75.*[6] The new standard, however, was not comprehensive.

When a serious accident with H_2S caused death in west Texas, the Railroad Commission of Texas (RCT) required that all oil companies conform to NACE *Standard MR-01-75* under RCT Rule 36,[7] enacted as a state law effective March 15, 1976. This action led to a special meeting of industry experts in April 1976 to revise and update the standard completely. The document as it exists today is similar to that produced in this exemplary session, with continual updating done by NACE Committee T-1F-1. Yet, even with the more comprehensive standard and more cautious design procedures, sour gas continues to cause casualties and property damage around the world. The principal reasons for these problems are unfamiliarity with the large knowledge base on sour gas, nonconformance to NACE *Standard MR-01-75,* and corrosion from H_2S.

The primary purpose of this monograph is to inform those who design and operate sour-gas systems about the important considerations for materials and factors that affect SSC and corrosion. Second, this monograph is intended to assemble in one volume pertinent data that describe the effect sour gas has on materials. Most of these data are scattered throughout the literature. While the monograph emphasizes materials behavior and corrosion, it includes other basic information on safety in H_2S environments and analysis techniques for sour gas. The highly toxic nature of H_2S cannot be overemphasized and must be kept in mind when considering the risk of any design intended to handle sour gas. Therefore, the reader must be aware of recommended safety procedures and equipment that should be incorporated into the design and operation of sour-gas facilities. If informed, prudent decisions are made during design and operation, then essentially trouble-free service can be expected in sour-gas systems.

This monograph does not provide a step-by-step approach to designing a sour-gas system. No such procedure exists, mainly because the area of corrosion and materials selection in sour-gas service is so complex. Instead, this monograph presents data that are considered to be important and necessary to those making decisions for the design and operation of sour-gas systems. Even after following all recommendations and guidelines presented, however, some degree of risk exists. Materials behavior in sour-gas systems is an evolving technology that occasionally displays exceptions to expected behavior; therefore, absolute guarantees are not possible.

The remainder of the monograph is presented in five chapters. Chapter 2 presents basic information on the definition of sour gas and the properties of some important sulfur compounds. Analytical methods to determine H_2S concentration, safety procedures, and equipment are discussed. The reader needs to become familiar with these considerations because the entire purpose of designing sour-gas systems is the safe containment and transport of a toxic gas.

Chapter 3 briefly presents the fundamentals of metallurgy and corrosion relative to sour gas to assist the reader in understanding the requirements for certain materials and the restrictions on others.

Chapters 4 through 6 discuss the materials concerns and considerations necessary when drilling, producing, and operating surface equipment in sour-gas environments.

References

1. Garwood, G.L.: ''Material Selection for Downhole and Surface Equipment for Sour Gas Condensate Wells,'' paper 53 presented at the 1973 NACE Corrosion/73, Anaheim, CA.

TABLE 1.1—SSC FAILURES (After Ref. 3, courtesy of NACE)

Description	Material	Heat Treatment	Hardness in Fracture Area (HRC)	Phase	Environment H_2S Content (%)	Location	Year
Carbon and low-alloy steels							
Casing	API Grade N-80			Condensate and gas	10	Ginger, TX	1951
Tubing	9 Ni tubing	Normalized and tempered		Gas	75	Pincher Creek, Canada	1951
Tubing	9 Ni tubing			Gas		McKamie-Patton field, AK	1951
Tubing	9 Ni tubing			Gas	7.5	McKamie-Patton field, AK	1951
Casing	API Grade N-80			Gas	3.5	Jumping Pound, Canada	1952
Tubing coupling	API Grade N-80		51	Gas	3.5	Jumping Pound, Canada	1954
Tubing coupling	API Grade N-80			Gas	>10	Okotoks, Canada	1958
Casing	API Grade N-80		25	Gas	Trace	Paloma field, CA	1956
Casing collars	API Grade N-80			Gas	>10	Okotoks, Canada	1958
Tubing upset	API Grade N-80	Not normalized	25 to 39	Gas	70	Panther River, Canada	1964
Tubing	API Grade C-75	Normalized and tempered	26 to 30*	Gas	70	Panther River, Canada	1966
Casing collars	Soo 95	Normalized and tempered	>25	Gas		South Texas	1966
Tubing	API Grade C-75	Normalized and tempered	28 to 42**	Sour crude		Goodwater field, MS	1970
Tubing	API Grade C-75	Normalized and tempered	22 to 24†	Sour crude		Pachuta Creek, MS	1970
Compressor valve springs	AISI 6150		38			Not reported	1968
Valve manifold	Free-machining steel‡		HB 156	Gas	>10	Wildcat Hills, Canada	1962
Retainer rings, wellhead tubing hanger			51			Canada	1962
Blowout preventer, Capstan screws	AISI 4140		41 to 43	Low temperature Brittle failure		Canada	1961
Sphere bolts	AISI 4140	Quenched and tempered	30 to 40	Condensate and gas	>10	Waterton, Canada	1961
Christmas tree caps	AISI 4340	Cast and normalized	27 to 30	Condensate and gas	>10	Waterton, Canada	1962
DF tubing hanger			26 to 29	Condensate and gas	>10	Waterton, Canada	1962
Tool-joint pin, drillpipe	Grade E		34 to 35	Gas and mud		Waterton, Canada	1963
Tool joints	Grade E AISI 4135			Gas	70	Panther River, Canada	1968
Drillpipe	S-135		36 to 37	Gas and mud	>10	Jonathan area, MS	1970
Sucker rods			23 to 25.5	Sour water			
Liquified-petroleum-gas tanks, weld area	Mild steel			LPG	Trace	Japan	1959
Compressor impeller	Low-alloy	Quenched and tempered§				Hydrotreating service, Canada	1968
Valve bonnet	Free-machining steel	Cold-finished	HB 174	Condensate and gas	10	Waterton, Canada	1963
Martensitic stainless and chromium steels							
Valve plug	AISI 410	Forged and heat-treated	27	Condensate and gas	42	Ginger, TX	1951
Valve body	AISI 410	Seat-flame-hardened	Core 25 to 27	Condensate and gas	42	Ginger, TX	1951
Gate-valve spring	AISI 410	Quenched and tempered		Gas	>10	Jumping Pound, Canada	1953
Gas-lift valve latch	AISI 403 or 410		38	Gas	>10	Burnt Timber, Canada	1961
Level lock arm and pin	AISI 410	Weld material (pin to arm)	Pin 32 Arm 35				1959
Dummy valve	AISI 410		38	Condensate and gas	>10	Waterton, Canada	1962
Wireline lubricator	9 Cr-1 Mo		32 to 43	Gas	15	Germany	1968
Austenitic stainless steel							
Latch spring	AISI 304	Cold-worked	47	Gas	>10	Burnt Timber, Canada	1962
Wireline	AISI 304			Gas		Carbondale, Canada	1967
Choke plug and stem	AISI 316			Condensate and gas	>10	Waterton, Canada	1962
Precipitation-hardened stainless steel							
S-1 plug	17-4 PH	H-950 age	39	Gas	>10	Wildcat Hills, Canada	1962
Plug	17-4 PH					Canada	1962
Nonferrous alloys							
Tubing hanger	Inconel™ X-750	Forged and heat-treated	32 to 35	Gas	35	Glenpool, MS	1972
Valve stem	Monel™ K-500	Hot-rolled and age-hardened	27 to 34.5	Gas	35	Thomasville, MS	1972

HRC = Rockwell C hardness *Mn-rich bands. **Cold-rotary straightened. †Microhardness of 41 in tong marks. ‡S = 0.28% and P = 0.08%. §114,000-psi yield.

2. "Symposium on Sulfide Stress Corrosion," *Corrosion* (1952) 8-1–8.
3. Tuttle, R.N.: "Deep Drilling—A Materials Engineering Challenge," *Materials Performance* (1974) **13,** 42–45.
4. *Sulfide Cracking Resistant Metallic Materials for Valves for Production and Pipeline Service,* Publication 1F166, NACE, Houston (1966).
5. *Recommendations of Materials for Sour Service,* Publication 1B163, NACE, Houston (1963).
6. *Standard MR-01-75, Metallurgy of Oil Field Equipment for Resistance to Sulfide Stress Cracking,* NACE, Houston (1975).
7. "Rule 36: Oil, Gas, or Geothermal Resource Operation in Hydrogen Sulfide Areas," *Statewide Rules for Oil, Gas and Geothermal Operations,* Oil & Gas Div., Railroad Commission of Texas, Austin (June 1991) 106–20.

SI Metric Conversion Factor

psi × 6.894 757 E+00 = kPa

Chapter 2
Definition, Test Methods, Safety, and Properties of Sour Gas

2.1 Introduction

The presence of sour gas in a reservoir has several possible sources. New production containing H_2S is often attributed to the decay of organic matter originally associated with the source material of the oil and gas present in the reservoir. The souring of reservoirs that were originally sweet is attributed to the presence of sulfate-reducing bacteria,[1] introduced into the reservoir while drilling or during water injection for waterflooding, or to the nonoxidative dissolution of mineral sulfides.[2] Regardless of which mechanism produces H_2S and sulfur compounds in the reservoir, the drilling, production, and handling of gas containing H_2S is the emphasis of this monograph.

Although much has been written about sour gas and its effect on personnel, materials, and the environment, a standard definition for sour gas or a specific concentration for H_2S that qualifies a gas as sour does not exist. The American Petroleum Inst. (API) does not specifically define sour gas but implies that gas containing any H_2S is sour. API *RP 49*[3] suggests guidelines to apply when an atmospheric concentration of H_2S gas$>$20 ppm (0.002 vol%) is encountered in the work area. This amount is a ceiling, not a permissible exposure for an 8-hour time-weighted average. Canada maintains the same 20-ppm ceiling. In the U.S. and Canada, the acceptable upper-limit concentration for an 8-hour exposure to humans is 10 ppm. As discussed in a later section, the Natl. Assn. of Corrosion Engineers (NACE) defines sour gas from a materials standpoint as an H_2S partial pressure of 0.05 psia [0.34 kPa] or greater. If sour gas is vented into the atmosphere or burned in a flare to produce SO_2, U.S. state or federal Environmental Protection Agency regulations may dictate what constitutes sour gas. *The Gas Engineers Handbook*[4] defines sour gas as having an H_2S content $>$1.5 grains/100 ft^3 [$>$1.5 grains/2.8 m^3] or a total sulfur content of 30 grains/100 ft^3 [30 grains/2.8 m^3]. At standard temperature and pressure, 1 grain H_2S=16.5 ppm.

In general, sour gas can be defined as any gas that contains measurable sulfur-bearing compounds of which H_2S is the primary constituent. While there are a multitude of other sulfur-bearing compounds, only a few, such as mercaptans, carbonyl sulfide (COS), carbon disulfide (CS_2), and occasionally elemental sulfur occur in natural gas streams. Sometimes, sulfur is produced as a solid and its presence may create significant plugging and corrosion problems in gas production and transportation.

The specific quantity of H_2S that imparts sour characteristics to a gas depends on whether one is concerned with materials, safety, or the environment.

2.2 Properties of Components

To understand the effect that sulfur compounds have on materials, safety, and the environment, we must examine the properties of the compounds and their respective acceptable concentrations. In addition to sulfur compounds, data on CO_2 are incorporated because this acid gas is often produced in sour-gas streams and can significantly increase the corrosivity.

Table 2.1 lists various sour-gas components and some of their properties. Table 2.1, however, is not a complete list of all organic and inorganic sulfur compounds that may be produced with natural gas. Because the chemistry of sulfur and its derivatives is quite complex, the reader is referred elsewhere[5,6] for more information on this subject. The compounds listed in Table 2.1 are representative of components often detected in gas wells and are pertinent to discussions in this monograph. Note that all the gases are heavier than air and as such will tend to accumulate along the ground or in low-lying areas. Moreover, H_2S is quite toxic, causing death in a short time at low concentrations. In fact, H_2S is one of the most toxic gases known to man.

Table 2.2 presents the toxicological ramifications of H_2S exposure. Small concentrations of H_2S can be tolerated for long times; however, above 100 ppm, the sense of smell rapidly becomes impaired and the inability to smell, or otherwise know, that H_2S is present can result in serious illness or death. COS and CO_2 are odorless but also are not as toxic as H_2S or SO_2. The mercaptans, of which there are numerous types, have a pungent smell even in trace amounts. Ethyl mercaptan is often used to odorize natural gas for commercial use.

The threshold limits presented in Table 2.1 are the maximum atmospheric concentrations of gases that can be tolerated by a worker for an indefinite period of time without adverse effects. These levels are quite low and generally are not encountered. In sour-oil and -gas operations, it is more common to be exposed to low amounts (1 to 5 ppm) of H_2S that breaks out of a drilling mud or produced water. At the other extreme, doses $>$50 ppm may be encountered when drilling or producing sour gas.

For the myriad organic sulfur compounds that may be produced, it is generally found that the higher the molecular weight the less toxic the compound is to humans and the less aggressive toward materials. Compounds with higher molecular weights, however, may be more environmentally damaging.

Because some sulfur compounds are highly toxic at small concentrations, it is imperative that their concentrations be measured accurately. Numerous methods exist for these analyses, some quite sophisticated and others just simple indicators. The methods used most frequently in the oil field are discussed.

TABLE 2.1—IMPORTANT COMPOUNDS AND THEIR PROPERTIES AT STANDARD TEMPERATURE AND PRESSURE

Compound	Chemical Formula	Specific Gravity	Threshold* Limit (ppm)	Lethal** Concentration	Explosive Flammability Limit (vol% in air)	Water Solubility at 77°F (gas volume/volume water)
Air	N_2/O_2	1.00	—	—	—	177 ft^3/ft^3
Carbon dioxide	CO_2	1.52	5,000	10%	—	0.73 ft^3/ft^3
Hydrogen sulfide	H_2S	1.18	10	600 ppm	4.3 to 46.0	2.3 ft^3/ft^3
Sulfur dioxide	SO_2	2.26	5	1,000 ppm	—	31.21 ft^3/ft^3
Methyl mercaptan (methanethiol)	CH_3SH	1.66	0.5	NA	NA	2.4 g/100 g†
Ethyl mercaptan	C_2H_5SH	NA	0.5	NA	NA	NA
Butyl mercaptan	C_4H_9SH	NA	0.5	NA	NA	NA
Carbonyl sulfide	COS	2.1	NA	1,200 ppm	11.9 to 28.5	0.8 mL/mL H_2O‡
Elemental sulfur	S	2.0§	—	—	—	Insoluble

NA = not available.
*Threshold = continuous exposure level with no adverse effects.
**Lethal = will cause death with short-term exposure.
†At 59°F.
‡At 56°F.
§Compared with water.

2.3 Determination (Analytical Methods)

Because H_2S is considered to be the primary constitutent of sour gas, it is the principal component detected by various analytical methods. Analysis for H_2S depends on whether it is being measured in the liquid or gas phase. Only analytical methods are presented here; H_2S detectors for safety around well and plant sites are discussed in Sec. 2.6.2.

One of the most common and accurate methods for determining the type and concentration of sulfur species is gas chromatography. In this method, gas is passed through an inert column from which components with the lowest molecular weights exit first, followed by increasingly heavier components. A flame photometric detector then analyzes each component as it comes off the column. **Fig. 2.1** shows a typical chromatograph of a low-sulfur-bearing natural gas.[7] Gas chromatography can detect a wide range of various compounds and measure their concentrations.

The sampling and transport of samples from the field can result in the loss of sulfur compounds by adsorption to the container walls and interaction of the various sulfur species to form other sulfur compounds not originally present in the gas when it was sampled. **Fig. 2.2** shows the results[7] of an experiment that began with the addition of 100 ppm of certain compounds. For example, methyl mercaptan was not present in the American Iron & Steel Inst. (AISI) 316 stainless-steel container at the start of the experiment but rapidly

TABLE 2.2—TOXICITY OF H_2S GAS FOR HUMANS

	Reaction to Duration of Exposure						
H_2S (ppm)	0 to 2 Minutes	2 to 15 Minutes	15 to 30 Minutes	30 Minutes to 1 Hour	1 to 4 Hours	4 to 8 Hours	>8 Hours
50 to 100				Mild irritation			
100 to 150		Coughing, eye irritation, loss of sense of smell	Disturbed respiration, pain in eyes, sleepiness	Throat irritation	Salivation and mucous discharge, sharp pain in eyes, coughing	Increased symptoms*	Hemorrhaging and death*
150 to 200		Loss of sense of smell	Throat and eye irritation	Throat and eye irritation	Difficult breathing, blurred vision	Serious irritating effects*	Hemorrhaging and death*
250 to 350		Eye irritation, loss of sense of smell	Eye irritation	Painful secretion of tears, weariness	Pain in eyes, difficult breathing	Hemorrhaging and death*	
350 to 450		Eye irritation, loss of sense of smell	Difficult respiration, coughing, eye irritation	Increased eye and nasal-tract irritation, dull headache	Dizziness, weakness, increased irritation, death	Death*	
500 to 600	Coughing, collapse, and unconsciousness*	Respiratory disturbances, eye irritation, collapse*	Serious eye irritation, heart palpitations, a few cases of death	Severe pain in eyes and head, dizziness, trembling of extremities, great weakness, death*			
600 to 1,500	Collapse,* unconsciousness, death	Collapse,* unconsciousness, death					

*Data secured from the Natl. Soc. Council (Data Sheet D-chem 16), which ran experiments on dogs. Dogs have a susceptibility to H_2S similar to humans.

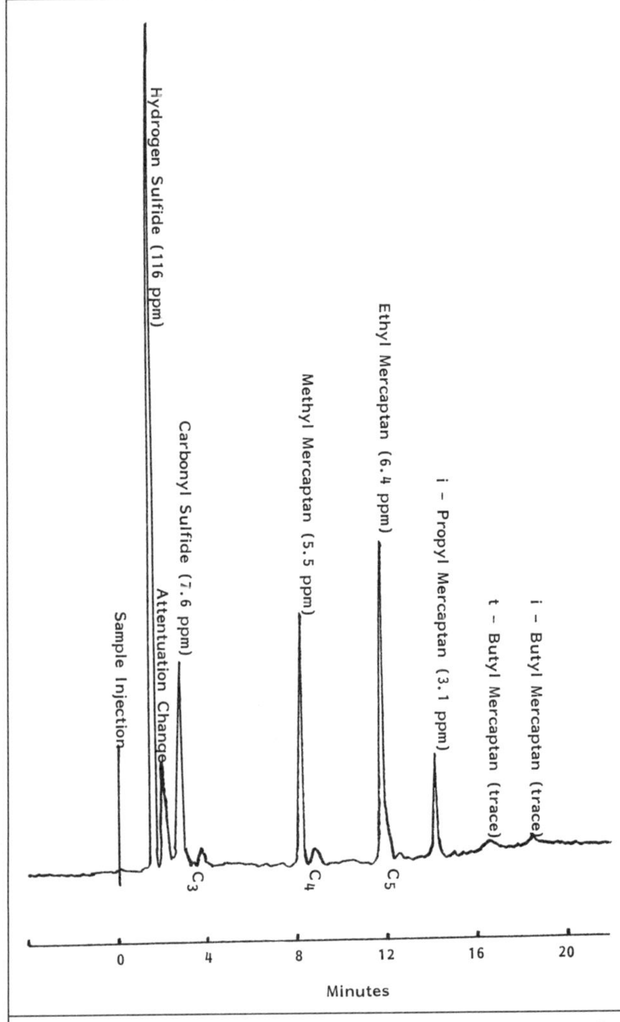

Fig. 2.1—Chromatograph of low-sulfur natural gas sample.[7]

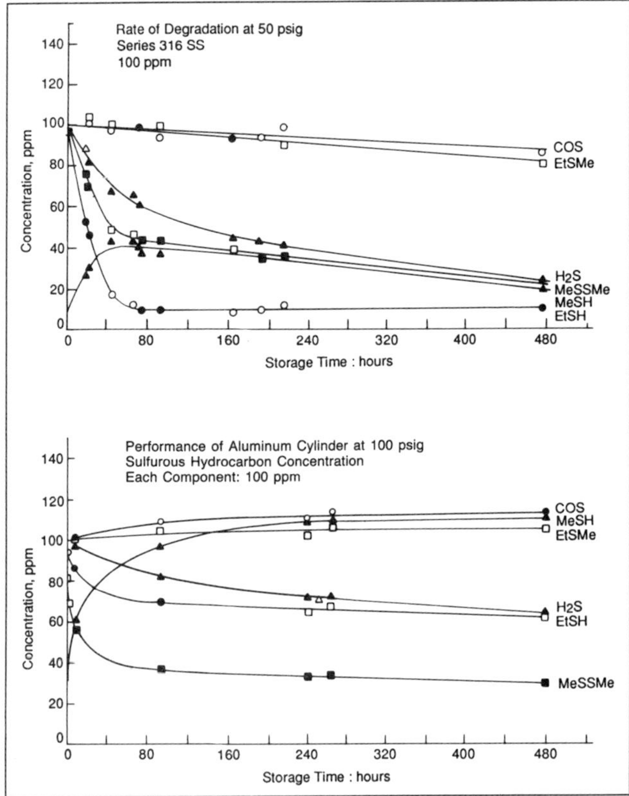

Fig. 2.2—Effect of container and storage time on sour-gas sampling. MeSSMe = dimethyldisulfide; MeSH = methyl mercaptan; EtSH = ethyl mercaptan; and EtSMe = methyl ethyl sulfide.[7]

formed at the expense of dimethyl disulfide. Several other compounds formed in the aluminum container. Thus, care in field sampling and expeditious analysis are of the utmost importance in obtaining valid sulfur-species concentrations and in determining the compounds actually present in the well.

Detector tubes or "sniffers" are also used to measure sour gas. **Fig. 2.3** shows the general appearance of such a tube, which such companies as Draeger and Gastec supply primarily for field use. The tube is packed with granules covered with a chemical indicator that reacts with H_2S. The two sealed ends are broken and a hand pump is attached to the high-concentration end. After pumping the gas into the low-concentration end with a prescribed number of strokes, the H_2S concentration is read directly from the tube as indicated by the color change. The American Soc. for Testing & Materials (ASTM) *D 4810-88*[8] gives the details for this test method. Although detector tubes are not as accurate as chromatography, they are much more convenient and portable. They are often used as a safety device to detect the presence of dangerous levels of H_2S at a specific location.

Sometimes it is necessary to measure the sulfur content of liquids, such as sulfides, in water or drilling mud. Simple colormetric kits are available for determining the sulfide or H_2S level in water, but these tests are not very accurate and are limited to $\leq 1,200$ ppm for sulfides in solution and ≤ 5 ppm for H_2S. Note, however, that the concentration of H_2S in the vapor phase over oil or water can be significantly higher (thousands of parts per million) than that dissolved in solution.

The Tutwiler method[9-11] is a much more accurate analysis that uses titration to determine sulfur compounds. This method is sensitive to ≥ 1.0 grain $H_2S/100$ ft^3 [≥ 1.0 grain $H_2S/2.8$ m^3] gas. (1 grain H_2S=16.5 ppm H_2S at 77°F [25°C] and 1 atm [101 kPa].) The gas sample is titrated with iodine in a starch solution until a blue color signals the endpoint.

API *RP 13B*[12] describes a standard method for determining sulfide in water-based drilling muds. This method, also known as the Garrett gas train, essentially uses CO_2 bubbled through a solution sample to drive H_2S into a detector tube for analysis.

Probably the least sophisticated method is the use of lead-acetate indicator paper. While not particularly quantitative, this method is sensitive and rapidly identifies the presence of H_2S. The rate at which the moist paper changes color to brown or black is a rough estimate of the H_2S concentration.

Although there are other methods for determining the concentration of H_2S, those above are the most commonly used in the petroleum industry. Once sour gas is encountered, its effect on both equipment and personnel is immediate. Thus, it is imperative that precautions and proper design be considered before possible exposure; otherwise, there may not be sufficient time to react.

2.4 Codes and Standards

In light of the toxicity, frequency of occurrence, and difficulties with handling sour gas, it is surprising that few industry codes and standards are available that specifically address H_2S.

The API deals with sour gas directly and indirectly in all its standards, depending on the specific application. No attempt is made here to detail all requirements regarding sour service. Instead, several representative specifications that deal with sour-service considerations in some depth will be discussed. Note, however, that API standards contain specific requirements for sour-gas-service design and materials specifications, and the trend is to incorporate stricter guidelines when specifications are revised or added. For example, the original API *Spec. 5AC*[13] for controlled yield-strength tubulars generally was intended to create a category of tubulars that had greater resistance to sulfide stress cracking (SSC) than those in API *Specs. 5A*[14] or *5AX*.[15] However, neither SSC behavior nor testing of these grades is specifically mentioned in API *Spec. 5AC*.

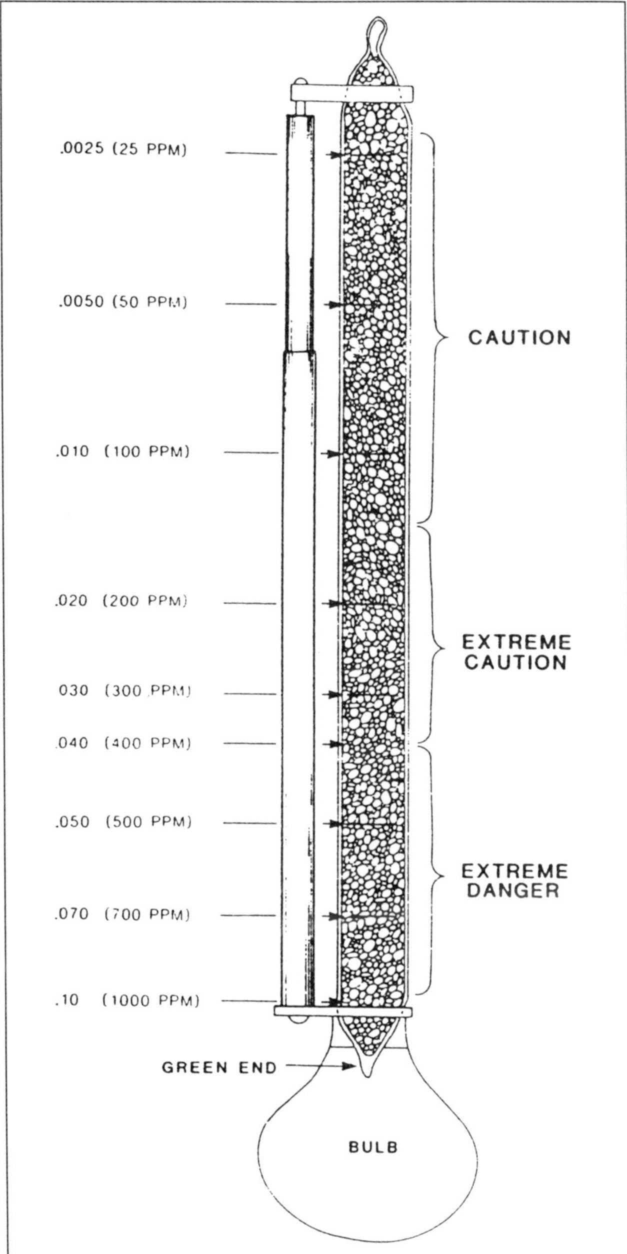

Fig. 2.3—Detector-tube analyzer for H_2S concentration.

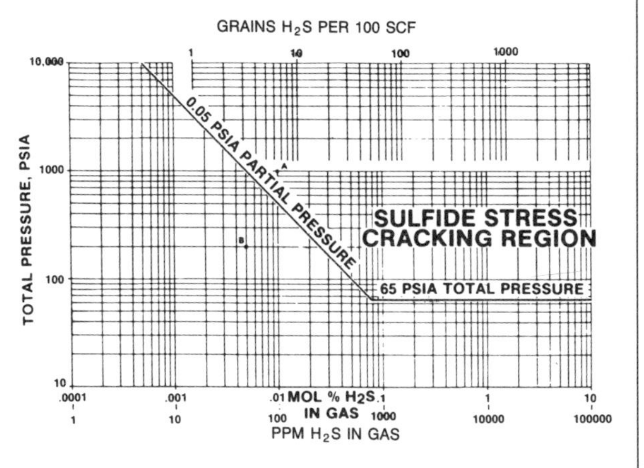

Fig. 2.4—Critical concentrations of H_2S and pressure for SSC in sour-gas systems.[19]

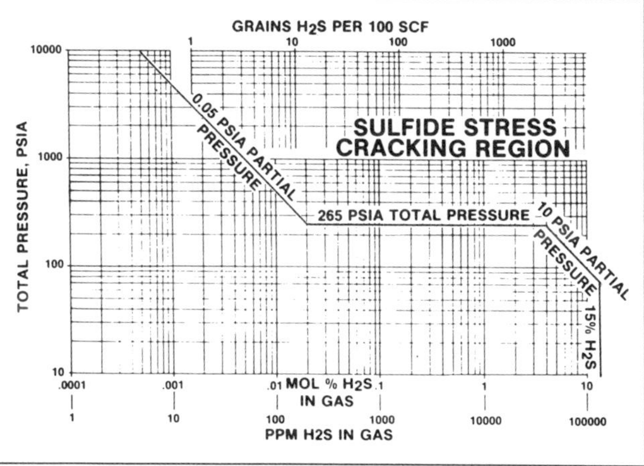

Fig. 2.5—Critical concentrations of H_2S and pressure for SSC in sour multiphase systems.[19]

The 1989 edition of API *Spec. 5CT*[16] combines API *Specs. 5A, 5AC,* and *5AX*. API *Spec. 5CT*, which includes tubular Grades C-90 and T-95, requires that these grades be qualified by NACE *Standard TM-01-77*[17] (Test Method 1), which is an SSC test, and sets a minimum acceptable threshold stress to be obtained for these grades in this test. Furthermore, hardness testing is required for each pipe length to ensure that it qualifies to Grades C-90 and T-95.

Likewise, previous versions of API *Spec. 6A*[18] for wellheads mention SSC and NACE *Standard MR-01-75*[19] but provide no specific requirements. With the advent of API *Spec. Q1*,[20] API *Spec. 6A* was completely revised to include Product Specification Levels (PSL's) 1 through 4, which consider the effects of H_2S, pressure, and location. The higher the PSL, the more comprehensive the requirements for quality assurance and control. The PSL recommended by API *Spec. 6A* for a certain application primarily is based on the H_2S level, but pressure and location are also considered.

Other API specifications, such as API *RP 7G*,[21] discuss the importance of SSC during drilling and suggest ways to prevent or reduce the potential for SSC. Finally, API *RP 49*[3] specifically deals with safe drilling of wells containing H_2S. API *RP 55*[22] details oil and gas production operations involving H_2S. Each applicable API specification should be consulted before designing for or operating in sour environments.

NACE *Standard MR-01-75* is the primary document for details about the application of materials in sour service from an SSC standpoint. This standard is referred to or invoked by numerous other codes and standards as the authoritative source on the use of materials in H_2S. NACE *Standard MR-01-75* lists the minimum requirements for metals in sour service and describes the conditions of pressure and H_2S content that may cause SSC of metallic materials (**Figs. 2.4 and 2.5**). Note, however, that NACE *Standard MR-01-75* does not address weight-loss corrosion from H_2S, stress corrosion cracking from other aggressive ions, quality control, or inspection requirements, all of which may be equally important in a decision regarding materials. Moreover, the general intent of NACE *Standard MR-01-75* is only applicable to materials behavior at room temperature. This document is being changed and updated constantly; therefore, it is always important to review a current edition of this or any other standard. Familiarity with NACE *Standard MR-01-75* is a must for those that expect to design and operate equipment in sour environments.

NACE *RP-0472-87*[23] is a recommended practice that is applied frequently in sour service but is not limited to H_2S environments. NACE *RP-0472-87* provides recommendations on the hardness of carbon-steel welds on equipment (such as pressure vessels, tanks, and drums) that is used in refining service to prevent cracking in aggressive environments. The *Boiler and Pressure Vessel Code*[24] does not specifically concern itself with environmental design factors; however, it is incumbent on the designer of pressure-containing equipment to appreciate the factors that govern the risk of SSC in high-pressure components in sour service and the means to mitigate the potential for catastrophic failures.

The Intl. Standards Organization (ISO) continues to produce standards in many areas in an effort to establish a complete set of international standards that are functional for all nations. While the ISO currently has no standards that either directly or indirectly address sour service, it is only a matter of time before such standards are developed and implemented.

2.5 Regulatory Agencies and Requirements

The regulatory aspects of drilling and producing sour gas involve many agencies at all government levels. A complete review of all regulatory requirements is beyond the scope of this monograph; however, the primary regulations and organizations responsible are presented. Suffice it to say, this is an ever-changing arena, and it is necessary to obtain details of government regulations for the particular area where sour gas will be drilled or produced.

2.5.1 U.S. Federal Agencies. The U.S. Occupational & Safety Health Admin. (OSHA) rules and regulations[25] set forth a maximum allowable human exposure of 10 ppm H_2S in air for an 8-hour workday. Of course, other, more stringent, state and local regulations may take precedence over this concentration limit.

Effective May 31, 1988, the U.S. Minerals Management Service rescinded Outer Continental Shelf (OCS) Orders 1 through 14 concerning oil, gas, and sulfur exploration, development, and production operations in the OCS to restructure and consolidate the rules into one convenient document.[26] This document is long and quite specific concerning drilling and operating in sour environments. Here, discussion is limited to Paragraph 250.67, "Hydrogen Sulfide," where zones known to contain H_2S are defined as any geologic formation where prior drilling, logging, coring, testing, or producing have confirmed that H_2S-bearing zones can potentially result in atmospheric concentrations of $H_2S \geq 20$ ppm. Ref. 26 gives additional definitions for zones where the absence of H_2S has been confirmed or where the presence of H_2S is unknown. The definitions are of the utmost importance to the applicability of the remainder of the regulation.

On Jan. 22, 1991, the U.S. Bureau of Land Management issued Onshore Oil and Gas Order 6, which identifies the necessary applications, approvals, and reports required to conduct H_2S operations. This order applies to all onshore federal and Indian (except the Osage tribe) oil and gas leases where H_2S is present or expected to be found in a concentration ≥ 100 ppm in the gas stream. The introduction of these regulations covering onshore and offshore operations will have far-reaching effects on the petroleum industry.

TABLE 2.3—STATE REQUIREMENTS FOR AMBIENT AIR-QUALITY STANDARDS FOR H_2S (1986)

State	Maximum Concentration (ppm)	Average Time (hours)
California	0.03	1
Connecticut	0.2	8
Kentucky	0.01	1
Massachusetts	0.014	24
Montana	0.03	0.5
Nevada	0.24	8
New York	0.1	1
Pennsylvania	0.1	1
Texas	0.08	0.5
Virginia	0.16	24

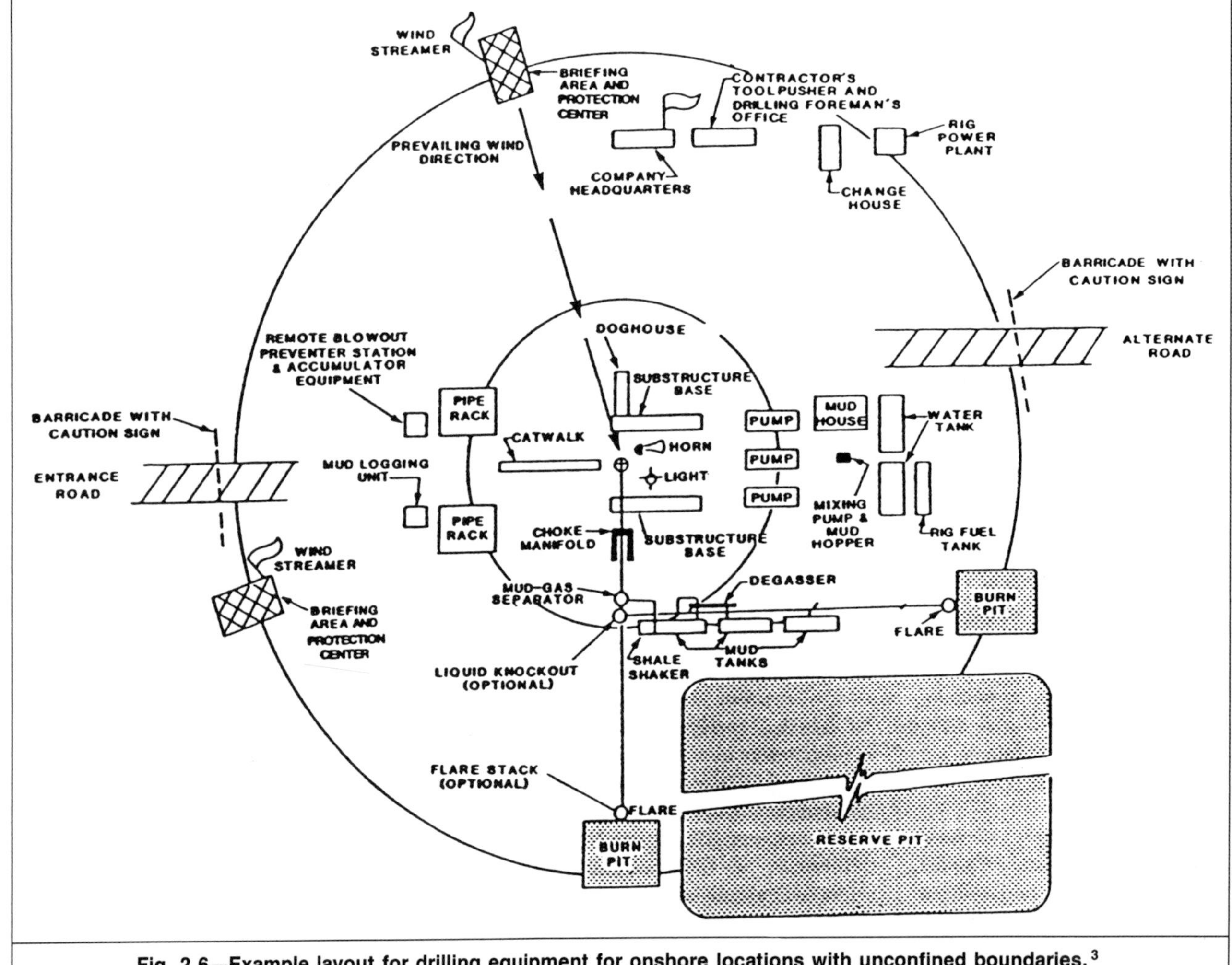

Fig. 2.6—Example layout for drilling equipment for onshore locations with unconfined boundaries.[3]

2.5.2 U.S. State and Local Agencies. Many states do not have regulations specific to sour-gas drilling and production but rather depend on federal requirements to dictate the need for regulation in this area. California and Texas, however, are quite active in developing regulations that govern H_2S in oil and gas operations.

The California Div. of Oil & Gas Publication M10[27] includes the stricter California/OSHA required limitation of 10 ppm H_2S exposure for an employee during an 8-hour workday. Ref. 27 also describes wellsite planning, safety, and materials considerations, much the same as API *RP 49* and the old OCS Order 1.

The Railroad Commission of Texas (RCT) Rule 36[28] regulates the drilling and production of wells containing H_2S in Texas. In Alabama, Rule 400-5 regulates the drilling and production of sour wells. These rules are applicable for operations where the concentration of H_2S is >100 ppm in the produced fluid. In addition to describing the necessary requirements for safety, security, and contingency planning, RCT Rule 36 invokes NACE *Standard MR-01-75* and API *RP 14E*[29] Secs. 1.7(c), 2.1(c), and 4.7 for materials considerations.

Table 2.3 presents some of the individual state requirements for ambient air-quality standards for H_2S over a certain time interval.

2.5.3 Canadian Regulations. In June 1987, the Alberta Energy Resources Conservation Board (AERCB) issued an interim directive[30] that addressed licensing and drilling of sour wells. Future directives will set requirements for completing, servicing, and producing critical sour wells. Additionally, the minimum separation distance for locating sour pipelines and associated facilities will be addressed. This directive defines a critical sour well (1) as a function of the H_2S release rate and the proximity to the corporate boundaries of an urban center, (2) any well for which the maximum potential H_2S release rate is ≥ 70.6 ft^3/sec [≥ 2 m^3/s], or (3) any well the AERCB classifies as a critical sour well.

2.6 Safety and Contingency Plans

Probably the most important considerations for sour-gas design are safety and contingency planning. If proper planning has not been instigated before drilling or operating in sour gas, serious safety problems can arise that will quickly become uncontrollable and catastrophic. API *RP 49* provides guidelines for safety and contingency planning.

In addition, there may be governmental rules and regulations covering safety, operation, and contingency plans for sour-gas drilling and production. Before drilling and producing, it is important to determine which agencies have jurisdiction and to establish the hierarchy of this jurisdiction. These rules must be observed at all times during sour-gas drilling and production.

2.6.1 Site Selection and Layout. Fig. 2.6 shows a typical layout for drilling equipment for onshore locations with unconfined boundaries.[3] Sites should be selected so that entrances can be barricaded if conditions so require, and auxiliary exits should be incorporated in case original exits are blocked or wind conditions prevent escape in that direction.

Prevailing wind data for specific sites should be obtained and used in site layouts so that protection centers and briefing areas are upwind or ≥ 200 ft [≥ 61 m] from the wellbore so that the prevailing winds are perpendicular to these areas. The drilling rig should be placed so that prevailing winds blow across the rig toward reserve pits. In anticipation of calm days, large blowers (bug blowers) or fans should be placed to blow across the cellar area toward the pits, across the rotary table, and at the shale shaker. The rig floor should be adequately ventilated by removing rig curtains and windbreakers.

H_2S training and safety drills should be conducted before drilling into suspect formations, if only to test detection and survival equipment and to train personnel.

A windsock should be on top the derrick and windstreamers set in at least three highly visible locations (e.g., entrances to the rig site and protection buildings) that are illuminated at night. Because crown wind direction is sometimes different from ground direction, personnel should be trained to observe wind direction frequently and to move in an upwind direction if H_2S is released.

Roadways and passageways should remain clear at all times for rapid evacuation and access to protective buildings and equipment. Furthermore, road access should be easy to barricade to prevent re-entry if an H_2S release occurs.

Controls to operate blowout preventer (BOP) equipment should be placed upwind a safe distance from the well. A backup or auxiliary closing system should be provided in case the primary system is inaccessible or fails.

At least two or three briefing areas should be ≥ 225 ft [≥ 69 m] from the BOP stack, upwind or perpendicular to the prevailing wind direction. Complete sets of self-contained breathing equipment should always be kept at each briefing area, and signs designating safe areas should be posted.

Flare lines should be installed from the degasser, choke manifold, and mud/gas separator to the flare stack. Two flare areas should be situated 90° from each other. The flare areas should be at least 150 ft [46 m] from the rig and other installations to protect workers during testing and trouble periods. The ground should be clear around flare areas to prevent brush and grass fires.

Flowlines and flare lines should be staked securely. Flowlines to flare areas should be as long (≥ 150 ft [≥ 46 m]) and as straight (free from 90° turns) as possible. After installation, flare lines should be tested with air, natural gas, or butane to ensure proper operation.

Every effort should be made to keep H_2S flare stacks lit at all times. This may be done with a propane pilot light. Special flare-gun shells are a relatively safe means of lighting a flare. A combustible gas indicator should be provided to identify the presence of an H_2S gas mixture. Note that the combustion product of H_2S is SO_2, which is also toxic.

Emergency relief valves and vent lines should be a safe distance from work areas. When venting into the atmosphere is unsafe, H_2S gas should be disposed of inside a closed system.

All lines, fittings, valves, etc., should be installed and maintained in a manner that eliminates all gas and oil leaks. All electrical wiring, devices, and lights should be explosion-proof to reduce the possibility of explosions.

The use of ground-level tank gauges, automatic custody-transfer units, and vapor-recovery systems reduces the exposure of personnel to H_2S gas.

For confined boundary locations, such as marine, urban, and mountainous areas, the same general considerations as for unconfined areas are necessary. Note, however, that less reaction time is usually available in smaller areas. **Fig. 2.7** shows a typical layout for a confined location.[3,26] More warning flags, signs, and streamers are needed to maintain visibility and consciousness of wind direction in confined areas. Additional fans or blowers may also be necessary to reduce the risk of exposure.

2.6.2 H_2S Detection. Several methods of H_2S detection were described in Sec. 2.3. However, the most common for field use are reiterated here.

Quantitative, electronic, H_2S monitors are available and recommended for permanent 24-hour operation in fixed locations. They are also required by some legislation. Monitors have 1 to 12 attached detection sensors that are positioned around the rig floor and mud pits. Each monitor also has a needle indicator that gives a continuous readout of H_2S concentration in parts per million. Systems are usually equipped with strobe lights that activate at a certain gas concentration and audible alarms that automatically sound when higher H_2S concentrations are present. Monitors must be calibrated and checked periodically to ensure that they are functioning properly.

The paper used in paper-type H_2S detectors has been impregnated with lead acetate that, when exposed to H_2S, forms lead sulfide. Lead sulfide darkens the paper to shades of brown that depend on the H_2S concentration. This method provides the easiest, most convenient means for workers to wear a detection device like a badge. The 3 to 5 minutes required to record a reaction on a paper detector, however, is a dangerous time lapse when large concentrations of H_2S are encountered. Therefore, paper detectors are used to indicate only when H_2S is present and not its concentration, even though the detector has an approximate range of 0 to 20 ppm H_2S.

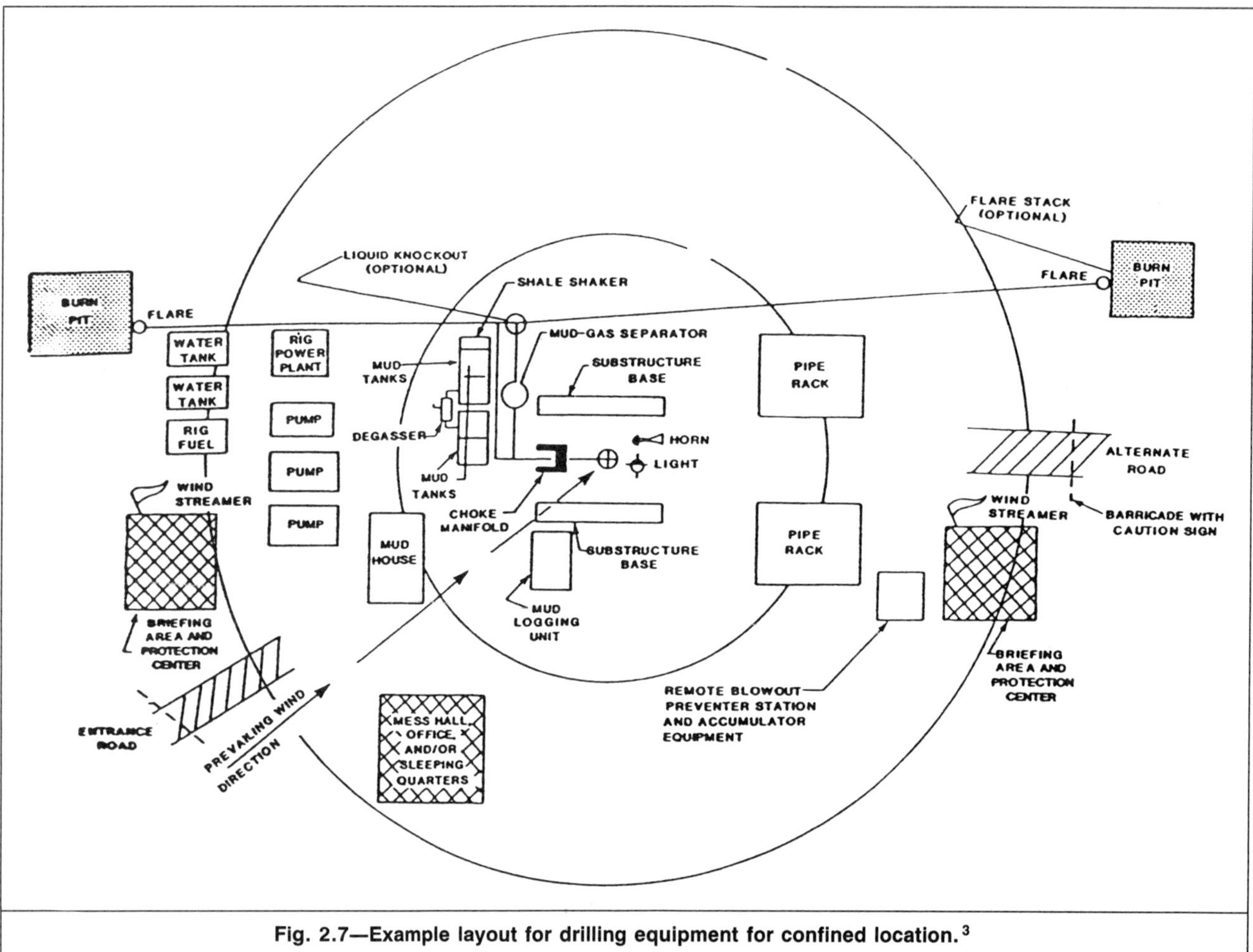

Fig. 2.7—Example layout for drilling equipment for confined location.[3]

A capsule detector is a granule-filled glass covered with a nylon sheath. The capsule is broken and attached to clothing with a string. When H_2S contacts the granules, they turn brown. This detector indicates the presence of H_2S up to a maximum concentration of 20 ppm. The useful life is 6 days.

Paper and capsule detectors should not be relied on for H_2S detection while drilling. Detector tubes, discussed earlier, are widely used for H_2S measurement and detection.

The belt-attached H_2S detector is a battery-operated electronic device with an audible alarm. The detector has a sensor head that will detect H_2S gas and measure concentrations between 0 and 50 ppm. The detector is usually preset to respond at 10 ppm; response time is about 35 seconds. This detector must be calibrated and checked periodically to ensure that it is functioning properly.

2.6.3 Radius of Exposure. Whether for drilling or producing environments, the potential well-area toxicity from H_2S must be known for planning. Other potential sources for H_2S release that must be considered are treating, processing, and storage facilities. The most stringent safety precautions must be taken in the areas of highest H_2S concentration.

The Pasquill-Gifford equations are used to calculate the radius of exposure. The equations for 100-, 300-, and 500-ppm radii of exposure are

$$r=(1.589 f_{H_2S} V)^{0.6258}, \quad \text{(2.1)}$$

$$r=(1.0218 f_{H_2S} V)^{0.6258}, \quad \text{(2.2)}$$

and $r=(0.4546 f_{H_2S} V)^{0.6258}$, ... (2.3)

respectively, where r=radius of exposure (ft [m]), V=maximum volume of gas that can escape (ft^3/D [m^3/d]), and f_{H_2S}=mole fraction of H_2S in the gas. **Figs. 2.8 and 2.9** show nomographs for 100- and 300-ppm H_2S radii of exposure.[27]

2.6.4 Safety Equipment. Air breathing equipment ranges from short-term escape units to long-term work types. Both types must be available at predetermined locations at the drillsite and in standby vessels offshore or company and contractor vehicles onshore.

Protective breathing apparatus should be stored in areas where they are quickly and easily available to all personnel. Such equipment should be located on the rig floor; in any working areas above the rig floor; at the mud-logging facility; in the shale-shaker, mud pit, mud storage, and briefing areas; in mud and cement pump rooms; in crew quarters; at heliports; and on standby vessels and company and contractor vehicles. **Table 2.4** provides guidelines[31] for selecting respirators, and Refs. 32 and 33 provide regulations on the selection, type, use, and maintenance of respirators. Two basic types of self-contained breathing apparatus exist.

1. Positive-pressure, fresh-air, breathing equipment that provides protection in any atmospheric H_2S concentration. This equipment has an alarm that signals when the breathing air supply is getting low; reserve air bottles are available.

2. Chemical units that convert exhaled breath (CO_2) into oxygen. These units are relatively light and can be used with a minimum of restriction on the wearer. An alarm system signals when the chemical supply is getting low; replaceable chemical canisters are available.

A regulator is that part of the respirator that reduces air pressure from the tank pressure to nearly atmospheric pressure. There are two types: the pressure-demand mode in which the wearer draws the air into the mask under slight vacuum and the positive-pressure mode in which the regulator allows a slight pressure buildup in the mask. The main difference between the two is that, if a leak occurs in the respirator or mask, the pressure-demand type leaks the atmosphere inward and the positive-pressure type leaks air outward. The latter is preferred to avoid contaminants being drawn into the mask; thus, it is required for use in atmospheres where the tolerance limit value for H_2S concentration is exceeded. Some units are

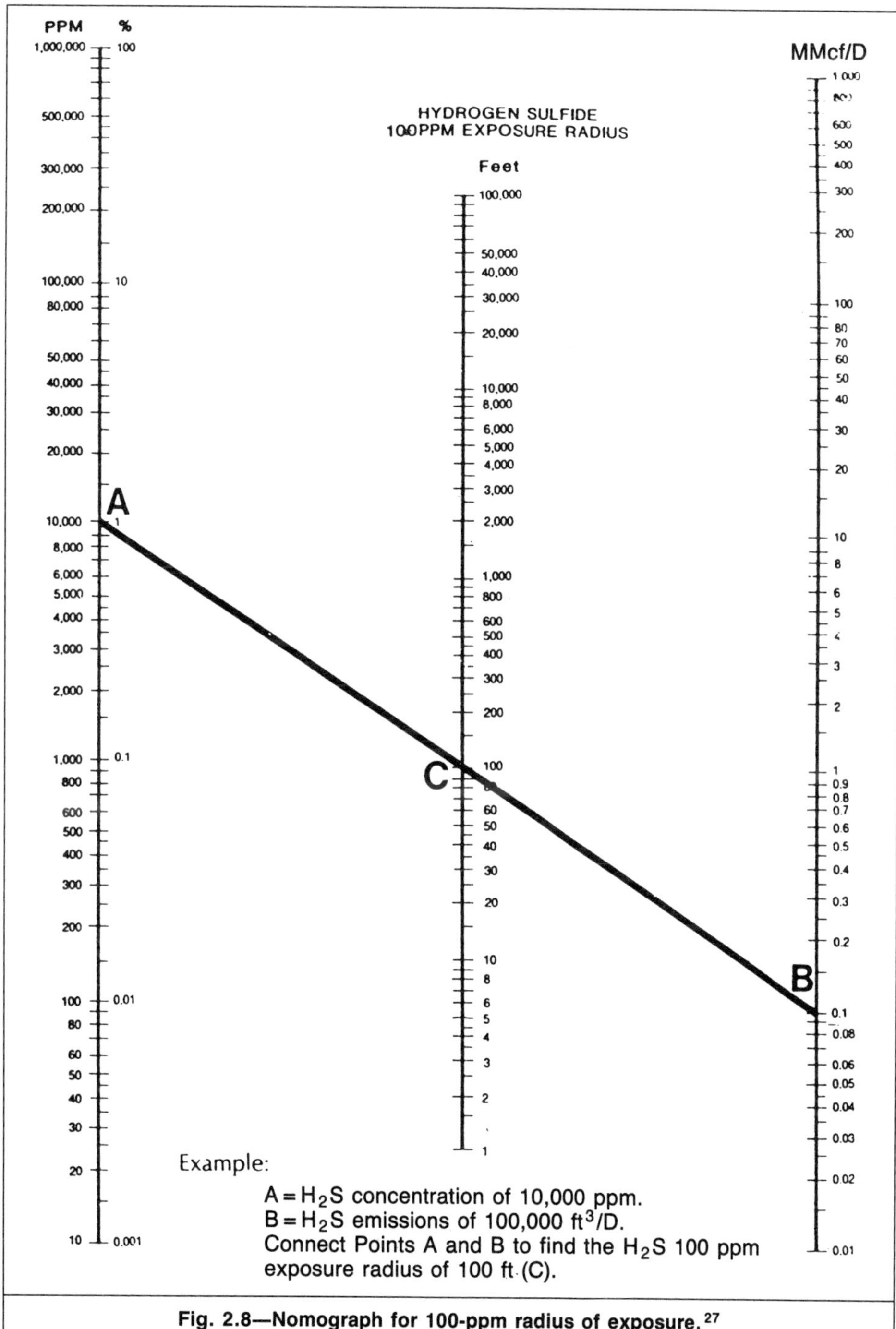

Fig. 2.8—Nomograph for 100-ppm radius of exposure.[27]

equipped with a bypass valve that allows delivery of partially regulated air to the mask in case of regulator failure. A mask with a full facepiece must be used, and the respirator must be approved by the U.S. Natl. Inst. for Occupational Safety & Health and the U.S. Mine Enforcement Safety Admin.

A person with a perforated eardrum should never work in an H_2S environment with concentrations >10 ppm, even with self-contained breathing equipment, because gas can enter the lungs through a damaged ear passageway. For this reason, physical examinations of crew members should include ear examinations.

If an area is suspected to be contaminated by H_2S, personnel should put on the self-contained breathing equipment, enter the area, and make tests with the hand-operated H_2S-detector tubes or the portable monitor instrument.

When an H_2S emergency exists, personnel should work in pairs; no one should enter a contaminated area alone. Moreover no one should enter an enclosed space where H_2S may have accumulated without wearing protective breathing equipment. If a coworker is more than an arm's length away, he should be secured with a lifeline and another coworker should be stationed in a clear area.

When H_2S is detected, warning signs should be placed in the immediate area and at the entrance to the location.

In the event of sudden gas release with no warning, personnel should put on protective breathing equipment, aid anyone in distress, proceed to designated clear areas, and wait for instructions from the driller, tool pusher, or other supervisory personnel.

If a person is down from H_2S and first aid must be administered, take the following steps.

1. Wear breathing equipment when removing a person from an area suspected to be contaminated by H_2S. Remove the victim to fresh air, and if the person is not breathing, start mouth-to-mouth resuscitation as soon as possible.
2. At the first opportunity, replace mouth-to-mouth resuscitation with resuscitation equipment.
3. Continue to administer oxygen when victim begins breathing.
4. Treat the victim for shock and call an ambulance and a doctor.

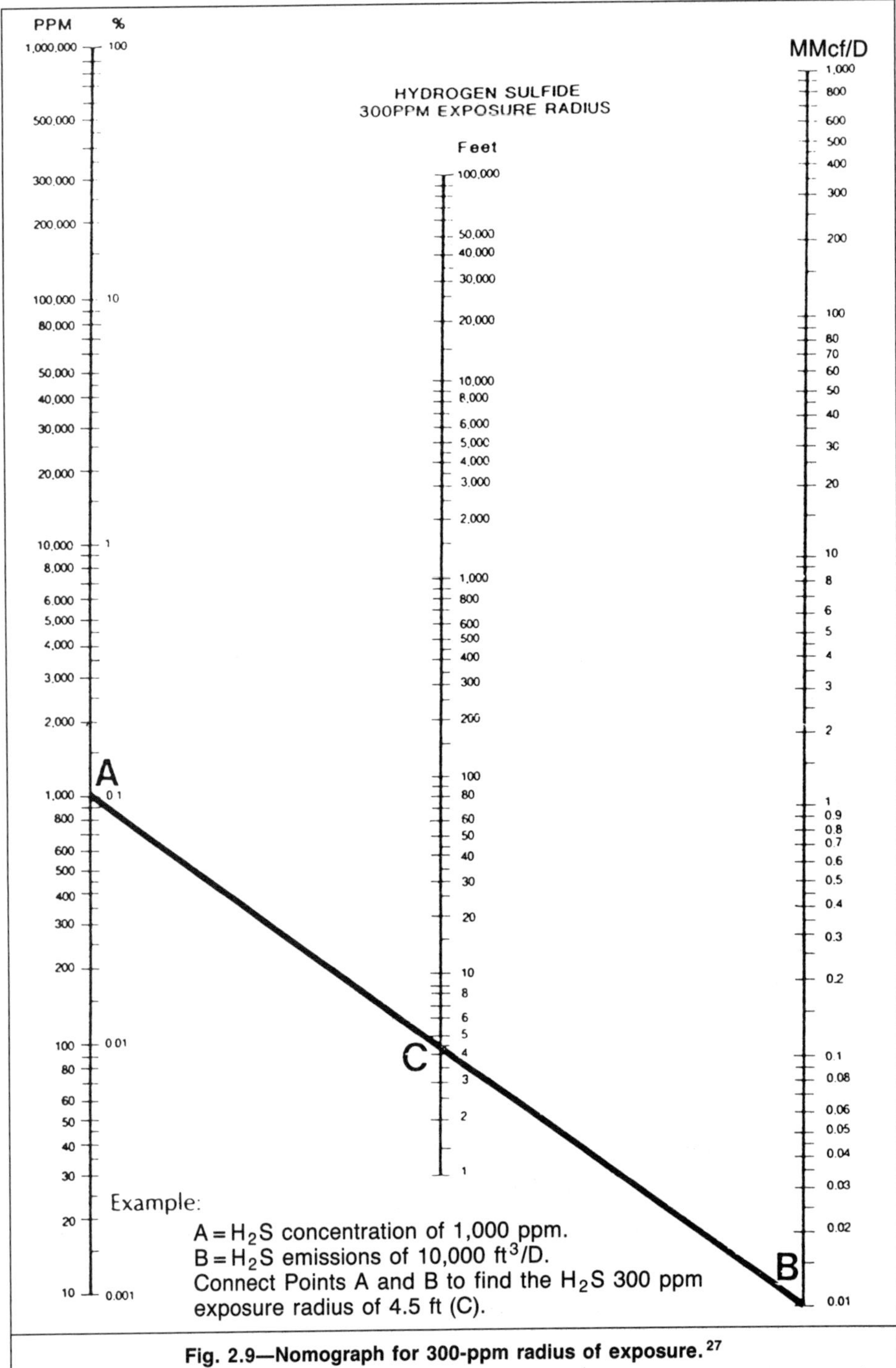

Fig. 2.9—Nomograph for 300-ppm radius of exposure.[27]

2.6.5 Contingency Plans. A contingency plan in the event of an H_2S release of significant proportion should contain the following details.

1. A means to activate the plan immediately upon detection of an accidental release of a potentially hazardous volume of H_2S.
2. Instructions and procedures for alerting the general public and public safety personnel about the emergency.
3. A list of telephone numbers and contacts for local supervisory personnel, the county sheriff, the state highway patrol, city police, an ambulance and/or helicopter service, the hospital, the fire department, doctors, contractors for supplemental equipment, the local air-control office and water conservation agency, and other applicable public agencies.
4. A plat detailing the area of exposure that includes locations of private dwellings, residential areas, and such public facilities as schools, businesses, roads, and similar areas where the public might reasonably be expected to be.
5. A list of names and telephone numbers for all residents within the area of exposure, with those people who have special health problems identified.
6. A list of names and telephone numbers of the responsible parties for each of the possibly occupied public areas, such as schools, churches, businesses, or other public areas or facilities within the area of exposure.
7. Provisions for advance briefing of the public within an area of exposure. Such advance briefings should explain the hazards and characteristics of H_2S, the necessity for an emergency action plan, the possible sources of H_2S within the area of exposure, instructions for reporting a gas leak, the means to notify the public of an emergency, and steps to take in case of an emergency.
8. If the area of exposure incorporates a densely populated locale or a locale where the population density may be unpredictable, a reaction plan is normally required. The reaction plan should include the locations of evacuation routes, safety and life support

TABLE 2.4—RESPIRATOR SELECTION GUIDE FOR H_2S (AFTER REF. 31)

H_2S Concentration	Respirator Type*
≤ 50 ppm	1. Any supplied-air respirator with full facepiece 2. Any self-contained breathing apparatus with full facepiece
>50 ppm	1. Self-contained breathing apparatus with full facepiece operated in positive-pressure mode 2. Combination Type C supplied-air respirator with full facepiece operated in positive-pressure or continuous-flow mode and auxiliary self-contained breathing apparatus operated in pressure-demand or other positive-pressure mode
Unknown, emergency entry into exposure area	1. Self-contained breathing apparatus with full facepiece operated in the positive-pressure mode 2. Combination Type C supplied-air respirator with full facepiece operated in the positive-pressure or continuous-flow mode and auxiliary self-contained breathing apparatus operated in positive-pressure mode
Unknown, escape from exposure area	1. Any self-contained apparatus 2. Any gas mask that provides adequate protection against H_2S (not to be used in confined spaces)

*Approved by the U.S. Dept. of Health, Education, & Welfare.

equipment, H_2S sources, telephone and communications equipment, and special instructions for conditions at particular installations and various weather conditions.

It is imperative that everyone associated with sour-gas drilling and production be trained to deal with H_2S and the requirements of emergency procedures. "Everyone" generally includes operating, rig, service-company, and any support personnel. At a minimum, training programs should cover the following.

1. Hazards and characteristics of H_2S.
2. Safety precautions.
3. Use, care, and servicing of protective breathing equipment, H_2S-detection instruments, resuscitation equipment, fire extinguishers, and emergency alarm systems.
4. The signs of personnel succumbing to H_2S.
5. First-aid procedures.
6. Effects of H_2S on metals.
7. A review of the contingency plan.
8. H_2S drills.

Producing and storage facilities generally are not covered by federal specifications. In Texas, however, the provisions of RCT Rule 36[28] apply. Information on producing and storage facilities from RCT Rule 36 are reprinted in Appendix A.

References

1. Maxwell, S.: "Assessment of Sulfide Corrosion Risks in Offshore Systems by Biological Monitoring," *SPEPE* (Sept. 1986) 363–68.
2. Marsland, S.D., Dawe, R.A., and Kelsall, G.H.: "Inorganic Chemical Souring of Oil Reservoirs," paper SPE 18480 presented at the 1989 SPE Intl. Symposium on Oilfield Chemistry, Houston, Feb. 8–10.
3. *RP 49, Recommended Practice for Safe Drilling of Wells Containing Hydrogen Sulfide,* second edition, API, Dallas (April 15, 1987).
4. *The Gas Engineers Handbook,* ninth printing, Industrial Press, New York City (1968).
5. *The Analytical Chemistry of Sulfur and Its Compounds,* J.H. Karcher (ed.), Wiley Interscience Inc., New York City (1972).
6. *Matheson Gas Data Book,* The Matheson Co. Inc., Newark, NJ (1961).
7. Price, J.G.W. and Cromer, D.K.: "Sulfurous Hydrocarbon Analysis and Suitable Sour Gas Sample Containers," 1978 Cdn. Natural Gas Producers Assn. Meeting, Calgary.
8. *D 4810-88, Standard Test Method for Hydrogen Sulfide in Natural Gas Using Length-of-Strain Detector Tubes,* ASTM, Philadelphia (1988).
9. *D 1266-87, Test Method for Sulfur in Petroleum Products,* ASTM, Philadelphia (1987).
10. *D 1838-89, Test Method for Copper Strip Corrosion by Liquified Petroleum Gases,* ASTM, Philadelphia (1989).
11. *D 2420-86, Test Method for Hydrogen Sulfide in Liquified Petroleum Gases,* ASTM, Philadelphia (1986).
12. *RP 13B, Recommended Practice for Standard Procedure for Field Testing Drilling Fluids,* 11th edition, API, Dallas (May 1985).
13. *Spec. 5AC, Specification for Restricted Yield Strength Casing and Tubing,* 15th edition, API, Dallas (May 1985).
14. *Spec. 5A, Specification for Casing, Tubing, and Drill Pipe,* 38th edition, API, Dallas (May 1985).
15. *Spec. 5AX, Specification for High-Strength Casing, Tubing, and Drill Pipe,* 14th edition, API, Dallas (May 1985).
16. *Spec. 5CT, Specification for Casing and Tubing,* second edition, API, Dallas (1989).
17. *Standard TM-01-77, Test Method for Laboratory Testing of Metals for Resistance to Sulfide Stress Cracking in H_2S Environments,* NACE, Houston (1990).
18. *Spec. 6A, Specification for Wellhead and Christmas Tree Equipment,* 16th edition, API, Dallas (Oct. 1, 1989).
19. *Standard MR-01-75, Sulfide Stress Cracking Resistant Metallic Materials for Oilfield Equipment,* NACE, Houston (1988).
20. *Spec. Q1, Specification for Quality Programs,* second edition, API, Dallas (April 1986).
21. *RP 7G, Recommended Practice for Drill Stem Design and Operating Limits,* 11th edition, API, Dallas (May 1984).
22. *RP 55, Recommended Practice for Conducting Oil and Gas Productions Operations Involving Hydrogen Sulfide,* first edition, API, Dallas (Oct. 1981).

23. *RP-0472-87, Methods and Controls To Prevent In-Service Cracking of Carbon Steel (P-1) Welds in Corrosive Petroleum Refining Environments,* NACE, Houston (1987).
24. "Rules for Construction of Pressure Vessels, Division 1," *Boiler and Pressure Vessel Code,* American Soc. of Mechanical Engineers, New York City (1989) Sec. VIII-2.
25. *Federal Register* (Oct. 18, 1972) **37,** No. 202, Part II.
26. "Oil and Gas and Sulfur Operations in the Outer Continental Shelf; Outer Continental Shelf Minerals and Rights-of-Way Management," U.S. Minerals Management Service Code of Federal Regulations, Parts 250 and 256, *Federal Register* (April 1, 1988) **53,** No. 63.
27. Dosch, M.W. and Hodgson, S.F.: "Drilling and Operating Oil, Gas, and Geothermal Wells in an H_2S Environment," Publication M10, California Div. of Oil & Gas, Sacramento (1981).
28. "Rule 36: Oil, Gas, or Geothermal Resource Operation in Hydrogen Sulfide Areas," *Statewide Rules for Oil, Gas and Geothermal Operations,* Oil & Gas Div., Railroad Commission of Texas, Austin (June 1991) 106–20.
29. *RP 14E, Recommended Practice for Design and Installation of Offshore Production Platform Piping Systems,* fourth edition, API, Dallas (April 1984).
30. "Sour Well Licensing and Drilling Requirements," ID 87-2, Alberta Energy Resources Conservation Board (June 1987).
31. "A Guide to Respiratory Protection," U.S. Dept. of Health, Education, & Welfare, *Code of Federal Regulations* (1976) No. 30, Part II, 52.
32. "Occupational Safety and Health Standards for General Industry," U.S. Occupational Safety & Health Admin., *Code of Federal Regulations,* No. 29, 1910, Table 2, Table Z-2 (A)(3), 1001.
33. "Criteria for a Recommended Standard for Occupational Exposure to Hydrogen Sulfide," Publication 77-158, Natl. Inst. for Occupational Safety & Health, U.S. Dept. of Health, Education, & Welfare, Washington, DC (1977).

SI Metric Conversion Factors

ft	× 3.048*	E−01	=	m
ft^3	× 2.831 685	E−02	=	m^3
°F	(°F−32)/1.8		=	°C
psi	× 6.894 757	E+00	=	kPa

*Conversion factor is exact.

Chapter 3
Fundamentals of Metallurgy and Corrosion for Sour Gas

3.1 Introduction

This chapter presents some of the fundamentals of metallurgy necessary to understand the behavior of metals in sour gas. For more background in metallurgy, several good texts and references are available.[1-4]

3.2 Metals and Alloys

All common metals, including those used in the oil and gas industry, are crystalline and fit into one of three basic crystal structures: face-centered cubic (FCC) (**Fig. 3.1**), body-centered cubic (BCC) (**Fig. 3.2**), or hexagonal close-packed (HCP) (**Fig. 3.3**).[1] These atomic arrangements determine such metal and alloy mechanical properties as strength, hardness, ductility, and thermal and electrical conductivity.

In pure metals, such properties as corrosion resistance, strength, fracture resistance, etc., can be improved by adding other elements—i.e., by alloying. Alloys represent the most common form of metals used for industrial purposes. Alloying elements can reside in the crystal structure of the host metal in one of two ways: by substitution on host atom sites or in between these atom sites (interstitial). **Fig. 3.4** is a schematic representation of a substitutional solid solution where an alloying-element atom replaces one of the host-metal atoms.[1] Examples of such solid solutions are iron-chromium-nickel stainless steels, lead-tin solders, and copper-zinc brass. **Fig. 3.5** shows an interstitial solid solution in which the alloying-element atom fits between the normal host-metal lattice sites.[1] The most common example of this type of solid solution is carbon in iron (steel).

Both alloying forms strengthen host metals, but interstitial alloying offers a greater increment of strength. Thus, a pure metal can be strengthened by alloying elements; however, the strength is limited by the solubility of the alloying element in the host metal. Once the solubility is exceeded, a precipitate (second phase) forms. Iron carbide (cementite) in steel is a good example of such a precipitate.

Other ways to increase the strength of metals are discussed later. One method, however, is appropriate to address at this point. Almost all metals of industrial significance are polycrystalline; i.e., they consist of many crystals produced when the alloy solidifies from the liquid. These crystals, generally called grains, grow until they impinge on one another, creating boundaries where they contact (**Fig. 3.6**). These grain boundaries differ in chemistry and orientation from the parent grain and therefore may also have different properties. Furthermore, the resulting grain size has considerable effect on the strength and toughness of an alloy. Generally, the finer the grain size, the higher the strength and toughness (fracture resistance).

3.3 Classification Systems

The possible combinations of elements that form alloys are almost infinite. To organize the wide variety of alloy compositions into some rational order, many countries have developed categories or classification systems for metals and alloys. No standard worldwide system exists; however, the Intl. Standards Organization is developing one. Currently, each country may have numerous alloy systems that are either incompatible with each other or with those from other countries. Several examples of U.S. classification systems are given here because the petroleum industry worldwide typically refers to them.

Table 3.1 describes the general concept for numbering alloys with the American Iron & Steel Inst./Soc. of Automotive Engineers (AISI/SAE) system. This system is advantageous because the number indicates the alloy composition. AISI/SAE, however, has requirements for chemical composition only, none for mechanical properties. The American Soc. for Testing & Materials' (ASTM's) classification system is not as informative because it uses only prefixes for ferrous (A) and nonferrous (B) alloys. The rest of the numbering in the ASTM designation offers no information about the alloy itself and, to identify the alloy and to learn other pertinent information, one must refer to the actual specification. However, unlike the AISI/SAE system that provides only a chemical range for the alloy, the ASTM specifications detail the manufacturing method, the chemical composition, the heat treatment, the mechanical properties, and the tests and inspections required for compliance.

The U.S. aerospace and automotive industries also have their own classification systems. Recently, the ASTM developed a unified numbering system (UNS) for all the more common alloys. The UNS has 18 series of designations for metals and alloys. Each UNS designation consists of a single letter prefix followed by five digits. The letter indicates the family of metals identified; for example, A indicates aluminum, P precious metals, and S stainless steels (**Table 3.2**). The ASTM hopes that the UNS eventually will become the predominant U.S. system for metals classification.

Other countries, however, do not necessarily have to use the UNS. Some countries have their own industrial standards. For example, Germany has standards for carbon and alloy steels, and Japan has standards for carbon, manganese, manganese-chromium, chromium, chromium-molybdenum, and nickel-molybdenum-chromium steels.

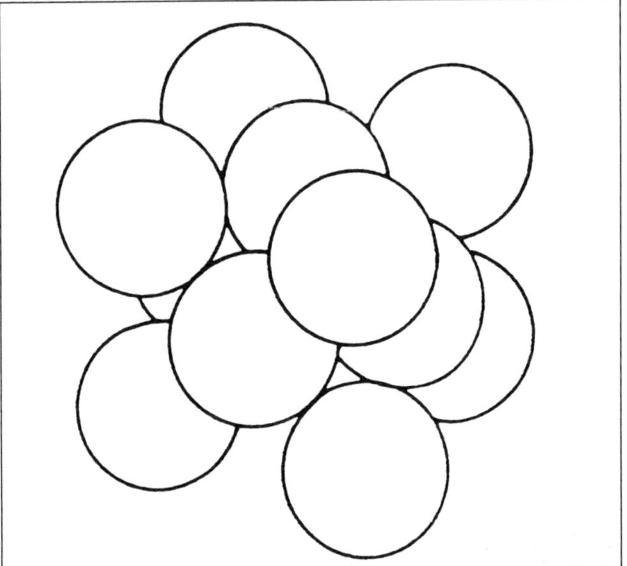

Fig. 3.1—FCC crystalline structure. (Source: Bruce D. Craig's *Practical Oil-Field Metallurgy.* © PennWell Books, 1984.)[1]

Fig. 3.2—BCC crystalline structure. (Source: Bruce D. Craig's *Practical Oil-Field Metallurgy.* © PennWell Books, 1984.)[1]

3.4 Mechanical Properties

The most common means of determining mechanical properties of metals is by performing a tensile test. A standard tensile bar (**Fig. 3.7**) is machined from the metal and pulled in tension until it elongates and then fractures.[5] The stress imposed on the tensile bar is expressed by

$$\sigma = P/A, \quad (3.1)$$

where σ=stress (load per unit area), psi; P=applied load; and A= cross-sectional area.

The engineering stress is based on the original cross-sectional area of the specimen. Likewise, as the tensile bar is pulled, it lengthens, and the resulting engineering strain or percent elongation is expressed as

$$\epsilon = \Delta L/L, \quad (3.2)$$

where ϵ=engineering strain, %; L=original length; and ΔL= change in length.

The yield strength is the stress at which a small specified amount of total strain (elastic plus plastic) or permanent (plastic) deformation has occurred. Below the yield strength, most strain is elastic and will be recovered when the specimen is unloaded. The slope of the curve in the elastic region is a constant referred to as the elastic or Young's modulus, E. In the elastic range, the stress can be related to the strain by this constant:

$$\sigma = E\epsilon. \quad (3.3)$$

The most common definition for yield strength is the 0.2% offset (**Fig. 3.8**).[1] This definition is used by ASTM and by the American Petroleum Inst. (API) in their *Spec. 6A*[6] for wellheads and Christmas trees. Fig. 3.8 also describes the 0.5% extension under load, another API method[7,8] for determining yield strength. The API method is not consistent because the yield for Grade P-110 casing is defined as a 0.6% extension, while the yield for Grade Q-125 casing is a 0.65% extension.

The ultimate tensile strength, usually simplified as tensile strength, is another commonly specified material property. Metals frequently

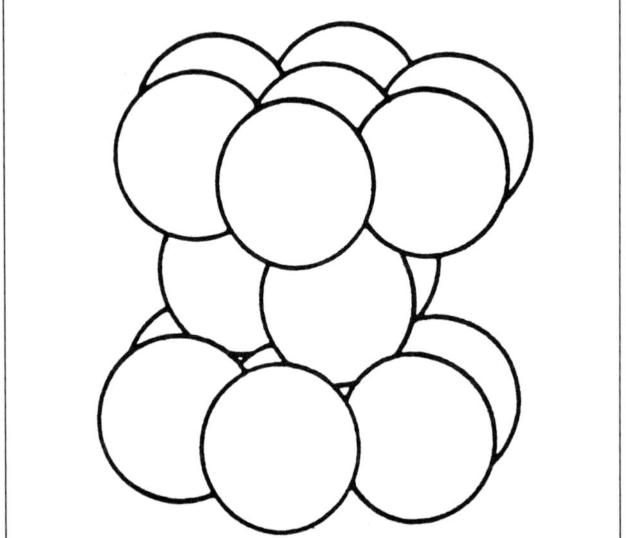

Fig. 3.3—HCP crystalline structure. (Source: Bruce D. Craig's *Practical Oil-Field Metallurgy.* © PennWell Books, 1984.)[1]

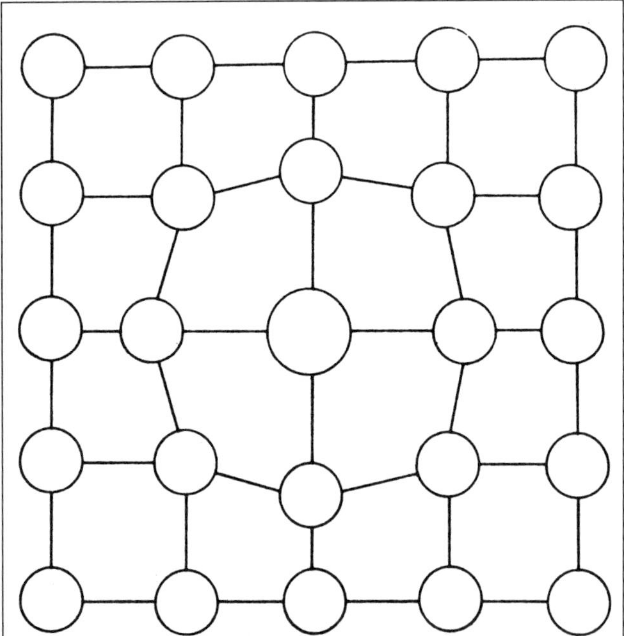

Fig. 3.4—Substitutional solid solution with larger atom. (Source: Bruce D. Craig's *Practical Oil-Field Metallurgy.* © PennWell Books, 1984.)[1]

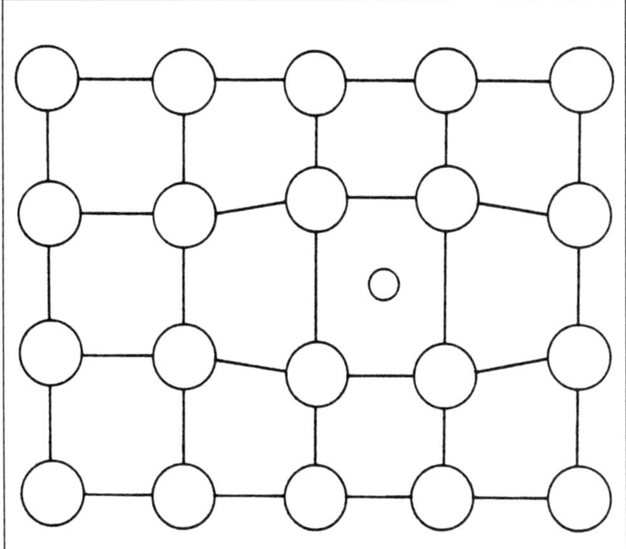

Fig. 3.5—Interstitial solid solution. (Source: Bruce D. Craig's *Practical Oil-Field Metallurgy*. © PennWell Books, 1984.)[1]

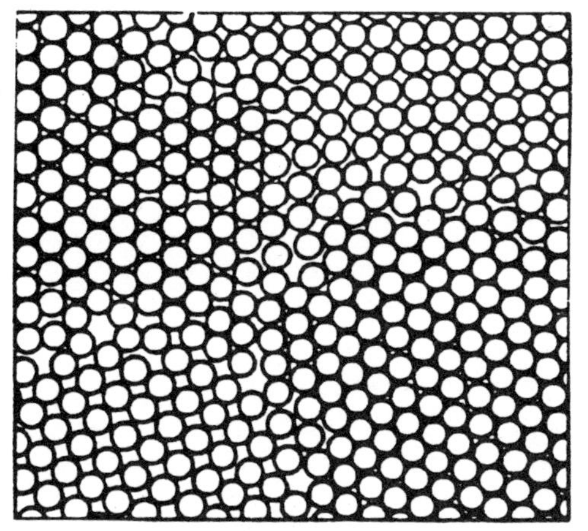

Fig. 3.6—Atomic structure of grains reflecting mismatch of atoms at grain boundary.

will work-harden above the yield point, creating a stronger metal. Eventually this increase in strength will be offset by a reduction in the cross section of the metal resisting the load. The ultimate tensile strength is the peak stress achieved before fracture. The percent elongation and the percent reduction in area are two other properties often included in mechanical properties data for metals. Both properties are a measure of a metal's ductility. The percent elongation is the change in length of the sample compared with the original length (usually 2 in. [5 cm]) of a certain interval. Likewise, the percent reduction in area is the percent the cross-sectional area of the specimen decreases compared with the original cross section.

3.5 Hardness Testing

The API, ASTM, and other materials specifications commonly specify tensile properties, but tensile tests are seldom conducted in field-level checks on metal properties. Tensile testing requires the destruction of a piece of the component to be tested. Hence, hardness tests are more commonly used for quality control. Hardness tests, however, only reflect the tensile strength of a metal, not its yield strength. Hardness tests are conducted by forcing an indenter of a known hardness and shape into the metal with a controlled force, with hardness being the measure of resistance to this penetration. The size and depth of the resulting indentation indicates the hardness and can be related to the approximate tensile strength of the steel. **Table 3.3** compares measurements from various hardness tests.[9] These correlations are strictly valid only for steels.

Although a multitude of hardness test methods exist, only a few are frequently associated with metals used in the petroleum industry (**Fig. 3.9**).[1] The Brinell test is used for shop and field testing or for rapidly evaluating numerous items (casing, line pipe, etc.). The Brinell test differs from other methods, such as the Rockwell hardness test, because the area of the indentation is measured rather than the depth of penetration. Some Brinell field testers use a 6,614-lbm [3000 kg] load and others use hydraulic means or dynamic impact (hammer blow) to produce the hardness impression.

The various testing methods are interrelated, and each has certain advantages and disadvantages. The overlapping Rockwell B and C hardness (HRB and HRC, respectively) scales, however, are the most commonly used methods in both the field and the laboratory. The HRB is used for softer materials with tensile strengths ranging from 57,000 to 115,000 psi [393 to 793 MPa], while the HRC is used for materials with tensile strengths from 110,000 to >330,000 psi [784 to >2275 MPa]. The HRC is not accurate below a value of 20 but is traditionally used for Grades L-80, C-90, and T-95, which often fall less than HRC 20.

The approximate tensile strengths derived from hardness tests are quite useful, especially in failure analysis when, because of limi-

TABLE 3.1—AISI/SAE SYSTEM OF STEEL DESIGNATIONS

Steel Type	AISI/SAE Code
Carbon steels	1xxx
Plain carbon	10xx
Free-cutting (screw stock)	11xx
High manganese	13xx
Nickel steels	2xxx
3.5% Ni	23xx
5.0% Ni	25xx
Nickel-chromium steels	3xxx
1.25% Ni, 0.6% Cr	31xx
1.75% Ni, 1.0% Cr	32xx
3.50% Ni, 1.5% Cr	33xx
Molybdenum steels	4xxx
C-Mo	40xx
Cr-Mo	41xx
Cr-Ni-Mo	43xx
Ni-Mo	46xx and 48xx
Chromium steels	5xxx
Low chromium	51xx
Medium chromium	52xxx
Chromium-vanadium steels	6xxx
1% Cr	61xx
Silicon-manganese steels	9xxx
2% Si	92xx

TABLE 3.2—UNS

AXXXXX	Aluminum and aluminum alloys
CXXXXX	Copper and copper alloys
EXXXXX	Rare earth and similar metals and alloys
FXXXXX	Cast irons
GXXXXX	AISI/SAE carbon and alloy steels
HXXXXX	AISI/SAE H-steels
JXXXXX	Cast steels (except tool steels)
KXXXXX	Miscellaneous steels and ferrous alloys
LXXXXX	Low-melting metals and alloys
MXXXXX	Miscellaneous nonferrous metals and alloys
NXXXXX	Nickel and nickel alloys
PXXXXX	Precious metals and alloys
RXXXXX	Reactive and refractory metals and alloys
SXXXXX	Heat- and corrosion-resistant steels*
TXXXXX	Tool steels, wrought and cast
WXXXXX	Welding filler metals
ZXXXXX	Zinc and zinc alloys

*Including stainless and valve steels and iron-based superalloys.

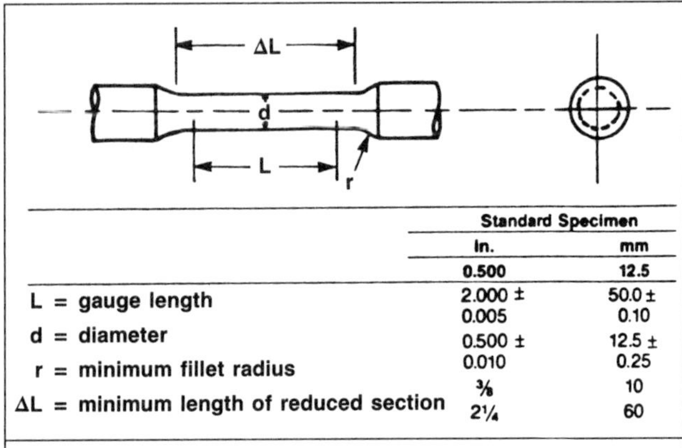

	Standard Specimen	
	in.	mm
	0.500	12.5
L = gauge length	2.000 ± 0.005	50.0 ± 0.10
d = diameter	0.500 ± 0.010	12.5 ± 0.25
r = minimum fillet radius	⅜	10
ΔL = minimum length of reduced section	2¼	60

Fig. 3.7—ASTM *A 370* standard tensile bar dimensions. (© ASTM. Reprinted with permission.)[5]

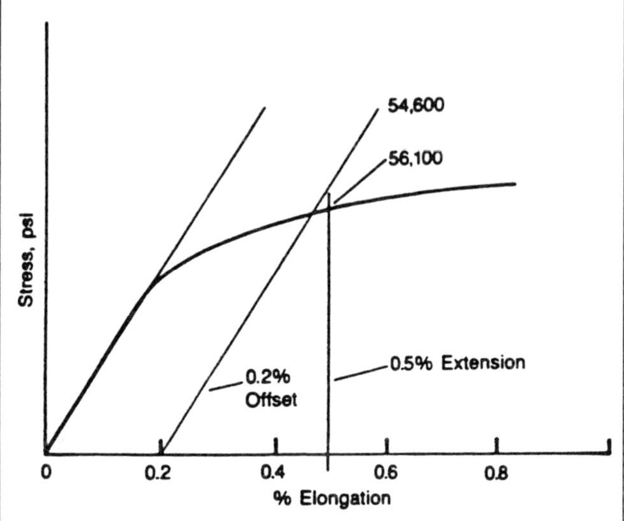

Fig. 3.8—Typical stress/strain curve for Grade J-55 steel showing two methods for determining yield strength. (Source: Bruce D. Craig's *Practical Oil-Field Metallurgy.* © PennWell Books, 1984.)[1]

tations in component size, obtaining the tensile strength by testing is not possible. Note that the yield strength for normalized or quenched and tempered carbon and low-alloy steels is about 75% to 90% of the tensile strength.

The other two hardness tests are known as microhardness tests when the loads are <2.2 lbm [<1 kg]. These tests are the Knoop hardness test and the Vickers hardness (HV) test, which is also known as the diamond pyramid (DPH) test. The size of the indentations is several thousandths of an inch. These tests are used in the laboratory to analyze microstructures, but portable microhardness testers are available for field use under special conditions.

The decision about which hardness test to use for a particular application depends on such factors as the number of tests to be performed, the sensitivity and accuracy required, the purpose of the tests, and the size and geometry of the component to be tested.

3.6 Strengthening Methods

For most applications, it is desirable to select an alloy that has high strength, good ductility, high fracture resistance, enhanced corrosion resistance, and reasonable cost.

Methods to enhance one of these properties, however, often diminish the other properties. Thus, these factors are often in conflict and must be optimized for the specific conditions of service. Primary among these tradeoffs is the processing of alloys to increase strength. Generally, increasing the yield and tensile strength will reduce an alloy's ductility and ability to resist fracture. Resistance to fracture is called toughness or fracture toughness.

Steels can be treated thermally to produce extremely high strength, but this reduces ductility and fracture toughness. By tempering the steel after hardening, some ductility (expressed as elongation and reduction of area) can be restored but with a loss in strength (**Fig. 3.10**).[10] The only way to enhance ductility and fracture toughness and to increase the strength of a particular alloy is to reduce the grain size.

Heat treatment of steels is a subject that involves many complexities; however, the fundamentals of heat treatment for steel are presented here to introduce the necessary terms for future reference and discussion in this monograph. Understanding the phases that form in steel as functions of temperature is important and best aid-

TABLE 3.3—HARDNESS vs. APPROXIMATE TENSILE STRENGTH FOR STEEL
(© ASTM. Reprinted with permission. After Ref. 9.)

Brinell								
3000-kg load Diameter (mm)	Tungsten Carbide 10-mm Ball	HRA* 60 kg Brale	HRB 100 kg 0.063-in. Ball	HRC 150 kg Brale	Rockwell Superficial 30-N	DPH Number**	Shore Sclera-scope Hardness Number	Approximate Tensile Strength (1,000 psi)
3.60	285	65.3	(105.5)	29.9	50.3	301	—	141
3.65	277	64.6	(104.5)	28.8	49.3	292	41	137
3.70	269	64.1	(104.0)	27.6	48.3	284	40	133
3.75	262	63.6	(103.0)	26.6	47.3	276	39	129
3.80	255	63.0	(102.0)	25.4	46.2	269	38	126
3.85	248	62.5	(101.0)	24.2	45.1	261	37	122
3.90	241	61.8	100.0	22.8	43.9	253	36	118
3.95	235	61.4	99.0	21.7	42.9	247	35	115
4.00	229	60.8	98.2	20.5	41.9	241	34	111
4.05	223	59.7	97.3	(18.8)	—	234	—	—
4.10	217	59.2	96.4	(17.5)	—	228	33	105
4.15	212	58.5	95.5	(16.0)	—	222	—	102
4.20	207	57.8	94.6	(15.2)	—	218	32	100
4.25	201	57.4	93.8	(13.8)	—	212	31	98
4.30	197	56.9	92.8	(12.7)	—	207	30	95
4.35	192	56.5	91.9	(11.5)	—	202	29	93
4.40	187	55.9	90.7	(10.0)	—	196	—	90
4.45	183	55.5	90.0	(9.0)	—	192	28	89
4.50	179	55.0	89.0	(8.0)	—	188	27	87

*Rockwell A hardness scale.
**Also known as HV number.

Common Hardness Tests

Test	Indentor	Typical Load	Shape of Indentation
Brinell	10 mm sphere (steel or tungsten carbide)	3,000 kg	○
Rockwell			
A	Diamond cone	60 kg	
C		150 kg	
B	1/16-in. diameter ball	100 kg	○
Vickers	Diamond pyramid	1 kg, 10 kg (variable)	⊠
Knoop	Diamond pyramid	1 kg, 10 kg (variable)	

Fig. 3.9—Common hardness test methods. (Source: Bruce D. Craig's *Practical Oil-Field Metallurgy.* © PennWell Books, 1984.)[1]

ed by reference to the iron-carbon phase diagram (**Fig. 3.11**). A phase is defined in the solid-state sense, as a homogeneous compound with a specific crystal structure. Fig. 3.11 shows that pure iron (left axis) goes through two solid-state transformations as a function of temperature. For instance, when cooling from the liquid state at 2,912 °F [1600°C], the first crystals to solidify have a BCC structure, but as cooling continues below 2,552 °F [1400°C], the crystal structure changes to FCC, and below about 1,652 °F [900°C] to room temperature, the final structure returns to BCC. These allotropic phase changes are largely responsible for the great versatility of steel.

While the addition of carbon presents a more complex picture, the same transformations are observed. The high-temperature BCC structure is known as delta ferrite. The FCC structure (austenite) represents a region of high carbon solubility in the iron matrix (2.08% C). The carbon is present in the iron as an interstitial solid solution. Austenite is also nonmagnetic.

The low-temperature BCC structure (alpha ferrite) has a limited solubility for carbon (0.02%C). Thus, carbon in excess of this solubility limit precipitates to being a carbide (Fe_3C) called cementite. Because most steels used in the petroleum industry contain ≤0.8% C, the remaining discussion is limited to steels in this range. The mixture of ferrite and cementite is called pearlite or bainite, depending on the shape and distribution of the cementite.

While the phase diagram is valuable for predicting phases formed at specific temperatures, it represents an equilibrium, or more correctly, metastable equilibrium. Therefore, it represents the phase behavior for extremely slow cooling. If the cooling rate is increased, equilibrium is not maintained and other phases form that cannot be predicted from this diagram. For instance, under rapid cooling (quenching) from 1,832°F [1000°C], the carbon will be retained

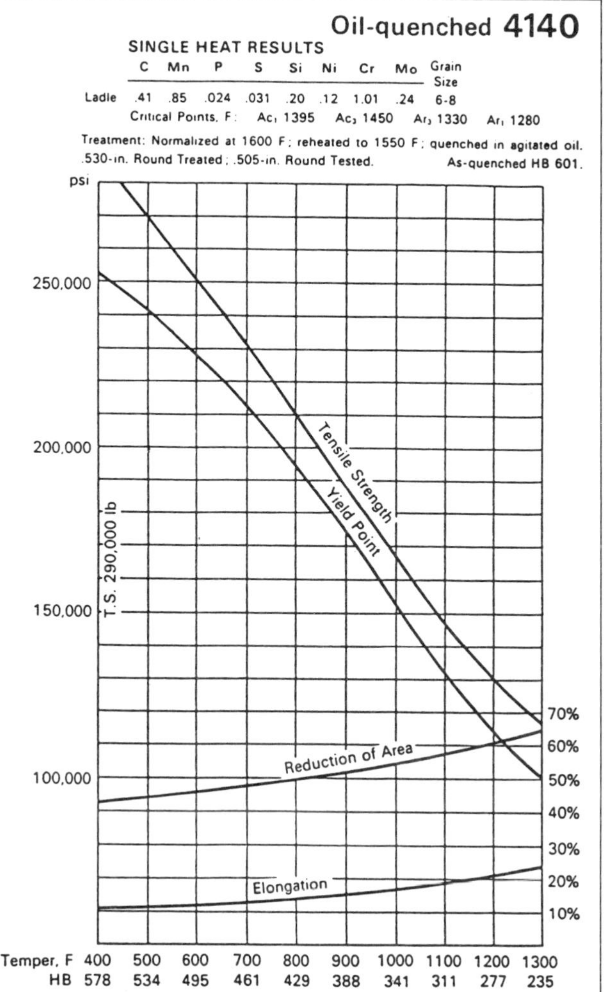

Fig. 3.10—Dependence of strength and ductility on tempering. (Courtesy Bethlehem Steel Corp.)[10]

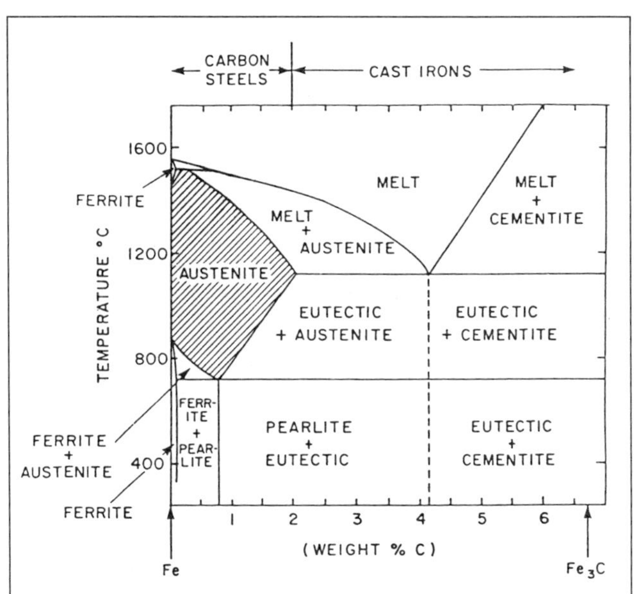

Fig. 3.11—Iron-rich side of the iron-carbon phase diagram.

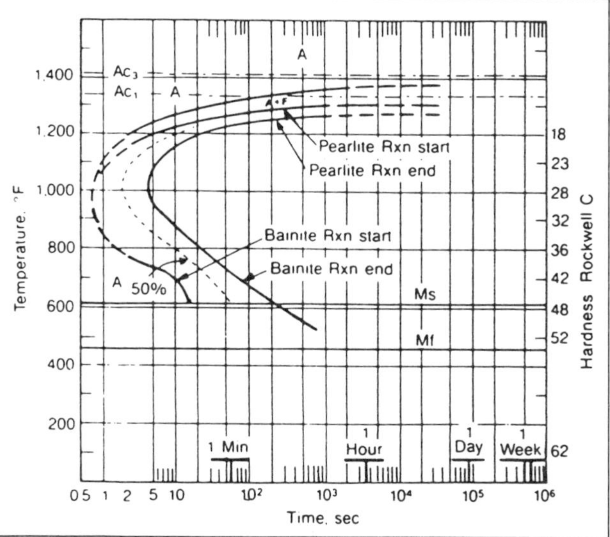

Fig. 3.12—TTT diagram for AISI 1040 steel. (Source: Bruce D. Craig's *Practical Oil-Field Metallurgy.* © PennWell Books, 1984.)[1]

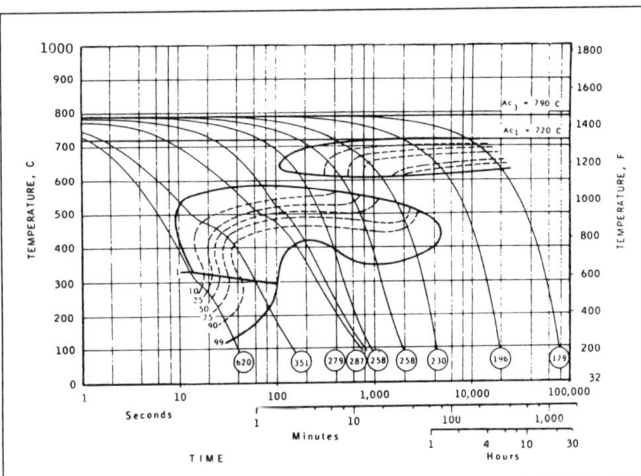

Fig. 3.13—CCT diagram for a medium carbon steel modified with molybdenum. (Source: Bruce D. Craig's *Practical Oil-Field Metallurgy.* © PennWell Books, 1984.)[1]

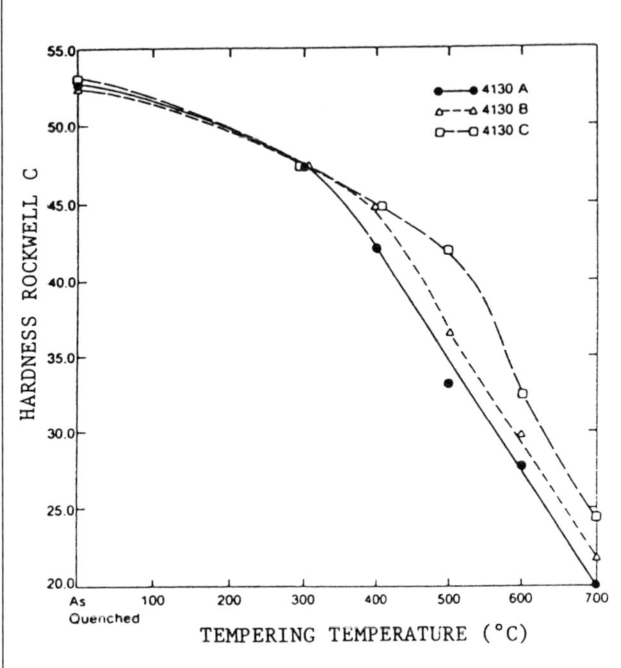

Fig. 3.14—Hardness of AISI 4130 (Line A) and two modifications (Lines B and C) as functions of tempering temperature.

in its interstitial positions and will not precipitate, causing tremendous strain in the crystal matrix as it tries to rearrange the structure from FCC to BCC. The result is an intermediate body-centered tetragonal structure called martensite. Intermediate cooling rates produce another microstructure called bainite. Understanding the development of these new nonequilibrium structures requires a diagram that incorporates the microstructure change with time as a function of temperature. **Fig. 3.12** is a time/temperature-transformation (TTT) diagram that shows phase development as a function of time and temperature.[1]

The basis of the TTT diagram is transformation under isothermal conditions. Thus, steel must be cooled instantaneously from the critical temperature to the temperature of interest and then held at that temperature. The various lines on Fig. 3.12 show the start and finish of the transformation to pearlite, ferrite, and bainite or martensite.

To illustrate the concept and use of Fig. 3.12, assume a steel is instantly cooled to 1,200°F [650°C] from the austenite region and held at this temperature for 1 minute. Lines crossed when the temperature is held constant are those indicating austenite and ferrite, the pearlite start, the pearlite finish, and the dotted line, indicating 50% completion of pearlite transformation. Thus, after 1 minute, the austenite has transformed completely to pearlite and ferrite. Although this diagram can describe many reactions and combinations, one of its obvious shortcomings is the instantaneous or idealized quench to the requisite temperature, which is impractical with actual components.

The continuous cooling transformation (CCT) diagram is more useful for predicting results of heat-treatment and compensates for this quench-time inconsistency. **Fig. 3.13** is a CCT diagram for a medium carbon (0.4%) steel.[1] Three regions, ferrite-pearlite

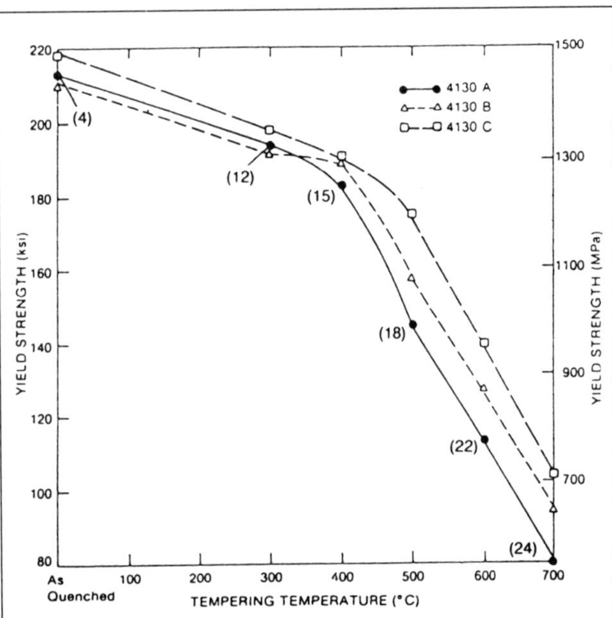

Fig. 3.15—Yield strength of the same alloys in Fig. 3.14 as a function of tempering temperature. Elongation values are given in parentheses.[11]

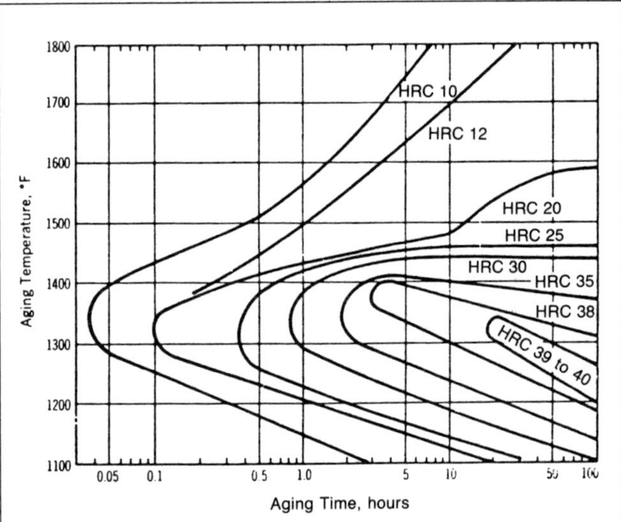

Fig. 3.16—Effect of aging conditions on hardness of Inconel 718. (Initial hardness, as-annealed condition, was HRC 4.) (Courtesy Inco Alloys Intl. Inc.)[12]

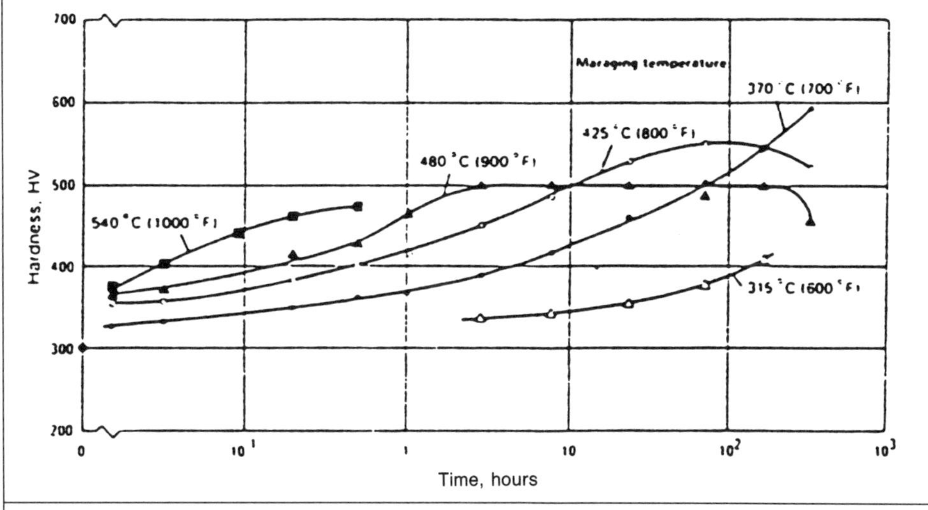

Fig. 3.17—Hardness of 18% Ni (250) maraging steel as a function of aging time and temperature.[13]

(F+P), bainite (B), and martensite (M) are shown. As the steel cools from the austenite region, it transforms to these products, depending on the region it passes through.

Lines 1 and 99 represent 1% and 99% transformation to the specific product noted as cooling proceeds from the upper left to the lower right. The values in the small circles at the bottom of the diagram provide hardness information from the resulting microstructure. Rapid cooling from the austenite, shown by the DPH 620 curve, produces almost 100% martensite, whereas slow cooling produces a structure composed of ferrite and pearlite, shown by the DPH 196 and 179 curves. The cooling line, representing DPH 351, shows a partial transformation to bainite, while the remaining austenite transforms to martensite.

At this point, it is advantageous to define certain heat-treating terminology. All these definitions begin with the steel already heated to the austenite region. All the products formed depend on the cooling rate. Annealing is the process of heating a work piece and then cooling it slowly in the furnace. Annealing produces a soft steel, with carbides that are spherical or a coarse pearlite. When steel is normalized, it is removed from the furnace and cooled in air (usually still air), producing a curve similar to that for DPH 230. Quenching is achieved by cooling steel faster than it cools with still air by use of forced air, water, brine, or oil. Quenching usually is accomplished by liquid immersion, producing curves similar to those for DPH 258 and higher.

The important concept from this discussion of TTT and CCT diagrams is that transformations are functions of both the cooling rate and the alloy content. Transformations are important in the manufacture of heavy-wall castings or forgings for valve bodies or heavy-wall pipe for deep wells. To achieve high strength, the steel must first be transformed to martensite. If the necessary cooling rate for carbon steel cannot be achieved in these heavy-walled products by quenching, then alloying elements must be added that will produce a fully martensitic microstructure with the slower cooling caused by heavy sections.

Hardenability is the ability to produce martensite by either rapid cooling or alloying. Hardenability should not be confused with hardness, which is a measure of resistance to penetration. The two are related in that the hardenability of a steel determines the depth and distribution of the hardness produced by quenching from the austenite region. Hardenability is a function of carbon content, alloying, austenite grain size, time and temperature during austenitizing, and cooling rate. The main elements that increase hardenability are carbon, manganese, molybdenum, chromium, silicon, nickel, and boron.

Once the martensitic structure is obtained, it is frequently tempered to improve toughness and ductility, although these are accompanied by a loss of strength. **Figs. 3.14 and 3.15** show the reduction in hardness and yield strength with tempering temperature for American Iron & Steel Inst. (AISI) 4130 steel and modifications of it with increased molybdenum.[11] Steel A is a standard AISI 4130 with 0.2% Mo, while Steels B and C contain 0.50% Mo and 0.75% Mo, respectively. These steels are typical of those used for manufacturing Grade C-90 casing. The elongation data (numbers in parentheses in Fig. 3.15), which are a measure of ductility, show that elongation doubles while yield strength decreases by 50% from a temperature of 572°F [300°C] to 1,292°F [700°C]. The microstructure also changes significantly. Microstructure changes are the primary factors influencing the strength and ductility of a steel. The relationship between a metal's microstructure and properties forms the basis of metallurgy.

Precipitation hardening or age hardening is another strengthening method. Various metals (e.g., aluminum alloys, some nickel-based alloys, and some stainless steels) are strengthened by precipitation hardening, which is a process of heating the alloy to a high solutionizing temperature (to dissolve all phases into one homogeneous phase), then cooling it rapidly. The alloy is then reheated (aged) for several hours at an intermediate temperature, during which a specific phase or compound precipitates from the solid solution. The precipitate size and type vary with aging time and temperature, which result in different properties in the alloy. **Fig. 3.16** shows the change in hardness with aging time and temperature for Inconel 718. Relatively long (≈50 hours) aging times are required to achieve a hardness comparable with steels (HRC 40).[12] Additionally, a time/temperature dependence exists, as demonstrated in **Fig. 3.17.**[13] Higher temperatures are required at shorter times to produce hardness values similar to those achieved at lower temperatures and longer times. All age-hardenable alloys display this type of time/temperature dependence.

Cold working is another method of strengthening alloys, especially alloys that are not heat treatable. As **Fig. 3.18** shows, if a metal is stressed beyond its yield point and then unloaded, the elastic portion of the strain is recovered but the plastic strain remains. If the specimen is reloaded, it will follow the new curve and reach the new, higher yield point before plastic deformation occurs. Thus, just as in heat treating to achieve strength, cold working will increase the yield strength and tensile strength but will reduce the ductility and toughness. **Fig. 3.19** shows the cold-work behavior of various alloys and the incremental increases in hardness with cold reduction.[12] Cold work can be accomplished by pilgering, drawing, rolling, and swaging. Cold pilgering and cold drawing are common methods for cold working corrosion-resistant alloys for sour-gas service. Cold pilgering involves pushing the alloy tube through rolls that rock back and forth on the outside surface, squeezing the pipe down and reducing its wall thickness. Cold drawing proceeds by pulling tubing through dies, which reduces the tubing's diameter and wall thickness simultaneously.

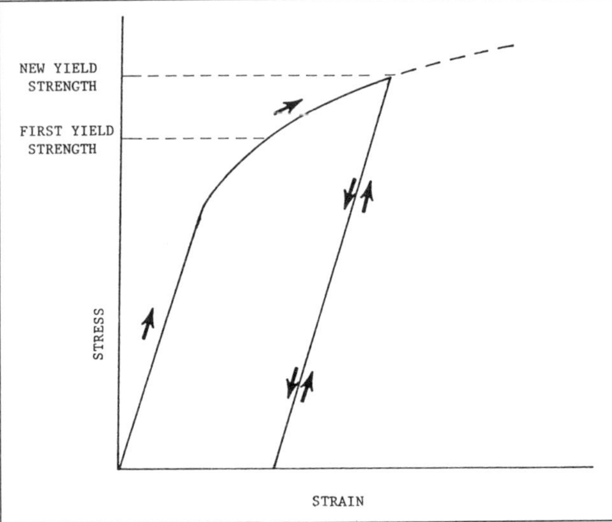

Fig. 3.18—Increase in yield strength from plastic deformation (cold working).

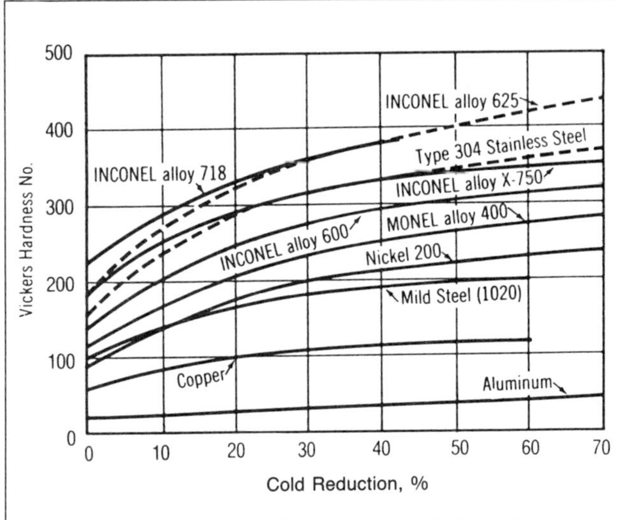

Fig. 3.19—Effect of cold work on the hardness of various alloys (courtesy of Inco Alloys Intl. Inc.).[12]

3.7 Sour-Gas Corrosion

Metal corrosion in sour-gas environments is an electrochemical process, which consists of anodes and cathodes. Metal corrosion can be divided into two basic reactions: oxidation and reduction. Oxidation represents the corrosion of the metal that occurs at the anode. Reduction is the reaction that occurs at the cathode. In an acidic solution, which is often found in the oil field, the following reactions are common:

$Fe \rightarrow Fe^{2+} + 2e$ (oxidation)

and $2H^+ + 2e \rightarrow H_2(gas)$ (reduction).

The oxidation and reduction reactions are dependent on each other; therefore, whatever affects one reaction affects the other. That is, if the reduction reaction is increased, the oxidation reaction (corrosion) also increases.

For H_2S in water, the particular sulfur species and concentration are functions of pH (**Fig. 3.20**).[14] At acid pH, the predominant species is H_2S, while at more basic pH, $S^=$ is the main constituent. HS^- is the dominant species at intermediate pH. The behavior of metals in solutions containing H_2S depends largely on the specific species in solution. Simplified total reactions for each species as a function of pH follow.

$Fe + H_2S = FeS + 2H^\circ$ (acidic),

$Fe + HS^- = FeS + H^+ + 2e$ (neutral),

and $Fe + S^= = FeS + 2e$ (basic).

There are actually numerous intermediate reactions and the reaction chemistry is complex.[15] For purposes of this discussion, however, the above reactions will suffice. Note in these reactions that, regardless of the sulfur species in solution, the final corrosion product is always iron sulfide. In practice, however, many different iron-sulfide corrosion products with a variety of crystal stuctures may form (**Fig. 3.21**).[16]

The corrosion of metals in H_2S depends on the concentration of H_2S in solution. The solubility in water of acid gases that form weak acids depends on the partial pressure of the gas and the solution pH. **Fig. 3.22** displays this dependence for H_2S in a 3% NaCl solution at different temperatures.* **Fig. 3.23** shows the effect of CO_2 additions with H_2S and the resulting pH.[17] Increasing concentrations of H_2S and CO_2 decrease the solution pH.

*Personal communication with G.P. Coker, Amoco Corp., Naperville, IL (1989).

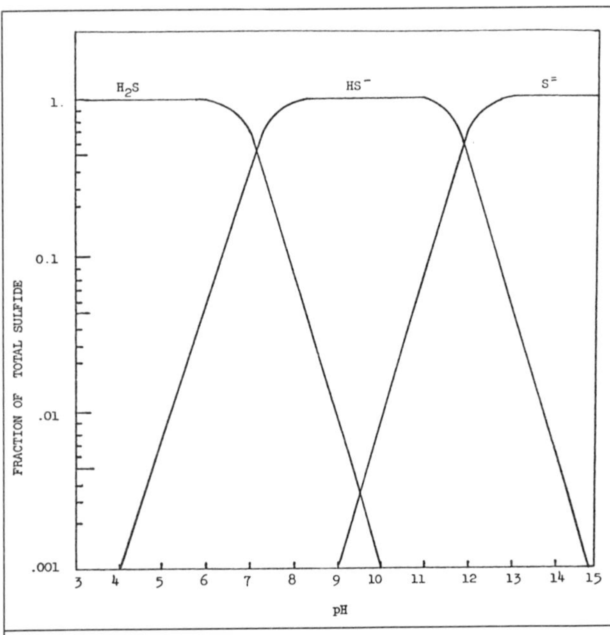

Fig. 3.20—Sulfur species as a function of pH (© NACE, 1966).[14]

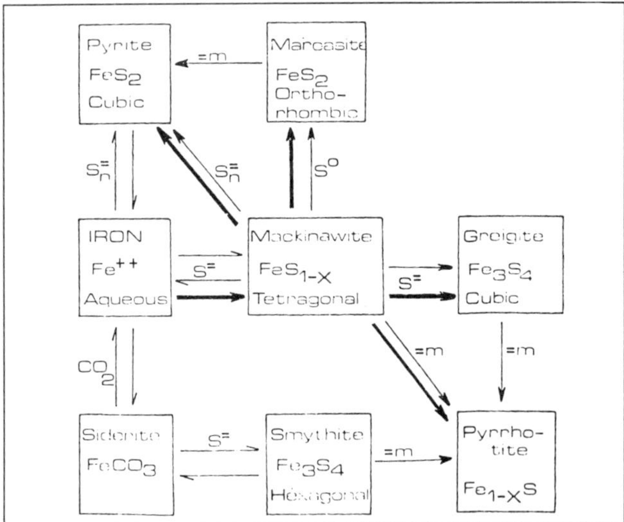

Fig. 3.21—Common forms of iron sulfide formed during the corrosion of steel in H_2S (Ref. 16) (courtesy of The Inst. of Metals).

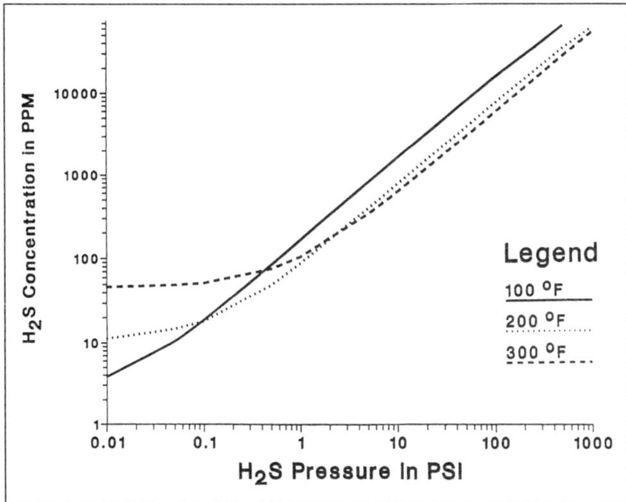

Fig. 3.22—H_2S concentration in water as a function of p_{H_2S} [G.P. Coker, Amoco Corp., Naperville, IL (1989)].

Fig. 3.24 shows the corrosion rate of carbon steel in a solution containing H_2S at ambient temperature.[18] Clearly, the corrosion rate diminishes significantly as the pH increases above pH 8. This, among other important factors (discussed later), is why high-pH drilling muds are beneficial for the resistance of drilling equipment to H_2S. The corrosion rate of steels in H_2S is also a function of the entire environment, including other gases and water chemistry. **Fig. 3.25** describes the typical corrosion experienced on carbon steel as a function of other constituents in the total environment.[19] If H_2S is the only constituent, a protective iron-sulfide film may form that significantly reduces corrosion, whereas the introduction of brine creates a continually corrosive condition. When CO_2 is included, the corrosion process becomes more aggressive and quite complex.

Another component that seriously aggravates H_2S corrosion is the presence of oxygen. Oxygen combined with H_2S can cause corrosion that is much worse than the additive effect of corrosion from each gas independently. Besides this synergism in corrosion, H_2S and oxygen have a chemical reaction that produces water and elemental sulfur:

$$H_2S+½O_2=H_2O+S.$$

This reaction is relatively slow at ambient temperature, but it can be catalyzed by cations in solution such as iron, manganese, cobalt, and nickel, or as recently discovered, by triethylene glycol.[20] The corrosion rate of steel in wet elemental sulfur is quite high (on the order of 1 in./yr [2.54 cm/a]).

Sulfur is not only formed by oxidation of H_2S; it also can be produced with sour gas. The production of elemental sulfur is observed most commonly in wells with high H_2S concentrations and high temperatures. Sulfur can be carried in gas streams as a physical suspension of particulate in the gas or dissolved chemically in H_2S or condensate, or it can follow from the decomposition of polysulfides. However, it is speculated that other reactions, such as

$$SO_4^{=}+CH_4=S+H_2O+CO_2$$

and $H_2S \longrightarrow H_2+S$ (in the presence of FeS_2),

may also occur.[21] The latter reaction reflects the possible role of pyrite (FeS_2) in catalyzing the dissociation of H_2S. Of course, regardless of the mechanism, the precipitation of elemental sulfur can create serious problems, including wellbore plugging and severe corrosion. **Table 3.4** shows examples of sulfur deposition in sour-gas wells as a function of the well parameters.[21] **Figs. 3.26 and 3.27** show that the solubility of sulfur in gas is a function of pressure, temperature, and H_2S content.[21] Likewise, sulfur precipitation depends on temperature and pressure. Additional effects of elemental sulfur in gas production on corrosion and cracking of high-alloy materials are discussed in Chap. 5.

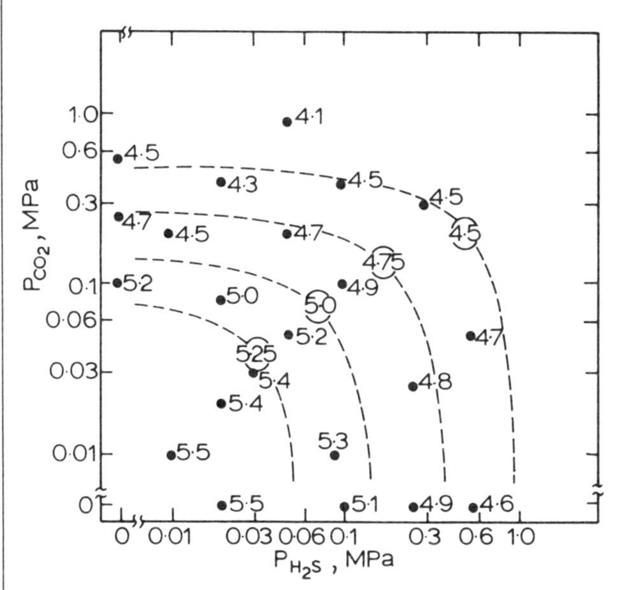

Fig. 3.23—Effect of H_2S and CO_2 on pH value of synthetic seawater.[17]

3.8 Sulfide Stress Cracking

From an equipment standpoint, the most serious aspect of sour gas is the potential for catastrophic failure that many metallic materials display in the presence of H_2S. Premature failure by fracturing, often below the yield strength, is called sulfide stress cracking (SSC).

The principal factors that contribute to SSC can be separated into two general categories: environment (H_2S concentration, pH, temperature, and applied stress) and materials (yield strength, microstructure, heat treatment, and alloying). Increasing the H_2S concentration can have a significant effect on susceptibility to SSC (**Fig. 3.28**)[14] because increasing the H_2S concentration increases the amount of hydrogen charged into an alloy (**Fig. 3.29**).[22] In fact, H_2S promotes hydrogen entry into alloys because it hinders the hydrogen recombination reaction. During electrochemical corrosion in acid solutions, the overall cathodic reaction is

$$2H^++2e^-=H_2(gas).$$

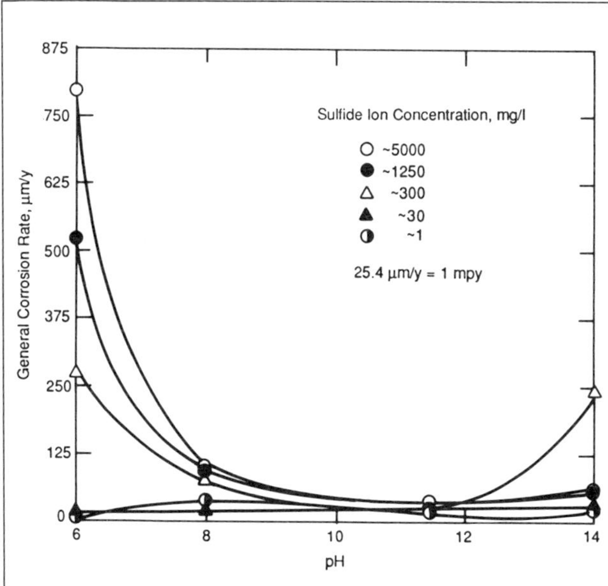

Fig. 3.24—General corrosion rate for AISI 1040 steel as a function of sulfide-ion concentration and pH (© NACE, 1981).[18]

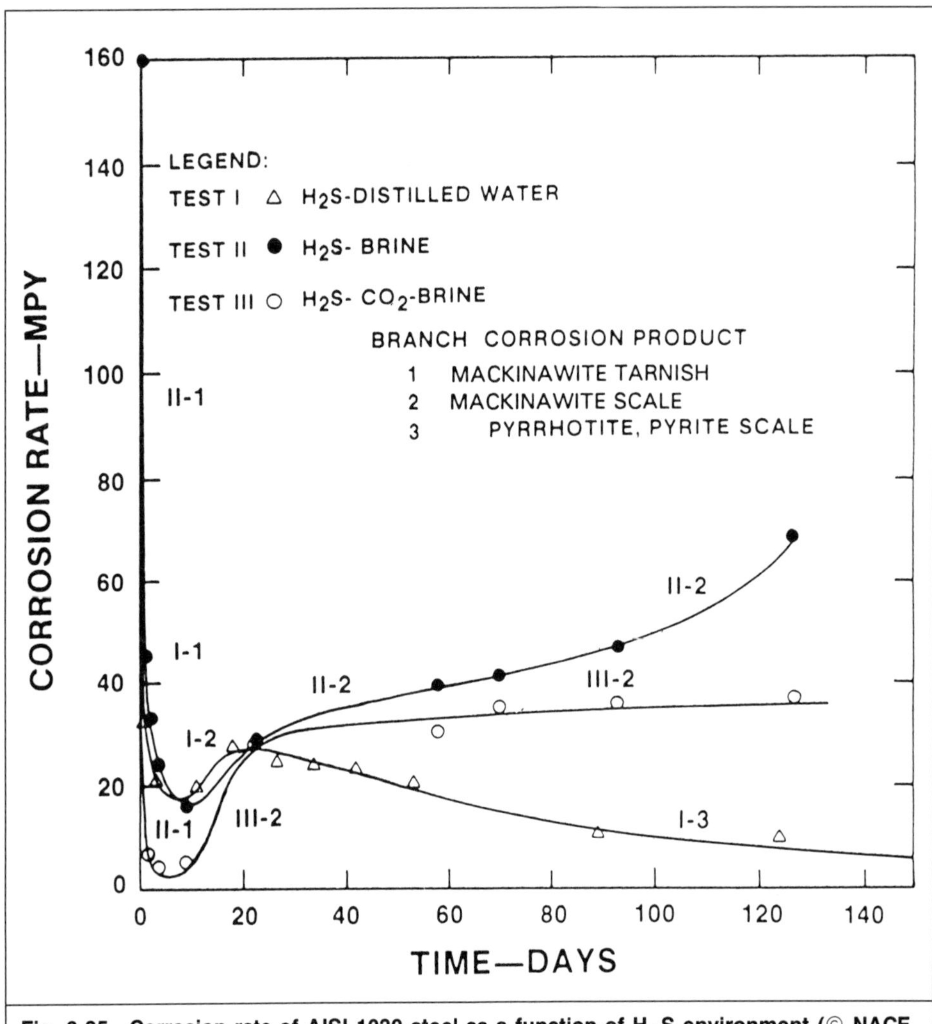

Fig. 3.25—Corrosion rate of AISI 1020 steel as a function of H_2S environment (© NACE, 1958).[19]

TABLE 3.4—SULFUR DEPOSITION IN SOUR-GAS WELLS (After Ref. 21)

Location	H_2S (%)	Bottomhole Temperature (°F)	Bottomhole Pressure (psi)	Comment
Buchhorst, Germany	4.8	273	5,875	Initial liquid sulfur flow, bottomhole
Devonian Wabamun B, Alberta	10.4	216	5,980	13,500- to 14,000-ft well string deposition, dry gas
Crossfield Wabamun, Alberta	34.4	175	3,600	Deposition in presence of condensate
Leduc and Woodbend, Alberta	53.5	230	4,673	Well string deposition in dry gas (11,000 ft)
Josephine and Mississippi, USA	78	390	14,000	Estimate 7,500 lbm/MMcf carried sulfur; deposition up to 2,000 lbm/MMcf
Murray Franklin, Texas	98	450 to 500	18,000	Liquid sulfur, bottomhole
Permian Reef, Alberta	90	250	5,400	Estimate 5,000 lbm/MMcf deposition and plugging

However, before hydrogen gas is formed, an intermediate step must occur:

$$H^+ + e \longrightarrow H^\circ.$$

Then, $H^\circ + H^\circ \longrightarrow H_2$.

H_2S or sulfide ions hinder the last reaction (recombination), allowing the hydrogen atoms (H°) to enter the alloy. Thus, SSC is actually a special case of hydrogen stress cracking (HSC), frequently called hydrogen embrittlement.

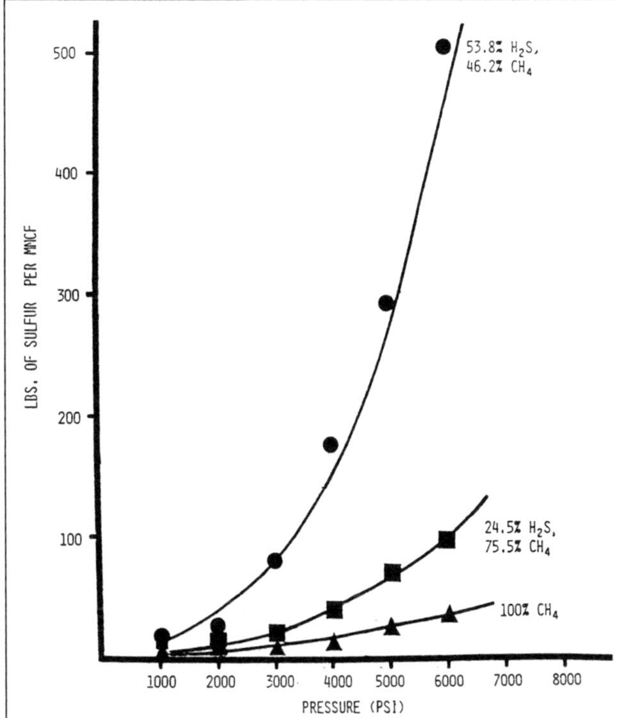

Fig. 3.26—Sulfur solubility vs. pressure and H_2S content at 250°F [121°C].[21]

Increasing the concentration of hydrogen ions by decreasing the pH increases the susceptibility to SSC compared with more neutral pH at the same H_2S concentration (**Fig. 3.30**).[23] **Fig. 3.24** shows this as a function of sulfur species.[24] A high degree of embrittlement is observed at low pH, but with increasing pH the embrittlement goes to zero.

Temperature has an important effect on SSC. The susceptibility of steels to fracture in H_2S reaches a maximum at about 77°F [25°C]. For temperatures less than or greater than this maximum, steels become increasingly more resistant to SSC (**Fig. 3.32**).[25] This factor is also consistent with an HSC mechanism.

To understand SSC, it is important to discuss the primary factors that contribute to HSC. HSC is the abrupt failure of a metal by fracture below its yield strength in the presence of a tensile stress and a hydrogen-bearing environment. As with SSC, HSC is a function of pH, temperature, applied stress, yield stress, microstructure, heat treatment, and alloying. These dependencies are identical to those for SSC; thus, all HSC laboratory data can be used to understand the problems of SSC. For instance, the temperature dependence of HSC is also found to be a function of the strain rate (**Fig.**

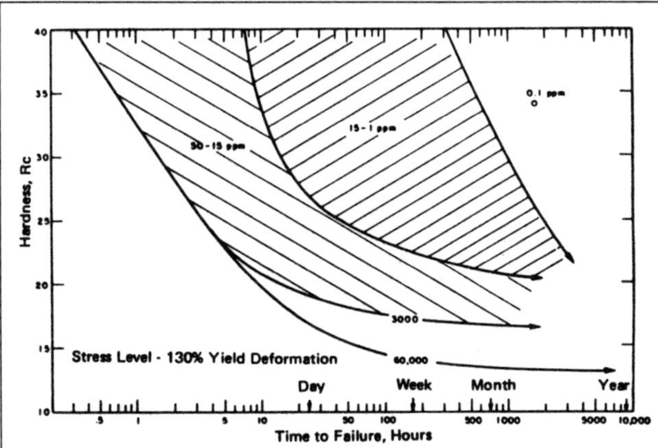

Fig. 3.28—t_f as a function of hardness and H_2S content in 5% NaCl solution (© NACE, 1966).[14]

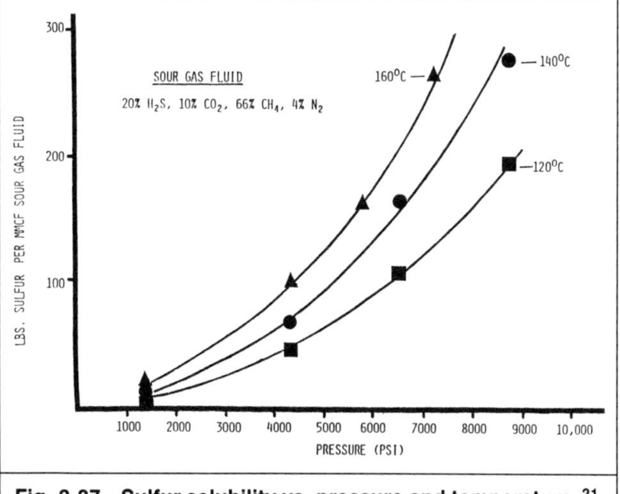

Fig. 3.27—Sulfur solubility vs. pressure and temperature.[21]

3.33).[26] Increasing the strain rate decreases the effect of hydrogen and essentially restores steel to its temperature-independent behavior. At slow strain rates (shown in Fig. 3.33 by crosshead speed), however, hydrogen has a marked effect on fracture strength.

Yield strength is possibly the most important factor governing the resistance of alloys to SSC. Increasing the yield strength seriously diminishes alloy resistance to SSC. Because hardness can be used to measure strength, however, the resistance of many metals to SSC is measured by their hardness. Hardness reflects the tensile strength of an alloy, and indirectly, its yield strength. Besides carbon steel, stainless steels and nickel-based alloys with high yield strengths may suffer from SSC. This widespread susceptibility of high-strength alloys to SSC led the Natl. Assn. of Corrosion Engineers (NACE) to produce their material recommendation (NACE *Standard MR-01-75*)[27] as a guideline in selecting materials for sour service. **Fig. 3.34** is an example of the relationship between the yield strength of steel and its threshold stress level for cracking in H_2S.[28] Note the significant difference in resistance to SSC depending on the heat treatment; quench and tempered steels are more resistant than steels that are normalized and tempered. The threshold stress is the stress below which failure does not occur and above which failure does occur.

In addition to yield strength, the applied stress is an important factor in resistance to fracture in H_2S. **Fig. 3.35** shows the reduction in time to failure with a minor change in applied stress.[29] Fig.

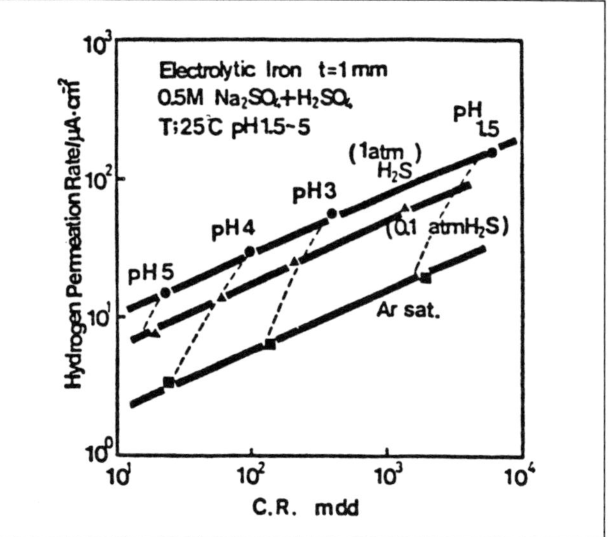

Fig. 3.29—Effect of pH and p_{H_2S} on hydrogen permeation rate through 0.04-in. [1-mm]-thick pure iron at 77°F [25°C].[22]

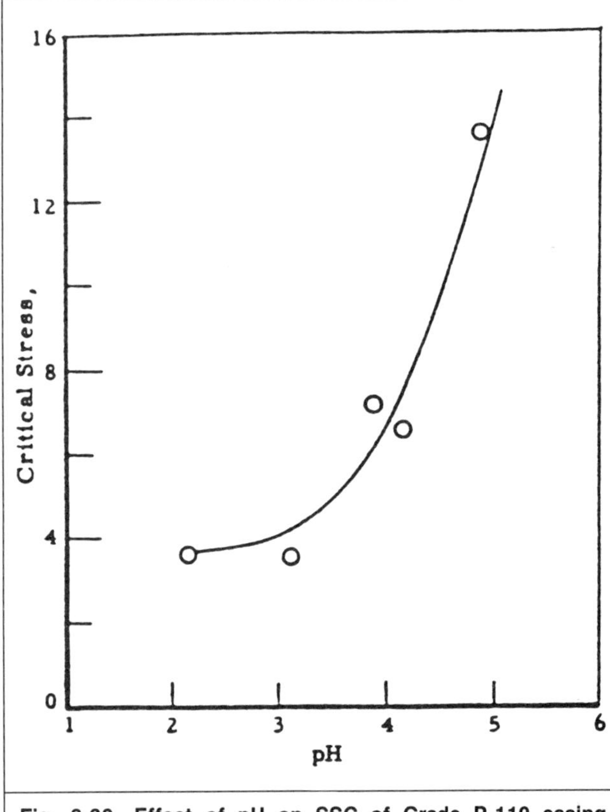

Fig. 3.30—Effect of pH on SSC of Grade P-110 casing (© NACE, 1968).[23]

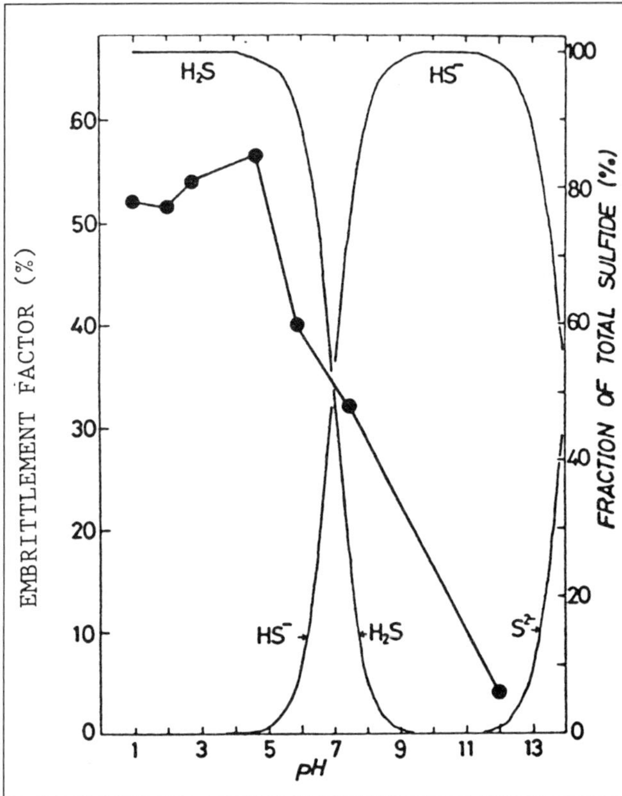

Fig. 3.31—Effect of pH and sulfur species on steel embrittlement (© NACE, 1976).[24]

3.35 also illustrates the concept of threshold stress. The large variation in threshold behavior is a result of different alloy composition and heat treatments.

Thus, microstructure, heat treatment, and alloying are interrelated and are also important in determining alloy resistance to SSC. All else being equal, including strength level, a steel with a highly tempered martensitic microstructure is the most resistant to SSC. Bainite and a mixture of ferrite and pearlite (normalized) are the next most resistant microstructures. In other alloys, all else being equal, a single-phase microstructure, excluding precipitates, generally provides higher resistance to SSC than a multiphase microstructure.

One of the many features observed in both SSC and HSC is that fractures most often initiate at internal locations in the alloy at areas of high local stress, which induces fractures from an internal site. Contrary to this behavior, stress corrosion cracking (SCC) most often initiates on the metal surface from a crevice or the bottom of a pit. SCC is the fracture of metals below their yield strength in response to tensile stresses and the presence of a specific ion, which varies depending on the alloy. For example, chlorides can cause cracking of austenitic stainless steels but not copper-based

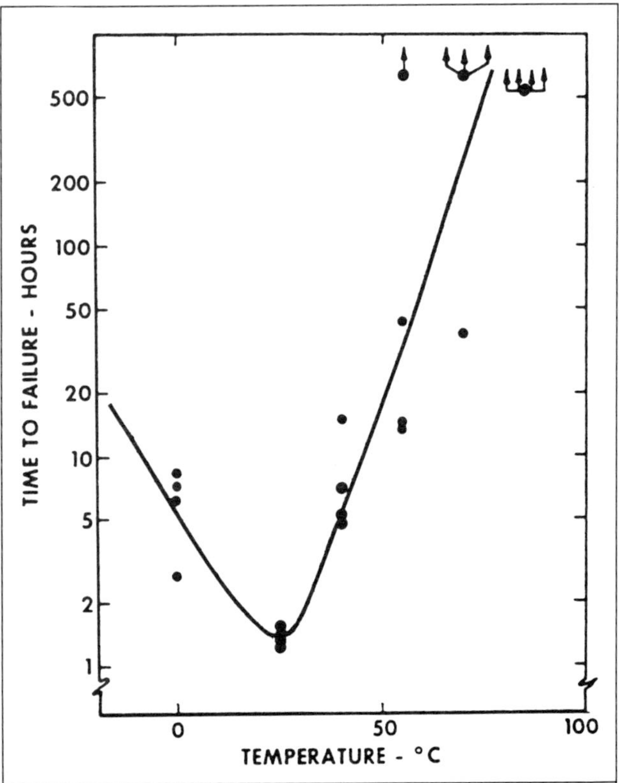

Fig. 3.32—Effect of temperature on SSC of high-strength steel wire (© NACE, 1972).[25]

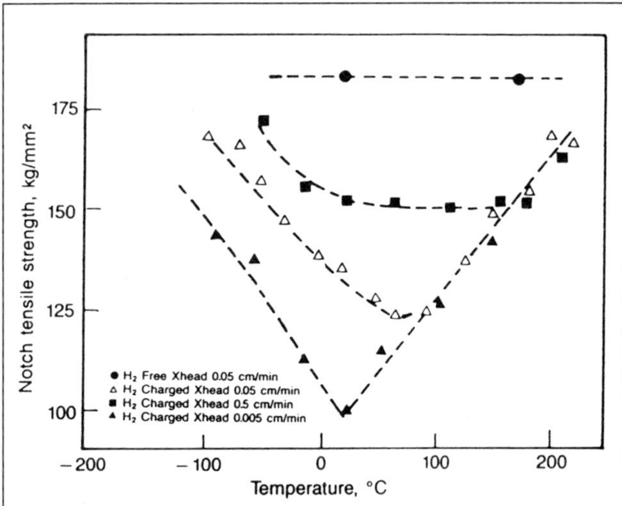

Fig. 3.33—Notch tensile strength of hydrogen-charged steel as a function of temperature and strain rate.[26]

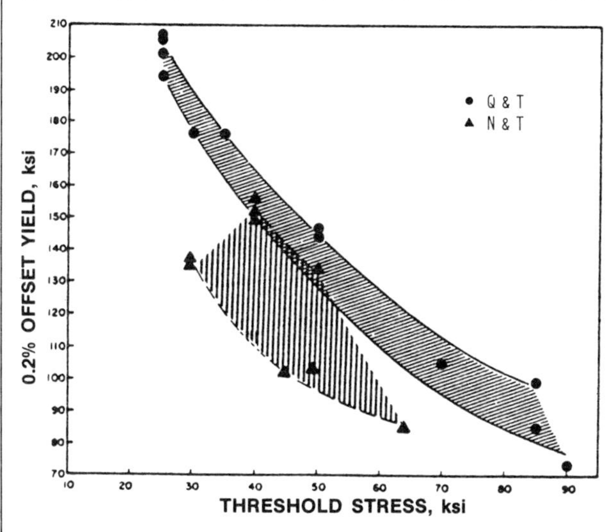

Fig. 3.34—Threshold stress for SSC as a function of yield strength for low-alloy steels (© NACE, 1967).[28]

alloys; however, ammonia will cause cracking of some copper alloys but not austenitic stainless steels. SSC is not ion specific but depends on the amount of hydrogen in the metal matrix. SCC is discussed further in Sec. 3.11.

The fracture mode of SSC passes through a transition from predominantly intergranular at high yield strengths to transgranular at lower yield strengths. In fact, at yield strengths below about 80,000 psi [552 MPa], fractures originate at nonmetallic inclusions.

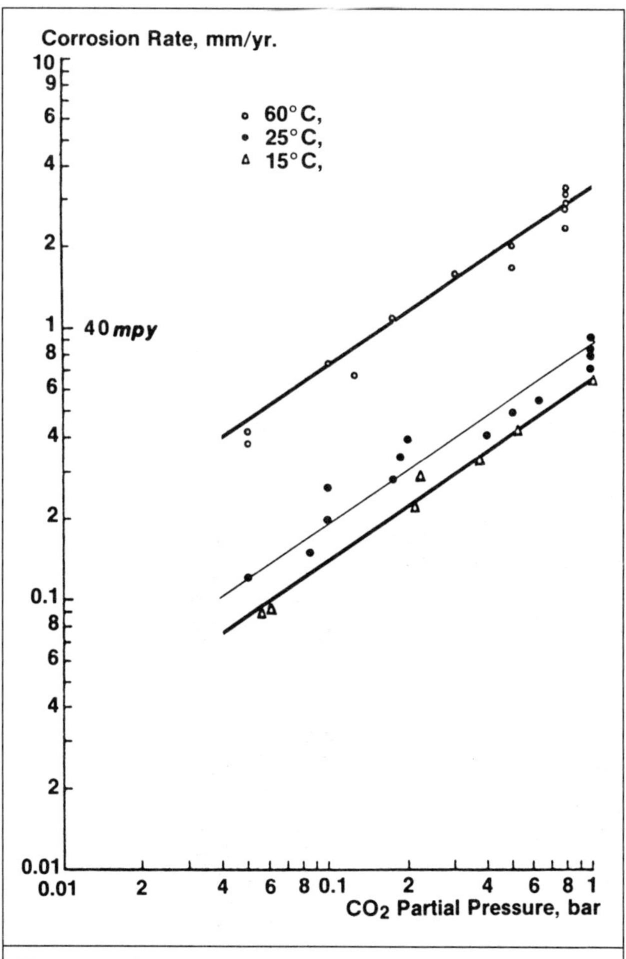

Fig. 3.36—Steel corrosion as a function of p_{CO_2} and T (© NACE, 1975).[30]

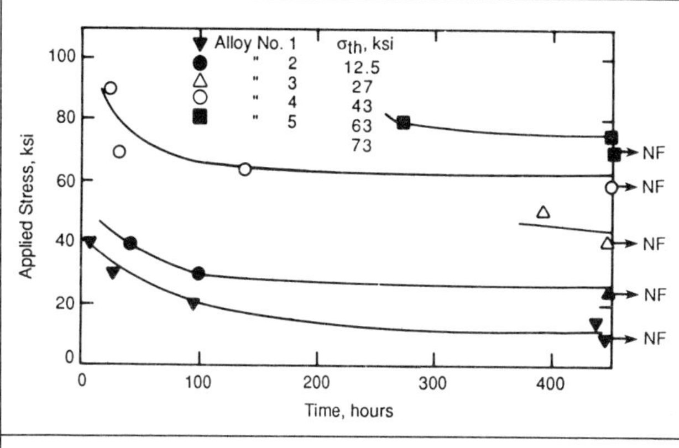

Fig. 3.35—SSC behavior for various low-alloy steels as a function of applied stress (© NACE, 1979).[29]

In quite low-strength unstressed steels exposed to H_2S, hydrogen cracking associated with inclusions has been observed as stair-step cracks linked together. This is called stepwise cracking or hydrogen-induced cracking. This phenomenon is addressed in Chap. 6. Thus, H_2S can cause cracking of steels and many other alloys across the entire strength spectrum.

3.9 CO_2 Corrosion

While this monograph is concerned with sour gas, the implications of CO_2, which often is produced with H_2S, cannot be ignored. Therefore, a brief discussion of CO_2 corrosion is presented.

CO_2 dissolves in water to form carbonic acid, which is a weak acid. However, low solution pH accelerates corrosion.

Corrosion from CO_2 can result in either a uniform thinning of the metal surface or a localized pitting attack. The primary factors that affect CO_2 corrosion are partial pressure, temperature, chloride content, and velocity. **Fig. 3.36** shows the effects of temperature and CO_2 partial pressure on the corrosion rate.[30] Increasing either or both factors increases the corrosion rate of carbon steel. Fig. 3.36, however, is indicative of corrosion only up to 1 atm [0.1 MPa] CO_2 partial pressure. At higher partial pressures, the linearity of the corrosion rate is maintained under flowing conditions (see the upper curve in **Fig. 3.37**) but reaches a plateau (lower curve) under static conditions.[31] The corrosion rate is limited on the lower curve because of the formation of a semiprotective iron-carbonate ($FeCO_3$) film. The stability of this film and its degree of protectiveness depend on the CO_2 partial pressure and temperature. At temperatures above about 160°F [71°C], the carbonate film is often quite tenacious and protective.

Fig. 3.38 demonstrates the temperature dependence of CO_2 corrosion and the effect of alloying with chromium.[32] While the behavior of carbon steel is erratic, increasing the chromium content to

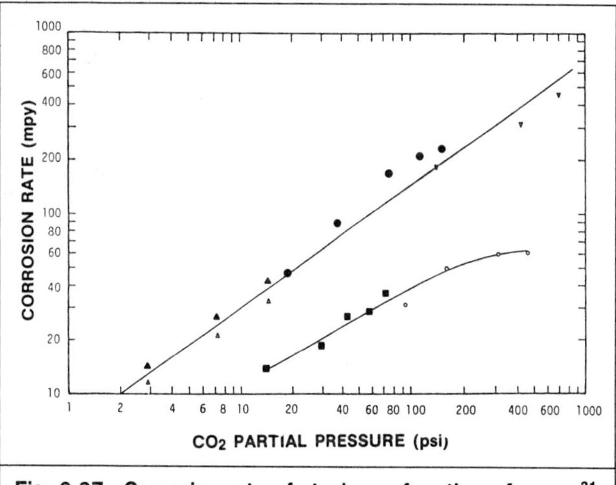

Fig. 3.37—Corrosion rate of steel as a function of p_{CO_2}.[31]

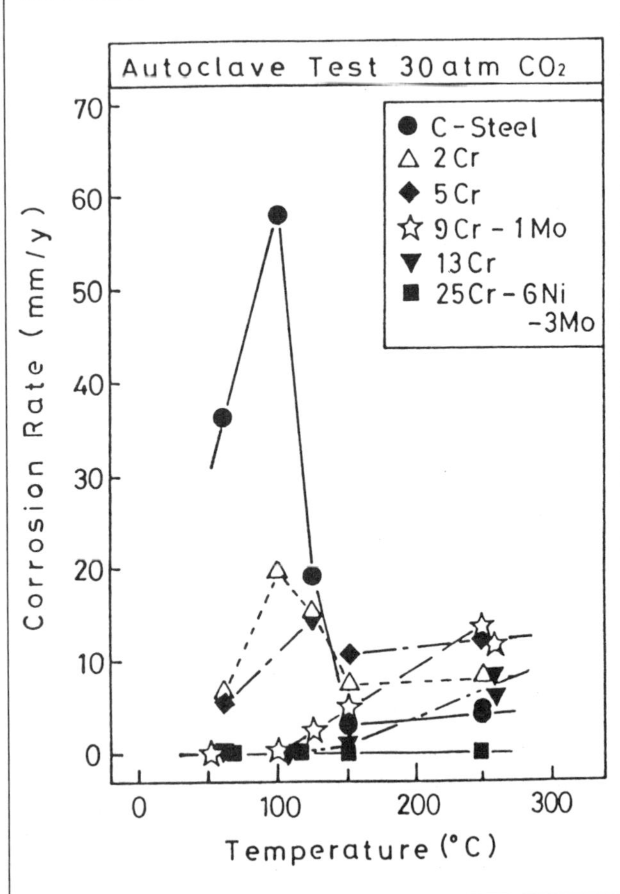

Fig. 3.38—Corrosion of carbon and chromium steels in CO_2 as a function of temperature.[32]

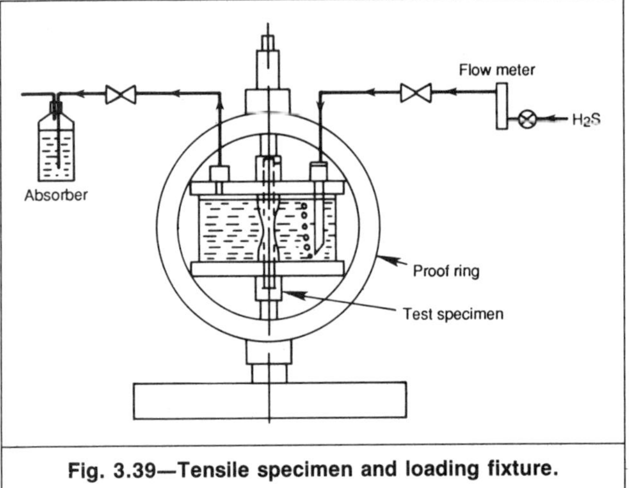

Fig. 3.39—Tensile specimen and loading fixture.

25% reduces corrosion to essentially zero.[32] The advantage of adding chromium to steel to reduce corrosion from CO_2 was established by NACE[33] under actual condensate well conditions. At least 9% Cr is necessary to provide protection against the carbonic-acid corrosion produced by CO_2. The 9% Cr steels, however, may be marginally resistant in some environments, so it is common practice to use 12% to 13% Cr steels for corrosion resistance in CO_2.

The addition of chlorides to the environment creates complex interactions, depending on the chloride concentration, the CO_2 partial pressure, and the temperature. When other species (e.g., H_2S and elemental sulfur) are added to the environment, the interactions and resulting corrosion become more complicated and difficult to predict. Small concentrations of H_2S, however, can cause SSC of 9% and 13% Cr steels, so they are not typically used in sour service. These complex environments (chlorides, CO_2, H_2S, etc.) are discussed in Chap. 5.

Although some laboratory evidence exists for cracking of carbon and low-alloy steels in CO_2 environments, to date, no field failures have been attributed to this cause. If CO and CO_2 are present together, then, depending on their ratio, these two gases may induce SCC.[1]

In the past decade, considerable insight into the causes of CO_2 corrosion and its mitigation has developed. For additional information, see Refs. 33 through 35.

3.10 Test Methods for SSC

Material selection and quality control are key steps in designing for sour-gas service. Regardless of prior experience and information

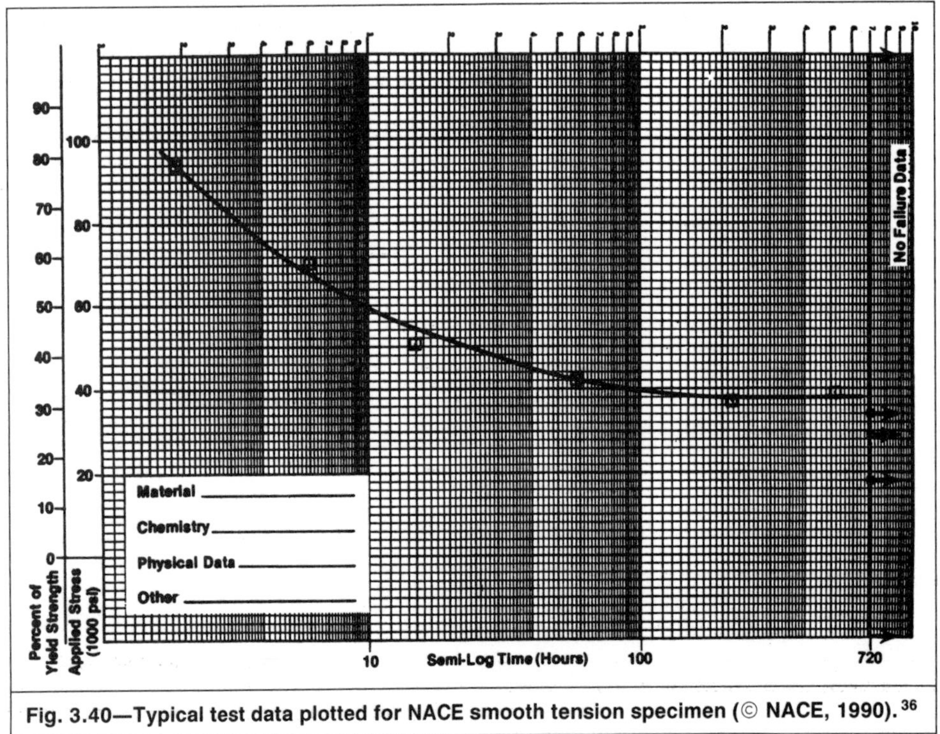

Fig. 3.40—Typical test data plotted for NACE smooth tension specimen (© NACE, 1990).[36]

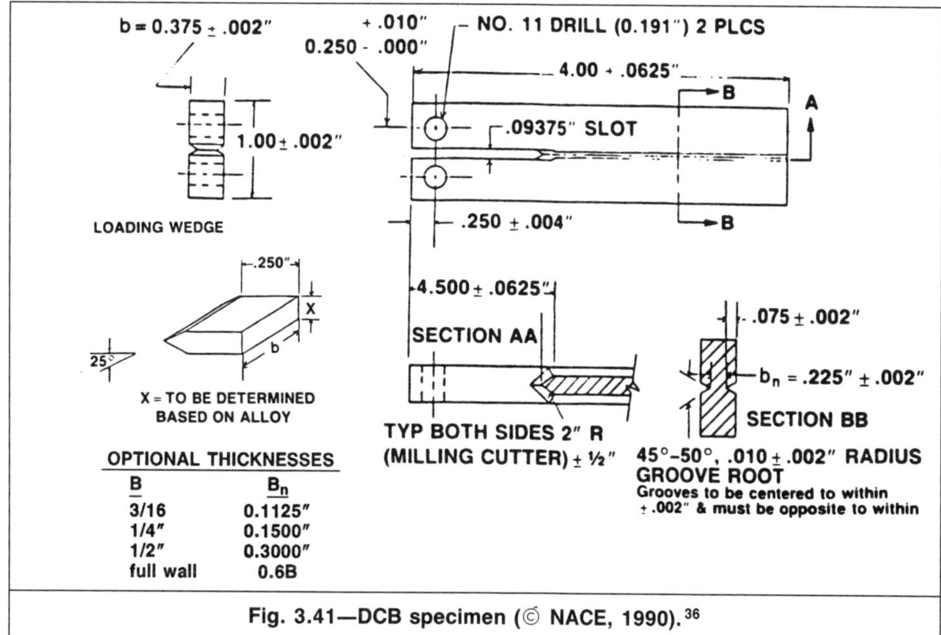

B	B_n
3/16	0.1125"
1/4"	0.1500"
1/2"	0.3000"
full wall	0.6B

Fig. 3.41—DCB specimen (© NACE, 1990).[36]

concerning a certain field or well environment, the ramification of a failure in a sour-gas system is so great that accurate understanding of how materials will behave in a specific environment is necessary to make proper design decisions. Numerous test methods are currently available to evaluate the behavior of materials in severe environments. All methods have advantages and disadvantages, and it is prudent to use more than one method to evaluate materials for a specific environment or application. Moreover, material performance data (e.g., threshold stress) are not absolute values; thus, judgment and experience must be applied. The most common test specimens used to determine SSC resistance are the smooth tensile bar, the double cantilever beam (DCB), the C-ring, and the bent beam. NACE has developed a standard test method that describes the use of each test.[36]

For the tensile bar test, tensile bars are loaded in tension, typically in a proving-ring fixture, to different percentages of the yield strength and exposed to a solution of distilled water containing 5% NaCl and 0.5% acetic acid through which H_2S is continuously bubbled. **Fig. 3.39** shows a typical proving-ring apparatus.[36] The time to failure is measured for each applied stress and the data are plotted as shown in **Fig. 3.40**.[36] Note that as the applied stress diminishes, a threshold level is reached below which fracture does not occur. This threshold is demonstrated by the data points with arrows on the 720-hour line at the right in Fig. 3.40 and indicates that no failure occurred after 720 hours of testing. This threshold concept is useful when comparing various alloys in the same environment, but it is not a material property to use for design purposes because actual field conditions are rarely identical to the laboratory test environment, and the threshold under field conditions may be quite different.

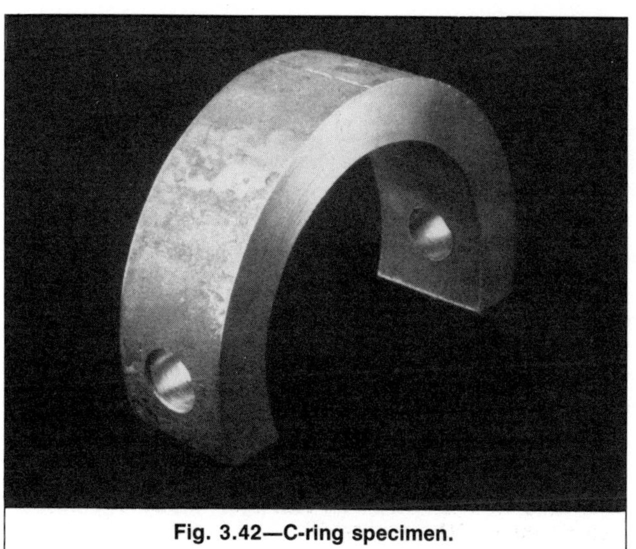

Fig. 3.42—C-ring specimen.

Materials engineers use fracture mechanics to evaluate the tolerance of structures to flaws. Fracture mechanics allows the calculation of a critical value, K_{IC}, that predicts the onset of unstable crack extension (i.e., fracture). The DCB test can measure, but not calculate, similar values for metals in H_2S. The DCB test uses fracture mechanics to derive a value of threshold stress intensity for environmentally assisted crack growth (**Fig. 3.41**).[36] Before specimens are exposed to a test environment such as that described in *Standard TM-01-77,*[36] DCB's are prepared by initiating a fatigue crack along the fracture plane of the specimen at the end of a machined notch. Interaction with the test environment and stress concentration at the crack tip cause the crack to propagate if the material is susceptible. The SSC threshold stress intensity, K_{ISSC}, is then determined. K_{ISSC} is characteristic of the specific material and test environment and is not a true material property for design purposes. In fact, neither a test method nor a mathematical means of determining a definitive threshold stress exists for SSC that is accurate enough for design purposes.

The C-ring is also commonly used to evaluate SSC resistance. This specimen, machined from a tube (**Fig. 3.42**), offers the advantage of simulating the behavior of tubulars stressed in the field environment. Quite often, full-dimension tubing specimens are used for testing. To increase the severity of the test, a notch is sometimes cut into the outside surface of the ring at the location of highest tensile stress. C-rings can be loaded by means of a bolt to fractions

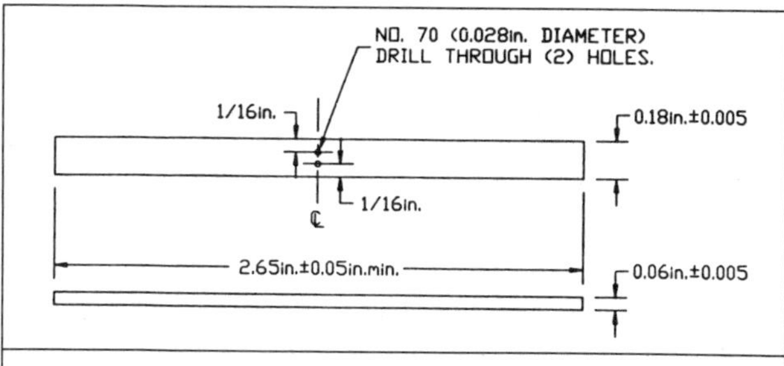

Fig. 3.43—Typical Shell bent-beam specimen (© NACE, 1990).[36]

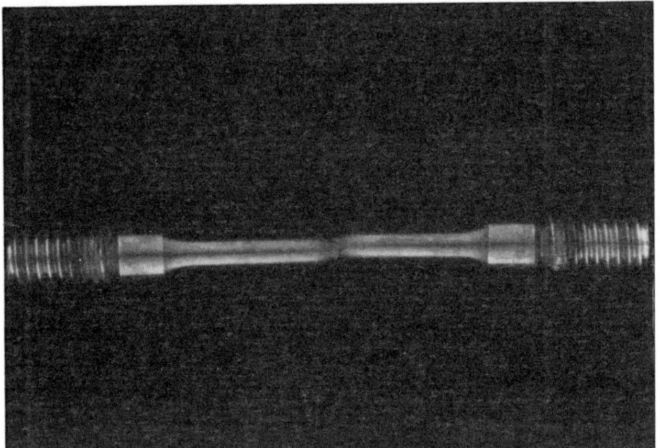

Fig. 3.44—SSRT specimen after testing (magnification approximately 1⅓X).

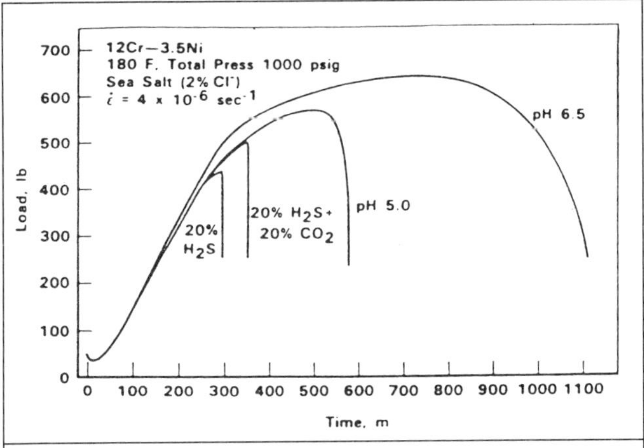

Fig. 3.45—Load vs. time to failure for SSRT at 180°F [82°C] in sea-salt brine (© NACE, 1986).[37]

of the yield strength to produce a curve similar to that shown in Fig. 3.40.

Frequently, many tests are required to screen potential materials for SSC resistance. One of the most economic means is to test a bent beam (**Fig. 3.43**).[36] The bent beam is a small, thin strip of metal removed from a large sample and can be smooth or have a notch or small holes. The specimen in Fig. 3.43, the Shell bent beam, has two holes drilled at the center and is named for the company that developed it. The beam may be loaded in three- or four-point bending. Small fixtures designed for the bent-beam method allow many of these specimens to be tested simultaneously in the same environment at different applied stresses. The actual applied stress on this test specimen is relatively subjective because it is difficult to calculate the stress concentration effect of the drill holes.

The four test specimens described are by no means the only ones used to evaluate SSC resistance. These specimens represent those most frequently used under conditions of static applied stress. Moreover, these tests provide data only on SSC and not on pitting or general corrosion from sour environments. Coupons are often tested for materials corrosion studies to detect general or localized attacks, such as pitting or crevice corrosion. These specimens are made in a variety of shapes and sizes and are exposed to test environments in the same manner as the SSC specimens, except no stress is applied.

Autoclaves are necessary to generate the high pressures and temperatures needed to simulate field environments in the laboratory. Corrosion coupons and the four SSC-specimen types have been adapted for testing in autoclaves. High-pressure/high-temperature autoclave testing will be required more frequently to simulate the harsher environments found by the petroleum industry. However, one disadvantage of autoclave testing is that it typically takes a long time (from a minimum of 1 month to 3 to 6 months).

The slow strain-rate test (SSRT) has gained recent popularity for evaluating the environmental cracking behavior of materials in sour environments. The advantage of the SSRT is that it is short (usually <2 days), compared with several weeks or months for the other tests described. The SSRT is especially useful for testing corrosion-resistant alloys. However, one serious disadvantage is that the test is severe, and hence, requires that results be interpreted. The specimen, a long, smooth tensile bar (**Fig. 3.44**) is strained at a constant rate (e.g., 1×10^{-6} in./in.-sec^{-1} 2.5×10^{-6} cm/cm·s^{-1}]) until failure occurs. The specimen is exposed to an environment for the duration of the test and the results are compared with those from a test performed in air or an inert environment (oil). **Fig. 3.45** shows typical SSRT data for a 12% Cr stainless steel.[37] Fig. 3.45 also shows that the addition of H_2S significantly affects the failure time and the maximum load to fracture. **Table 3.5** gives the parameters used to evaluate SSRT data. Significant reduction in elongation, ϵ_e; reduction in area, A_r; and/or time to failure suggest sensitivity to the test environment. Additionally, secondary cracks in the gauge section tend to confirm susceptibility to stress cracking. Presently, however, there are no commonly agreed upon values for these ratios that represent pass or fail criteria. Note that, because it is so severe, the SSRT technique may eliminate alloys that could be resistant to cracking under normal field conditions. Thus, decisions regarding materials for sour service should not be made solely on the basis of SSRT data. The SSRT provides a means of ranking the resistance of alloys to a specific environment and is often useful in establishing the rank of candidate alloys for additional testing. The SSRT is also quite useful in establishing such parameters as critical temperature for cracking, as **Fig. 3.46** shows for Incoloy 825 in an H_2S environment.[38]

TABLE 3.5—PARAMETERS USED TO EVALUATE SSRT DATA
Time to failure (fracture), t_f
Percent elongation: $\epsilon(t_y - t_f)100 = \epsilon_e$
Ratio of elongation to elongation in air, ϵ_e/ϵ_a
Percent reduction in area, $A_r = 100[1-(d_f/d)^2]$
Ratio of reduction in area to reduction in area in air, A_r/a_r
Tensile strength from slow-rate strain curve
Secondary (visible) cracks outside necked region of gauge section
Strain rate, $\dot{\epsilon} = 10^{-7}$ to 10^{-1} seconds^{-1}

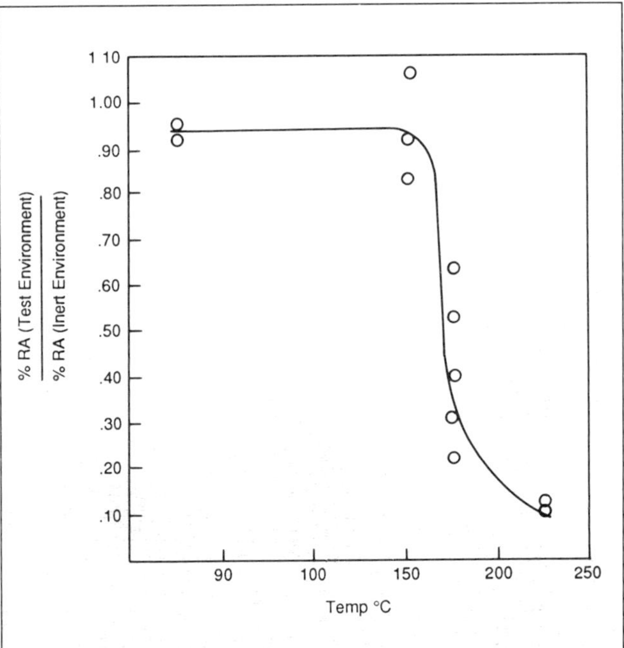

Fig. 3.46—Critical cracking temperature for UNS NO8825 in sour brine (© NACE, 1988).[38]

TABLE 3.6—MATERIAL/ENVIRONMENT COMBINATIONS FOR WHICH SSC MAY OCCUR (After Ref. 39)

Material	Environment
Aluminum alloys	NaCl-H_2O_2 and NaCl solutions, seawater, air, and water vapor
Copper alloys	Ammonia vapors and solutions, amines, water, and water vapor
Gold alloys	$FeCl_3$ and acetic acid-salt solutions
Inconel	Caustic soda solutions
Lead	Lead acetate solutions
Magnesium alloys	NaCl-K_2CrO_4 solutions, rural and coastal atmospheres, and distilled water
Monel	Fused caustic soda and hydrofluoric and hydrofluosilicic acids
Nickel	Fused caustic soda
Ordinary steels	NaOH, NaOH-Na_2SiO_2, calcium, ammonium, and sodium nitrate solutions; mixed acids (H_2SO_4-HNO_3); HCN and acidic H_2S solutions; seawater; and molten Na-Pb alloys
Stainless steels	Acid chlorine ($MgCl_2$ and $BaCl_2$) and NaCl-H_2O_2 solutions, seawater, H_2S, NaOH-H_2S solutions, and condensing steam from chloride waters
Titanium alloys	Red-fuming nitric acid, seawater, N_2O_4, and methanol-HCl

*Fontana, M. and Green, H. Corrosion Engineering, McGraw-Hill Inc., 1967. Reproduced with permission from McGraw-Hill.

3.11 SCC

SCC requires the presence of a tensile stress and a corrosive environment. Other factors, however, can distinguish SCC from SSC. The principal contributing factors to SCC are the environment (pH, specific ion, concentration of ion, temperature, and applied stress) and materials (yield strength, alloying, microstructure, and heat treatment).

Almost every alloy is subject to catastrophic cracking when stressed in a specific environment. All aggressive environments do not crack all alloys; instead, certain chemical species and alloy combinations produce SCC. Such ions as hydroxides, chlorides, and nitrates may cause cracking of carbon and low-alloy steels. **Table 3.6** shows some of the solutions and compounds that cause SSC in various alloys.[39] This list is incomplete because specific ions or environments are added continually as new alloy/environment combinations that produce SCC are encountered in field operations and the laboratory.

The concentration of a specific ion is also a factor. As the concentration increases, susceptibility to SCC increases, even if all other factors remain the same.

Temperature is one important factor in determining the susceptibility of an alloy to SCC and in distinguishing the failure mechanism between SSC and SCC. For SCC, an alloy's susceptibility usually increases with increasing temperature, while for SSC, an alloy's maximum susceptibility occurs near room temperature. **Fig. 3.47** shows this behavior for carbon steel exposed to NaOH.[40] The logarithmic scale for time to failure shows the significant effect small changes in temperature have on the life of steel in this environment.

Applied stress and yield strength factors are identical for SSC and SCC behavior. Increasing the applied stress and the yield strength, however, reduces alloys' resistance to SCC.

Alloying elements can significantly affect the resistance of alloys to SCC. Copson's[41] classic study on stainless-steel wires in boiling chloride demonstrates the relationship between the concentration of nickel and SCC (**Fig. 3.48**). The role of alloying is quite complex because the enhancement of SCC resistance by alloying with a particular element may pertain to one specific environment only. The addition of this particular element may actually increase susceptibility in other environments. Thus, the alloying approach to SCC must be examined carefully for other potential applications.

As with SSC, the microstructure and heat treatment of an alloy may measurably alter its resistance to SCC. Normalized carbon and low-alloy steels have less resistance to SCC than quenched and tempered steels of the same hardness. An annealed duplex stainless steel (ferrite and austenite phases), however, typically has better chloride SCC resistance than a fully austenitic stainless steel because of the difference in SCC resistance of the two phases in the duplex stainless steel. Although chloride SCC has been emphasized because of the high concentration of chlorides in oilfield waters, other halides (bromides, iodides, and fluorides) are just as detrimental to cracking of some stainless steels.

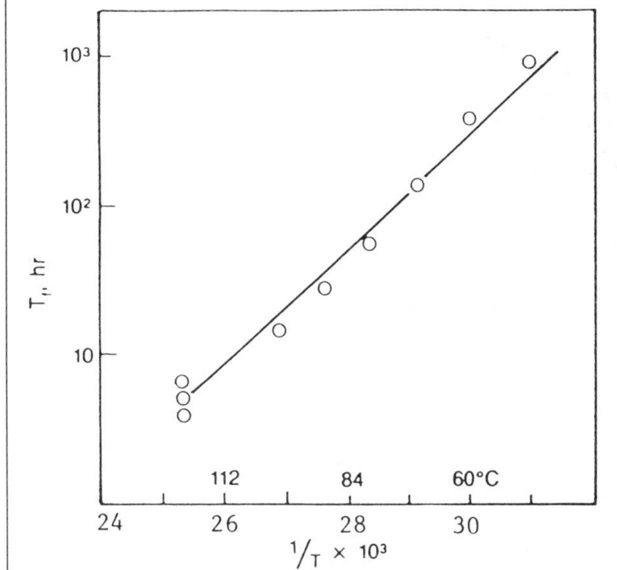

Fig. 3.47—Effect of temperature on SCC of steel in boiling 33% NaOH (© NACE, 1969).[40]

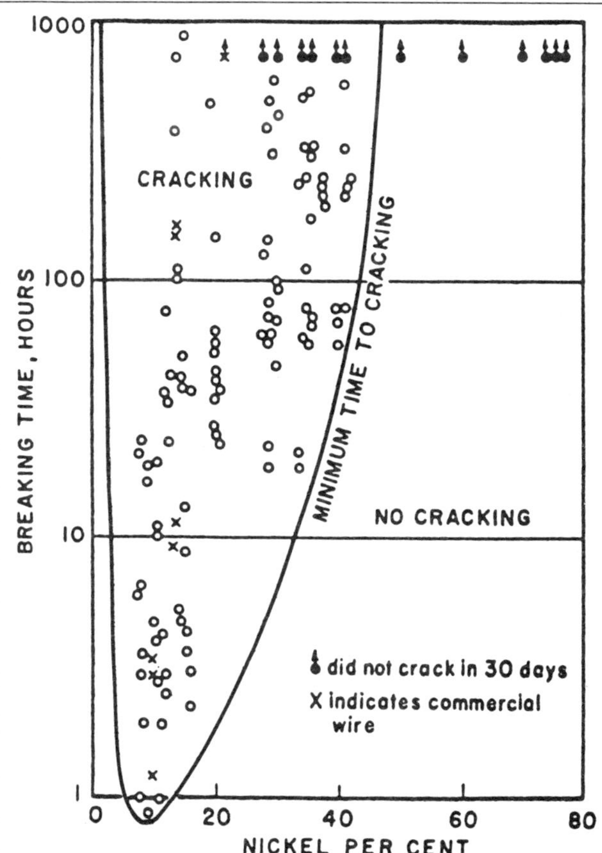

Fig. 3.48—SCC of iron-chromium wires in boiling magnesium chloride as a function of nickel content (courtesy of TMS).[41]

Many different metal and environmental systems display SCC but are not important to the discussion in this monograph. Further information on this subject is available in Ref. 1. However, another important SCC medium observed in sour systems is polythionic acid cracking, which most often occurs in austenitic stainless steels that have been sensitized (heated at temperatures between 900 and 1,500°F [482 and 816°C]). Polythionic acid ($H_2S_xO_6$, where $x=3$ to 6) can be formed by a variety of means but most often is ascribed to iron sulfide formed at high temperature in an H_2S environment, then hydrolyzed from humidity and oxygen during equipment shutdown and exposure to the atmosphere.[42] Incoloys 800 and 801 also have been reported[43] to crack in polythionic acid when sensitized. Polythionic acid cracking is avoided by use of stabilized stainless steels such as AISI's 347 or 321. Lower carbon, such as in AISI 304L or 316L, may also be helpful, but they may still crack. Polythionic acid cracking typically is not encountered in the oil field but is observed in gas plants and refineries.

Hydrogen damage to titanium alloys is a form of cracking that completes the picture of environmental cracking. In alpha-phase titanium alloys and alpha-beta titanium alloys, hydrogen combines with titanium to form a second phase (precipitate) referred to as a hydride (i.e., TiH_2). This is a brittle phase that can lead to brittle fracture of the alloy (hydriding). Hydriding is a distinct form of hydrogen damage and not a form of SSC or SCC. Synonymous with steels, the beta titanium alloys do not hydride but may fail by HSC or hydrogen embrittlement in severe environments.

Two less common alloy systems for sour service are copper- and aluminum-based alloys. Both alloy systems are infrequently used in sour service for different reasons. The copper-based alloys (coppers, brasses, and bronzes) are generally quite susceptible to rapid corrosion in environments containing H_2S. Copper-based alloys have been used successfully[44] only under waterflood conditions with $\lesssim 5$ ppm H_2S. Copper-based alloys should never be used in sour-gas systems.

Aluminum alloys typically are quite resistant to H_2S but are generally limited by their relatively low strength to less severe applications such as instrument housings and containers. Aluminum drillpipe (with steel connections) has been used successfully for drilling in sour formations.[1]

Although this chapter has described the behavior of various metals in sour environments, it would not be complete without mentioning welding. Welding of any of the metals and alloys described will significantly alter the metallurgical structure, strength, ductility, and resistance to fracture, as well as SSC and SCC resistance, compared with these properties in the base metal. The effect of welding on steels and their resistance to SSC are discussed in Chap. 6. However, other alloy systems may behave differently when welded, and carbon-steel data should not be relied on to predict the SSC and SCC resistance of other alloy weldments. In general, welding will be detrimental to SSC and corrosion resistance in H_2S unless precautions are taken to minimize its effect. Hence, it is of the utmost importance to ensure that proper testing, design, and construction of welding structures are carried out before equipment is installed in sour-gas facilities.

Because many mechanisms can cause metals to fail in sour environments, more than a passing knowledge of the subject is required and care should be taken in the selection and fabrication of metals for sour-gas applications.

Nomenclature

a_r = reduction in area in air, in.^{2}
A = cross-sectional area, in.^{2}
A_r = reduction in area, in.^{2}
b = width of DCB specimen, in.
b_n = width between side grooves on DCB specimen, in.
b_s = thickness of DCB wedge, in.
d = gauge diameter, in.
d_f = diameter of SSRT fracture surface, in.
E = elastic (Young's) modulus
K_{IC} = critical stress intensity
K_{ISSC} = SSC threshold stress intensity, ksi $\sqrt{\text{in.}}$
L = original length, in.
ΔL = change in length, in.
p_{CO_2} = CO_2 partial pressure, psi
p_{H_2S} = H_2S partial pressure, psi
P = applied load, psi
r = radius, in.
t_f = time to failure (fracture), seconds, minutes, or hours
t_y = time to yield point for SSRT, seconds
T = temperature, °F
ϵ = engineering strain
$\dot{\epsilon}$ = strain rate, seconds
ϵ_a = elongation in air, %
ϵ_e = elongation, %
σ = stress load per unit area, psi

References

1. Craig, B.D.: *Practical Oilfield Metallurgy,* PennWell Publishing Co., Tulsa, OK (1984).
2. Reed-Hill, R.E.: *Physical Metallurgy Principles,* Van Nostrand Reinhold, New York City (1968).
3. Smith, W.F.: *Structure and Properties of Engineering Alloys,* McGraw-Hill Book Co., New York City (1981).
4. *Metals Handbook,* ninth edition, American Soc. for Metals Intl. (1968) **1.**
5. *A 370, Test Methods and Definitions for Mechanical Testing of Steel Products,* ASTM, Philadelphia (1990).
6. *Spec. 6A, Specification for Wellhead and Christmas Tree Equipment,* 16th edition, API, Dallas (Oct. 1, 1989).
7. *Spec. 5CT, Specification for Casing and Tubing,* third edition, API, Dallas (Dec. 1, 1990).
8. *Spec. 5L, Specification for Line Pipe,* 39th edition, API, Dallas (June 1, 1991).
9. *E 140, Standard Hardness Conversion Tables for Metals,* ASTM, Philadelphia (1984).
10. *Modern Steels and Their Properties,* Bethlehem Steel Co., Bethlehem, PA (1972).
11. Craig, B.D. and Krauss, G.: "The Structure of Tempered Martensite and Its Susceptibility to Hydrogen Stress Cracking," *Metallurgical Trans.* (1980) **11A,** 1799–1805.
12. *INCONEL alloy 718,* Publication No. IAI-19, fourth edition, Inco Alloys Intl. Inc., Huntington, WV (1985).
13. Lang, F.H. and Kenyon, N.: "Welding of Maraging Steels," *Bulletin 159,* Welding Research Council (1971) 3.
14. Hudgins, C.M. *et al.*: "Hydrogen Sulfide Cracking of Carbon and Alloy Steels," *Corrosion* (1966) **22,** 238–51.
15. Ogundele, G.I. and White, W.E.: "Some Observations on the Corrosion of Carbon Steel in Sour Gas Environments: Effects of H_2S and $H_2S/CO_2/CH_4/C_3H_8$ Mixtures," *Corrosion* (1986) **42,** 398–408.
16. King, R.A. and Wakerley, D.S.: "Corrosion of Mild Steel by Ferrous Sulphide," *British Corrosion J.* (1973) **8,** 41–45.
17. Saki, N. *et al.*: "The Evaluation of Environmental Conditions and the Performance of Line Pipe Steels Under Wet Sour Gas," paper 131 presented at the 1982 NACE Corrosion/82, Houston, March 22–26.
18. Gupta, D.V.S.: "Corrosion Behavior of 1040 Carbon Steel," *Corrosion* (1981) **37,** 611–16.
19. Meyer, F.H. *et al.*: "Corrosion Products of Mild Steel in Hydrogen Sulfide Environments," *Corrosion* (1958) **14,** 109t–15t.
20. Bruckhoff, W. *et al.*: "Rupture of a Sour Gas Line Due to Stress Oriented Hydrogen Induced Cracking: Failure Analyses, Experimental Results and Corrosion Prevention," paper 389 presented at the 1985 NACE Corrosion/85, Boston, March 25–29.
21. Hyne, J.B. and Derdall, G.D.: "How To Handle Sulfur Deposited by Sour Gas," *World Oil* (Oct. 1980) 111–16.
22. Sato, E., Hashimoto, M., and Murata, T.: "Corrosion of Steels in a Wet H_2S and CO_2 Environment," paper presented at the 1981 Asian Pacific Corrosion Control Conference, Kuala Lumpur.
23. Treseder, R.S. and Swanson, T.M.: "Factors in Sulfide Corrosion Cracking of High Strength Steels," *Corrosion* (1968) **24,** 31–37.
24. Kawashima, A., Hashimoto, K., and Shimodaira, S.: "Hydrogen Electrode Reaction and Hydrogen Embrittlement of Mild Steel in Hydrogen Sulfide Solutions," *Corrosion* (1976) **32,** 321–31.
25. Townsend, H.E. Jr.: "Hydrogen Sulfide Stress Corrosion Cracking of High Strength Steel Wire," *Corrosion* (1972) **28,** 39–46.
26. Graville, B.A., Baker, R.G., and Watkinson, F.: "Effect of Temperature and Strain Rate on Hydrogen Embrittlement of Steel," *British Welding J.* (1967) **14,** 6, 337–42.

27. *Standard MR-01-75, Sulfide Stress Cracking Resistant Metallic Materials for Oilfield Equipment,* NACE, Houston (1988).
28. Snape, E.: ''Sulfide Stress Corrosion of Some Medium and Low Alloy Steels,'' *Corrosion* (1967), **23,** 154–72.
29. Wilde, B.E. and Doyle, M.J.: ''A Comparison Between Threshold Stress and Crack Initiation Stress Intensity for Sulfide Stress Corrosion Cracking,'' *Corrosion* (1979) **35,** 273–76.
30. DeWaard, C. and Milliams, D.E.: ''Carbonic Acid Corrosion of Steel,'' *Corrosion* (1975) **31,** 177–81.
31. DeBerry, D.W. and Clark, W.S.: ''Corrosion Due To Use of Carbon Dioxide for Enhanced Oil Recovery,'' Contract No. DOE/MC/08442-T1, U.S. DOE (1979).
32. Ikeda, A., Ueda, M., and Mukai, S.: ''CO_2 Behavior of Carbon and Chromium Steels,'' paper 4 presented at the 1983 NACE Corrosion/83, Anaheim, April 18–22.
33. *CO_2 Corrosion in Oil and Gas Production,* NACE, Houston (1984).
34. *Advances in CO_2 Corrosion,* NACE, Houston (1985) **1.**
35. *Advances in CO_2 Corrosion,* NACE, Houston (1986) **2.**
36. *Standard TM-01-77-90, Laboratory Testing of Metals for Resistance to Sulfide Stress Cracking in H_2S Environments,* NACE, Houston (1990).
37. Agarwal, A.K., Steigelmeyer, W.H., and Payer, J.H.: ''Corrosion and Stress Corrosion Cracking Behavior of a Martensitic 12Cr-3.5Ni-Fe Alloy in Simulated Sour Gas Environments,'' paper 169 presented at the 1986 NACE Corrosion/86, Houston.
38. McIntyre, D.R., Kane, R.D., and Wilhelm, S.M.: ''Slow Strain Rate Testing for Materials Evaluation in High Pressure H_2S Environments,'' *Corrosion* (1988) **44,** 920–26.
39. Fontana, M. and Green, N.D.: *Corrosion Engineering,* McGraw-Hill Book Co., New York City (1967).
40. Bohnen Kamp, K.: *Fundamental Aspects of Stress Corrosion Cracking,* NACE, Houston (1969) 374.
41. Copson, H.R.: ''Effect of Composition on Stress Corrosion Cracking of Some Alloys Containing Nickel,'' Thor N. Rhodin (ed.), *Proc.,* Symposium on Physical Metallurgy of Stress Corrosion Fracture, Pittsburgh (April 2–3, 1959), **4,** 256; TMS (TMS-AIME), Warrendale, PA (New York City).
42. Samans, C.H.: ''Stress Corrosion Cracking Susceptibility of Stainless Steels and Nickel-Base Alloys in Polythionic Acids and Acid Copper Sulfate Solution,'' *Corrosion* (1964) **20,** 256t–62t.
43. Stephens, C.D. and Scarberry, R.C.: ''*Proc.,* 25th NACE Annual Conference (1969) 583–87.
44. *RP-04-75, Recommended Practice for Selection of Metallic Materials to Be Used in All Phases of Water Handling for Injection Into Oil Bearing Formations,*'' NACE, Houston (1975).

SI Metric Conversion Factors

bar	× 1.0*	E−01	=	MPa
ft	× 3.048*	E−01	=	MPa
ft^3	× 2.831 685	E−02	=	m^3
°F	(°F−32)/1.8		=	°C
in.	× 2.54*	E+00	=	cm
ksi	× 6.894 757	E+03	=	kPa
lbm	× 4.535 924	E−01	=	kg
mil	× 2.54*	E+01	=	μm
psi	× 6.894 757	E+00	=	kPa

*Conversion factor is exact.

Chapter 4
Drilling in Sour Gas

4.1 Introduction

An operator can face any number of equipment and operations problems while drilling a sour-gas well. Some of the greatest problems have been encountered in sour-gas wells, although the industry has been successful in drilling them. Yet, with all the difficulties, relatively little information has been published specific to the performance of materials and corrosion of equipment in sour-gas drilling. This chapter reviews some of the problems that represent major trouble areas in sour-gas drilling.

The primary way to avoid materials problems in sour gas during drilling is to prevent H_2S from entering the drilling mud in the first place (i.e., drilling overbalanced). This chapter presents some measures to take during well planning so that, if and when H_2S enters the wellbore and the mud, the well can still be controlled. The measures presented here only address sulfide stress cracking (SSC) of drilling components and not countermeasures for handling high-pressure gas kicks during drilling. These aspects of well control are detailed in other texts such as Ref. 1.

4.2 Drillstem Components

Tool joints, drillpipe, drill collars, and other drillstem elements represent components that may fail rapidly when sour gas is encountered. Drillpipe tool joints are commonly manufactured from American Iron & Steel Inst. (AISI) Series 4100 [chromium-molybdenum (Cr-Mo)] low-alloy steel. The composition ranges from AISI 4135 to 4140; however, AISI 4145H is also used. For heavy-weight drillpipe, AISI 1340 [carbon-manganese (C-Mn)] tool joints may be used. Recently, AISI Series 4100 steels with increased molybdenum and niobium modifications were introduced for tool joints because of their greater resistance to SSC in H_2S environments. Tool joints normally are quenched and tempered to a Rockwell C hardness (HRC) range of 30 to 37, resulting in yield strengths of 120 to 150 ksi [829 to 1034 MPa]. **Table 4.1** shows the American Petroleum Inst.'s (API) *Spec. 7*[2] requirements for tool joints. API *Spec. 7* requires a minimum yield strength of 120,000 psi [829 MPa], a minimum tensile strength of 140,000 psi [967 MPa], and a minimum elongation of 13% for all new tool joints of all sizes. The same tool-joint metallurgy is used for all drillpipe grades. A minimum Brinell hardness (HB) number of 285 indicates a tensile strength of about 140,000 psi [967 MPa] and is acceptable on both the box and the pin end. The tool joints are welded, usually by friction, to the drillpipe.

Drill collars made of AISI 4135 and 4140 or 4145H steels are quenched and tempered to a range of HB 285 to 341. Drill collars are used to add weight to the drill bit and to keep the drillpipe in tension so that fatigue effects are minimized. Table 4.1 gives the minimum tensile requirements for drill collars according to API *Spec. 7*.

Use of nonmagnetic drill collars in a drillstring during directional and nondirectional drilling allows for magnetic surveys of hole trajectory. These collars and associated elements are made from a variety of alloys, with the most common being austenitic (nonmagnetic) stainless steels. Beryllium copper alloys and the original Monel collars (Monel K500) are used less often because of their high cost. The term Monel collar, however, continues to be used to identify any nonmagnetic drill collar, regardless of the alloy.

Drilling jars, stabilizers, subs, core barrels, and other tools are made from AISI 4140 or 4145H steel in the quenched and tempered condition. Sometimes quenched and tempered AISI 4340 or 4340H steel is used for these items. The basic difference between AISI Series 4300 and 4100 steels is that AISI Series 4300 steels contain about 2% nickel, which improves toughness and hardenability, both of which are needed for thick sections.

Table 4.1 also lists the standard API grades of drillpipe.[3] Steels used for drillpipe are C-Mn or Cr-Mo, with the latter usually being an AISI Series 4100 steel. Aluminum (typically aluminum alloy Type 2014) drillpipe is used less. Aluminum drillpipe must be made with high-strength steel tool joints because of the low torsion resistance of aluminum joints and the severe galling tendencies of threaded aluminum. Titanium is also being considered for drillpipe and tool joints. Drillpipe of titanium Alloy Ti-6Al-4V, with the same alloy tool joints, has been produced. These tool joints are welded onto the pipe in the same manner that steel tool joints are welded on steel drillpipe.

Grade E-75 drillpipe is usually normalized. Grade X-95 is most often normalized and tempered, while Grades G-105 and S-135 are usually quenched and tempered. Typical hardness values for the various grades range from HRC 20 to 28 for Grade E-75, HRC 25 to 30 for Grade X-95, HRC 29 to 34 for Grade G-105, and HRC 34 to 38 for Grade S-135. Thus, the hardness of API tool joints equals that of Grade S-135 drillpipe, regardless of the grade of pipe to which they are welded.

The high strength and hardness of many drillstem components make them quite susceptible to SSC. Failure from SSC can be rapid because of the hardness. Moreover, because the tool-joint material, even on Grade E-75 pipe, is equivalent to Grade S-135, use of Grade E-75 pipe in sour-gas drilling does not eliminate SSC, it only reduces the risk.

TABLE 4.1—API REQUIREMENTS FOR TOOL JOINTS, DRILL COLLARS, AND DRILLPIPE

Tool Joints (API *Spec.* 7[2])

Minimum yield strength, psi	120,000
Minimum tensile strength, psi	140,000
Minimum elongation, %	13

Drill Collars (API *Spec.* 7[2])

O.D. (in.)	Minimum Yield Strength (psi)	Minimum Tensile Strength (psi)	Minimum Elongation (%)
3⅛ to 6⅞	110,000	140,000	13
7 to 10	100,000	135,000	13

Drillpipe (API *Spec.* 5D[3])

Grade	Yield Strength (ksi) Minimum	Yield Strength (ksi) Maximum	Minimum Tensile Strength (ksi)	Chemistry (%, maximum) Phosphorus	Chemistry (%, maximum) Sulfur	Heat Treatment
E	75	105	100	0.030	0.030	Heat treated
X-95	95	125	105	0.030	0.030	Q&T/N&T*
G-105	105	135	115	0.030	0.030	Q&T/N&T
S-135	135	165	140	0.030	0.030	Q&T/N&T

*Quenched and tempered or normalized and tempered.

The advantage of the drilling process compared to petroleum production is the ability to control the environment (i.e., the drilling mud) and to reduce potential problems created by it, especially corrosional SSC. Use of chemical inhibitors, pH control, and scavengers can substantially reduce corrosion and SSC of the drillstem. Quite often, simple pH control and deaeration can control corrosion, extending the service life of a drillstem. Corrosion can cause pitting that reduces the normal fatigue life of the drillpipe.

Tool joints in general are particularly susceptible to SSC because of their high strength. The exposure to H_2S need not occur over a long period of time. Short exposure during a kick may be sufficient to cause SSC. Most often, pin failures occur that display a fracture that follows the circumference of the tool joint around the root of the last engaged thread. The hydrogen that enters the steel to cause SSC diffuses through the steel to regions of high stress, where it can cause cracking. This region represents both the highest applied stress and a stress concentration caused by the thread itself. Stress calculations and measurements have shown that the stress at the last engaged thread can achieve or exceed the yield strength. Although box connections fail less frequently because of lower stresses, they can be subjected to high hoop stresses. Therefore, cracking in the box frequently occurs in a longitudinal direction. Drill collars fail in the same fashion as tool joints but less often because the applied stresses are lower and temperatures are higher near the bottom of the drillstem. As previously discussed, higher temperatures reduce the risk of SSC.

A large body of field experience and recently published laboratory data[4] confirm the low resistance of drillpipe and tool joints to SSC (**Figs. 4.1 and 4.2**). As expected, Grade S-135 pipe is quite susceptible to SSC while Grade X-95 can tolerate traces of H_2S. In high H_2S concentrations, for which scavenging may not be completely effective, the lower-strength Grades E-75 and X-95 are more tolerant. Remember, however, that the API tool joints on all drillpipe are equivalent to Grade S-135 and therefore are quite susceptible to SSC. Because steel's resistance to SSC reaches a minimum near 77°F [25°C], the greatest risk for cracking occurs at the top of the hole where high-strength pipe is most often run. This problem is reduced if tapered strings are used to reduce the applied stress. Because Grade X-95 steel has a value of HRC 25 to 30, it usually resists SSC better than the higher-hardness Grades G-105 and S-135 steels in the event of a kick. Grade X-95 is more resistant to SSC in the quenched and tempered condition than when normalized and tempered. Generally, all steel drillstring components are susceptible to SSC and may fail in as little time as a few minutes or hours when exposed to H_2S; thus, it is essential to maintain a scavenger in the mud or to use an oil-based drilling mud.

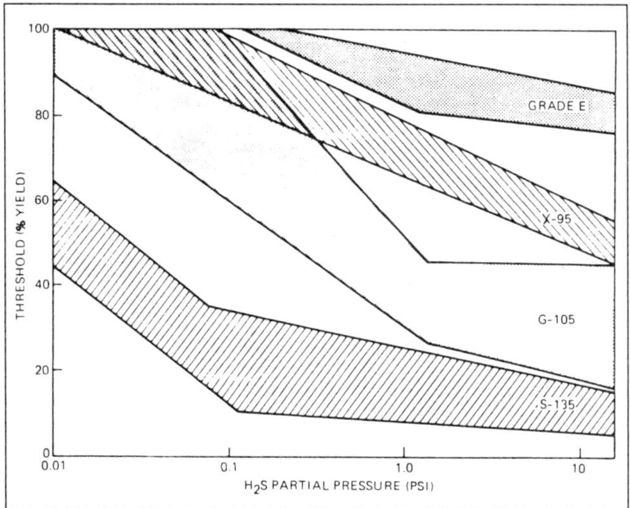

Fig. 4.1—Threshold stress for SSC of drillpipe as a function of H_2S concentration (©NACE, 1985).

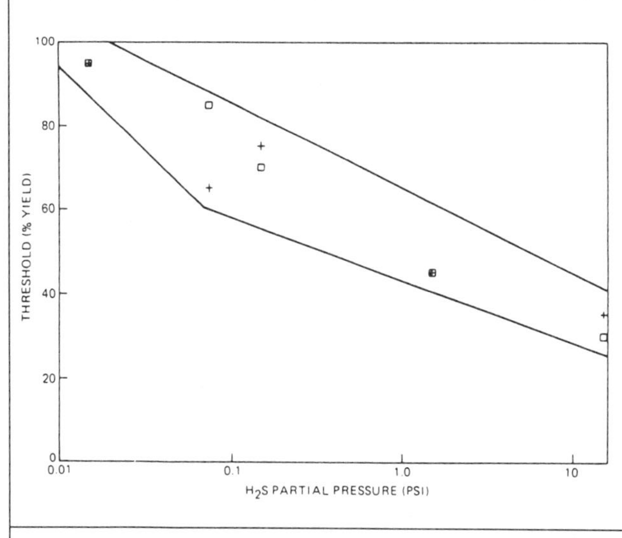

Fig. 4.2—Threshold values for tool-joint samples (©NACE, 1985).

TABLE 4.2—MECHANICAL PROPERTIES OF SPECIAL SOUR-SERVICE DRILLPIPE AND TOOL-JOINT GRADES

	Yield Strength (psi)		Minimum Tensile Strength (psi)	Minimum Elongation in 2 in. (%)	Maximum HRC
Grade	Minimum	Maximum			
Drillpipe Grade 75	75,000	90,000	95,000	18	22
Drillpipe Grade 95	95,000	110,000	105,000	16.5	28
Tooljoint	95,000	110,000	105,000	16.5	28

TABLE 4.3—THERMAL DEGRADATION OF LIGNOSULFONATE MUD AT HIGH PRESSURE (AFTER REF. 5)

	Lignosulfonate Solution		
	A	B	C
Temperature, °F	450	450	425
Pressure, psi	12,000	10,000	10,000
Initial pH	8.3	8.5	8.3
Final pH	6.1	5.9	5.9
H_2S, ppm	15	2.5	20
Aging time, hours	16	16	16

TABLE 4.4—THERMAL DEGRADATION OF LIGNOSULFONATE MUD AT HIGH pH (AFTER REF. 5)

	Lignosulfonate Solution		
	A	B	C
Temperature, °F	375	375	375
Pressure, psi	300	300	300
Initial pH	12.6	12.8	12.6
Final pH	8.1	8.2	9.1
H_2S, ppm	15	25	2.5
Aging time, days	7	7	7

Several manufacturers offer new drillpipe grades with claimed improved resistance to SSC. These grades are manufactured so that the mechanical properties (yield strength, hardness, etc.) are controlled more closely than API requirements, and the tool-joint properties and metallurgy more closely coincide with the pipe body. **Table 4.2** is an example of such drillpipe properties. These components have been used to drill sour-gas wells successfully. However, drilling mud conditioning is still required to ensure that these grades are not exposed to H_2S for long times.

Although H_2S most often is derived from the reservoir, degradation of certain drilling muds can also produce H_2S and thus contribute to SSC. **Table 4.3** illustrates the potential problem with lignosulfonate muds at high temperatures.[5] Data[5] accompanying Table 4.3 show that, even in high-pH (>12.0) lignosulfonate mud, sulfide can evolve because of decomposition of the mud (see **Table 4.4**).

Sulfate-reducing bacteria (SRB) are yet another source of H_2S in drilling. SRB are probably present in the mud or may be carried with the makeup water for drilling mud. Even though high-pH drilling mud may not be conducive to SRB growth, it will not necessarily kill them. Thus, SRB remain dormant until environmental conditions (i.e., pH and temperature) in the mud or formation change and enhance growth. SRB produce H_2S by metabolizing sulfate in the environment.

One metallurgical alternative to steel that is occasionally used is aluminum drillpipe. Its chief advantages are lighter weight and greater flexibility than steel, which allow for deeper drilling with a mixed string. Although the yield strength (58,000 psi [400 MPa]) and tensile strength (64,000 psi [441 MPa]) of Type 2014-T6 aluminum are below that for Grade E-75 drillpipe, these factors have been mitigated by using thick sections. Aluminum is also more resistant to H_2S and CO_2 corrosion than steel pipe and does not exhibit SSC.

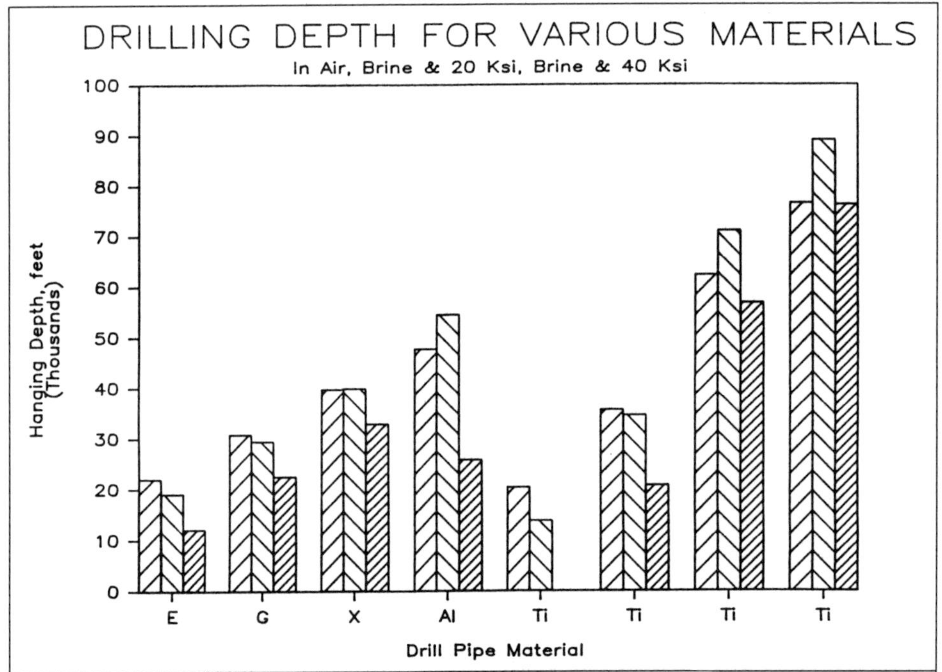

Fig. 4.3—Maximum hanging depth for various API grades of drillpipe: aluminum drillpipe and four different titanium alloys. Left bar in each series is for pipe hung in air. Middle bar is for pipe in brine with 20-ksi [138-MPa] overpull. Right bar is in brine with 40-ksi [276-MPa] overpull.[8]

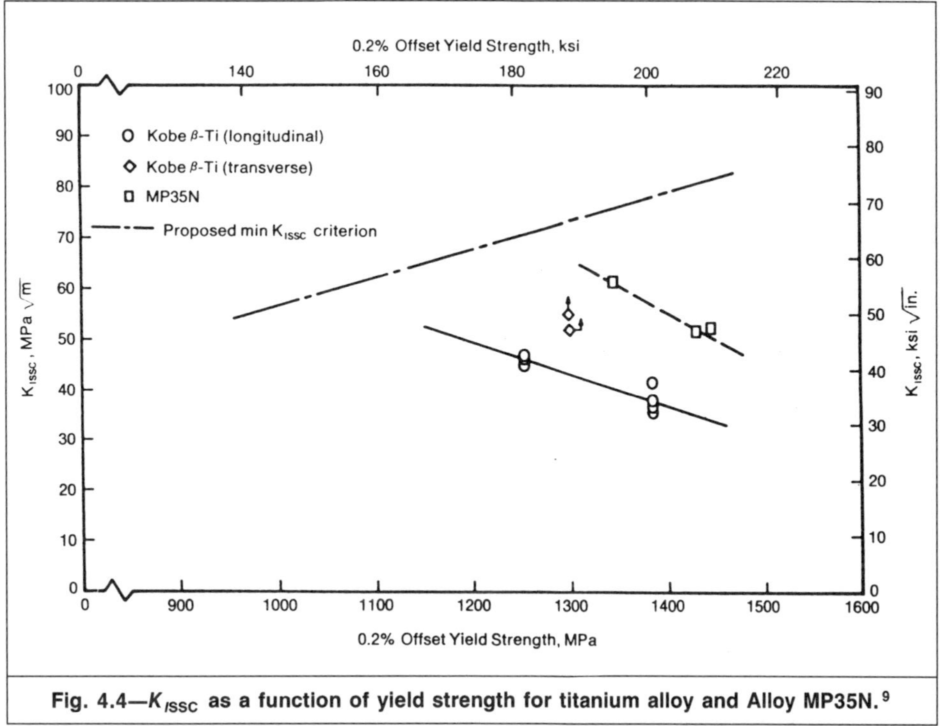

Fig. 4.4—K_{ISSC} as a function of yield strength for titanium alloy and Alloy MP35N.[9]

One of several disadvantages of aluminum drillpipe is its low corrosion resistance to muds with pH > 10.5; increasing pH above this can cause serious corrosion. Chlorides at levels > 180,000 ppm can also cause severe pitting that, in turn, can cause loss in fatigue life in salt muds.[6] Aluminum drillpipe also suffers reduced strength at elevated temperatures (>250°F [>121°C]). The low yield strength and limited elevated temperature resistance of aluminum drillpipe combine to eliminate it as a possible alloy for drilling deep, hot wells that contain H_2S.

The trend toward deep drilling beyond 25,000 ft [7 620 m] requires the use of very-high-strength drillpipe to achieve the desired depth. Grade S-135 pipe has the necessary strength but is highly susceptible to SSC. Steel drillpipe is also too heavy for wells currently being planned or drilled to 50,000 ft [15 240 m]. A lightweight alloy with a high strength/weight ratio is desirable for this work. While aluminum drillpipe has been effective from 25,000 to 30,000 ft [7 620 to 9 144 m], it has a temperature limitation.[7] Currently, titanium alloys are thought to be an alternative to steel and aluminum for both the strength/weight ratio and SSC resistance. **Fig. 4.3** illustrates the advantages of several titanium alloys over steel Grades E, G, and X and aluminum for hanging weight in air and brine, with different overpull tensile loads.[8] Fig. 4.3 shows that two titanium alloys (an alpha+beta and a beta) could easily exceed 51,000 ft [15 545 m] in a brine mud with 40,000-psi [276-MPa] overpull. **Figs. 4.4 and 4.5** show the enhanced SSC resistance of a beta titanium alloy as a function of yield strength and the yield strength/density ratio.[9] Note that a comparison strictly on yield strength favors the cold-worked nickel-cobalt Alloy MP35N over titanium. The lighter weight of titanium, however, reduces the effective string load and, therefore, the necessary drawworks capacity. Another advantage of titanium is that it can be heat treated to high strengths, and titanium-alloy tool joints can be friction welded onto the pipe.

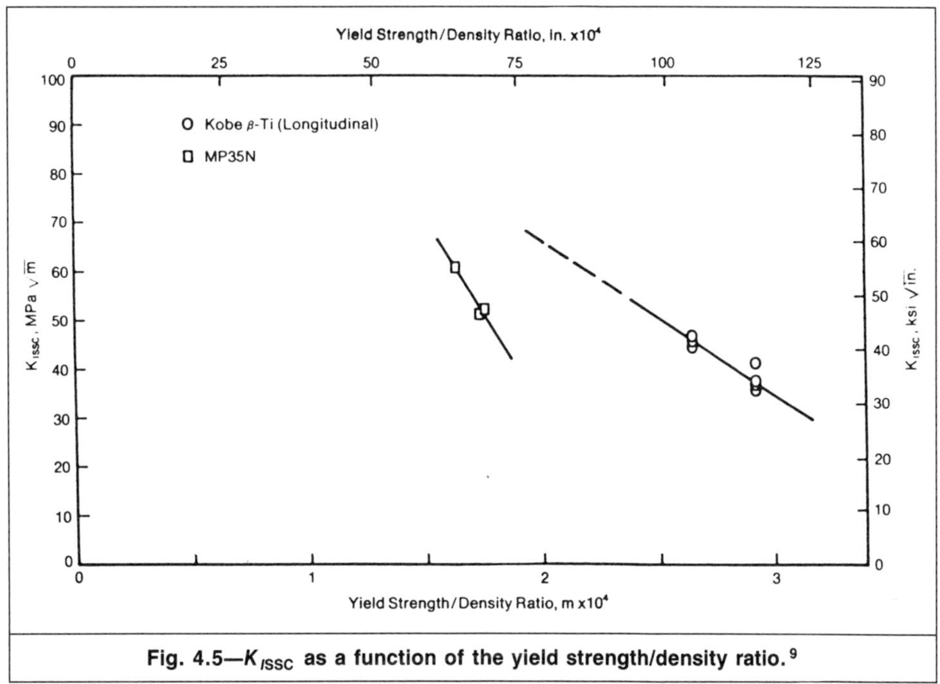

Fig. 4.5—K_{ISSC} as a function of the yield strength/density ratio.[9]

TABLE 4.5—EFFECT OF MUD TYPE ON CORROSION (AFTER REF. 10)

Mud Types	H_2S Present on Coupons	Hydrogen Embrittlement	Corrosion Rate (mil/yr)
Oil-based, 3 lbm/bbl lime	No	No	5.30
Oil-based, 8 lbm/bbl lime	No	No	3.99
Low lime	No	No	3.23
High lime	No	No	3.42
Nondispersed*	Yes	Yes	26.60
Lignite/lignosulfonate*	Yes	Yes	107.47
Lignite/lignosulfonate†	Yes	Yes	70.02

*Low lime with saturated salt, polymer, and starch.
**Starting pH from 9 to 11.
†Starting pH from 11.

4.3 Mud Chemistry

The critical advantage of drilling vs. producing in sour gas is that the environment (drilling mud) can be controlled. Proper attention to mud chemistry can mitigate most problems encountered during drilling in sour gas. **Table 4.5** shows the effect of mud type on corrosion and cracking in the presence of H_2S.[10] Oil-based muds offer the greatest protection to the drillstem from corrosion and cracking when H_2S is present because water (electrolytc) is not present as the continuous phase to form a corrosion cell.[10]

Alkaline water-based muds also can reduce the deleterious effects of H_2S if the mud pH is maintained sufficiently high to keep sulfides dissolved (**Fig. 4.6**).[11] Note that, even at pH 12, a mud with 5,000 ppm dissolved sulfides can have an H_2S-gas concentration 20 ppm above the mud, which is the maximum short-term exposure for personnel under certain regulations. Additional intrusions of H_2S or CO_2 can substantially and rapidly lower the mud pH, producing a dangerous or lethal level of H_2S gas above the mud. The rapid shift in H_2S-gas concentration above the mud dictates that we not rely on pH control to protect personnel on the rig floor from H_2S exposure. Likewise, pH control is unreliable as the sole prevention for SSC.

Various methods can be used to modify mud chemistry and to reduce the effects of H_2S. None of these methods, however, will prevent the sudden release of H_2S that occurs during a gas kick. Therefore, it is good practice to drill overbalanced if H_2S is expected so that scavengers have time to work. As noted earlier, simple pH control in the basic range can be quite effective in reducing the corrosivity and thereby the potential for SSC caused by H_2S. H_2S scavengers can also be added to water- and oil-based muds over a wide pH range. The more common H_2S scavengers are zinc carbonate ($ZnCO_3$), basic zinc carbonate [$3Zn(OH)_2 \cdot 2ZnCO_3$], zinc oxide, zinc chelates, and iron oxide. $ZnCO_3$ and $3Zn(OH)_2 \cdot 2ZnCO_3$ react with H_2S as follows.

$$ZnCO_3 + H_2S \rightarrow ZnS + H_2CO_3$$

and $3Zn(OH)_2 \cdot 2ZnCO_3 + 5H_2S \rightarrow 5ZnS + 2H_2CO_3 + 6H_20$.

Zinc oxide is used in oil-based drilling mud to scavenge H_2S; zinc chelates, which have a high water solubility, are effective in water-based mud over a wide pH range.[12,13] An important consideration in the use of H_2S scavengers is the reversibility of the reaction with pH. Zinc sulfide (ZnS) has been found to be highly stable even to pH 3.5; thus, reversion to H_2S is not a problem if the mud pH decreases. Such scavengers as iron oxide, however, may revert under less acidic pH, releasing H_2S back into the environment.

Iron sponge (i.e., iron oxide) is another additive used to control H_2S. Iron sponge consists of fine particles of iron oxide that have a large surface area. The large surface area is necessary because the reaction with H_2S occurs on the particle surface. Because of this dependence on the surface reaction, iron oxides are not effective during a large gas kick. Iron oxide/H_2S reactions are[14]

$$Fe_3O_4 + 4H_2S \rightarrow 3FeS + 4H_2O + S,$$

$$FeS + S \rightarrow FeS_2,$$

and $Fe_3O_4 + 6H_2S \rightarrow 3FeS_2 + 4H_2O\ 2H_2$.

The first reaction occurs predominantly in basic solutions, while the other two commonly occur in neutral and acidic solutions.

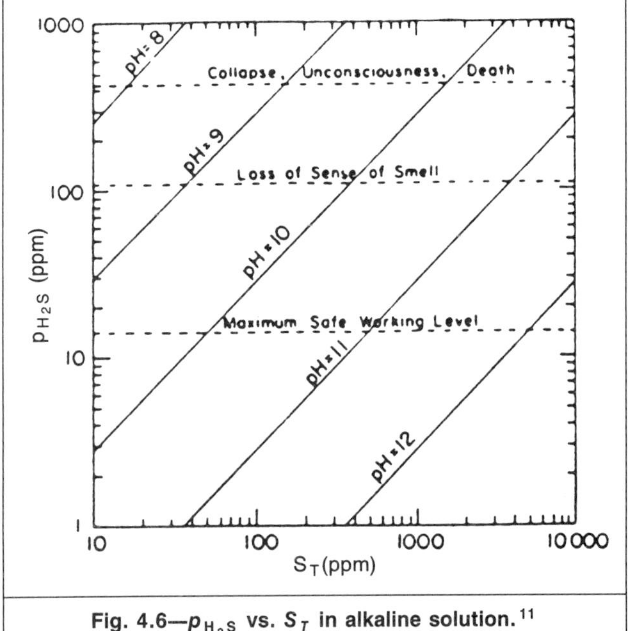

Fig. 4.6—p_{H_2S} vs. S_T in alkaline solution.[11]

Continually adding filming amine corrosion inhibitors to the drilling mud also reduces corrosion, but these inhibitors frequently are not effective in high-solids muds. Further, they should always be used in conjunction with H_2S scavengers because the mud solids will often preferentially adsorb some inhibitor, reducing the amount available for inhibition of the steel drillstem.

One of the best ways to handle H_2S in drilling operations is to use oil-based or invert muds. These muds contain some water, but oil is the primary (continuous) phase so the electrolyte resistivity increases to a level that stifles corrosion reactions because oil, not water, wets the steel surface. The oil/water emulsion, however, must be stable to maintain this property.

Another common problem with drilling in H_2S is that iron sulfide (FeS) scale develops from the corrosion of drillstem components. While the gradual accumulation of FeS on drilling equipment in low-H_2S environments may not create an immediate problem, the drilling equipment is often used in other wells. If FeS accumulates on the tool joints and the drillpipe is run into another well where the mud pH dips to acidic levels, H_2S will be released because FeS corrosion scale will dissolve. The generation of locally significant levels of H_2S can then immediately produce SSC in the equipment, especially the hard tool joints. Removing the FeS scale from tool joints and the bottomhole assembly (BHA) after drilling in a sour environment will solve this problem.

A common spot-test method to detect the presence of FeS on metal surfaces uses sodium arsenite (indicator) mixed in a solution of water and hydrochloric acid with a small amount of detergent. Development of a bright yellow precipitate indicates that FeS is present.

The Garrett gas train (GGT) and the mud-duck are two accurate methods used to detect sulfides in drilling mud at the surface. The GGT, an API-recognized procedure,[15] uses a series of cham-

TABLE 4.6—NDE METHODS AND DEFECTS OBSERVED

Drillpipe		
Inspection Type	Area Inspected	Defects Observed
Connection visual	Threads and rotary shoulders and grade marks on pin neck and tool joint	Grade mismatch, damaged threads, and damaged rotary shoulder seal
Connection dimensional	Threads and tool joints	Miscut threads and other features, misidentified connections, and excessive wear
Connection MT (wet-fluorescent method)	Internal and external surfaces of threaded areas (box and pin)	Fatigue cracks, heat checking (box), and SSC
Upset MT (dry-powder method)	From cylindrical part of tool joints to 3 ft onto pipe. Similar for heavy-wall drillpipe with mid-tube upsets/wear knots	Fatigue cracks, excessive mechanical damage, upsetting and forging laps not detected during pipe manufacture, and SSC
Pipe body visual	Internal and external surfaces of pipe and tool joints	Corrosion damage, cement and/or mud residue, and mechanical damage such as slip cuts and mashes
Pipe body OD gauge	Pipe body OD from upset to upset	Wear, dents, mashes, load-induced diameter variations, and SSC
Pipe body wall UT (normal beam)	Spot measurement of wall thickness at points of apparent maximum wear	Thin wall tube (wrong weight or excessive wear)
Pipe body EMI (flux leakage)	Full length from upset to upset	Transversely oriented cracks and mechanical damage
Pipe body end-area UT (shear wave)	Pipe upset and weld area	Fatigue cracks and poor welds
Drill Collars		
Inspection	Area Inspected	Defects Observed
Connection visual	Threads and rotary shoulders	Damaged threads and damaged rotary shoulder seal
Connection dimensional	Threads	Miscut threads and other features, misidentified connections, and excessive wear
Connection MT (wet-fluorescent method for steel collars) and Connection PT (for nonmagnetic collars)	Internal and external surfaces of threaded areas (box and pin)	Fatigue cracks, heat checking (box), and SSC of nonmagnetic collars

bers (a train). Mud filtrate and sulfuric acid are added to the first chamber, and a draeger tube at the end of the train measures the amount of H_2S evolved from the acidified mud filtrate.

The mud-duck is an ion-selective electrode that is specific to the total sulfides in the mud. The advantage of this method is the ability to measure sulfide concentration in alkaline water-based mud continuously.[16]

4.4 Monitoring Procedures

As discussed earlier, monitoring the sulfide in the drilling mud indicates whether the H_2S concentration is increasing because of such events as mud degradation, microbial activity, or intrusion from the formation. However, the effect of H_2S scavengers, inhibitors, and alkalinity on reducing corrosion can be evaluated by either indirect (coupons and probes) or direct (inspection of drilling equipment) methods. The latter topic is addressed in Chap. 6.

The following corrosion monitoring techniques directly indicate corrosion only, not SSC. If corrosion is controlled well, however, the risk of SSC is reduced.

Drillpipe corrosion rings are probably the most common method of analyzing drillstring corrosion. These machined rings are accurately weighed and installed in the drillstring and exposed to the drilling environment from as few as 50 hours up to several days. The rings are then removed, cleaned, and reweighed. The weight loss divided by the surface area and exposure time prorated to 1 year generate a corrosion rate expressed in (lbm/ft^2)/yr (see SI Conversion Factors for conversion). This expression for corrosion rate is common to drilling operations; however, more universal units are mils per year [where 1 mil=0.001 in. [0.00254 cm] and mil/yr=25.4×(lbm/ft^2)/yr [mm/a=0.62×(lbm/ft^2)/yr].

Corrosion rates $\leq$2.0 (lbm/ft^2)/yr [$\leq$0.1 kPa/a] are considered acceptable for most drilling conditions, if pitting is not significant. Corrosion rates $>$2.0 (lbm/ft^2)/yr [$>$0.1 kPa/a] with no pitting can be tolerated for short times.

Machined, preweighed metal strips called coupons are used to determine the corrosion rate in the same manner as corrosion rings. Coupons are more often installed at surface locations, such as mud-pump outlets. Coupon corrosion rates are reported in mils per year.

While corrosion rings and coupons are the least expensive form of corrosion monitoring and provide a great deal of information, they require substantial exposure time to present a realistic representation of what is actually occurring. Numerous electrical probes are available that have essentially instantaneous response and may provide corrosion rate data immediately or continuously. Several of these probes are discussed in Chap. 6.

A serious drawback of these probes, and the reason they are not used as extensively as corrosion rings in drilling, is the inability to install them in the drillstring itself, which reduces the accuracy of evaluating the actual drilling environment. Probes, however, are quite useful in surface equipment.

All these corrosion-monitoring methods are indirect and do not specifically reflect the actual condition of the equipment. Evaluation of the actual condition of drilling equipment requires nondestructive examination (NDE) and/or destructive testing.

The multitude of NDE methods have relative advantages and disadvantages, depending on the particular defect to be evaluated. Magnetic particle inspection (MT), liquid penetrant inspection (PT), electromagnetic inspection (EMI), and ultrasonic inspection (UT) are used most commonly on drillstem elements. Mechanical gauging and measurement are also used to check for wear and mechanical damage. **Table 4.6** shows typical inspection methods, the area inspected on drillpipe and drill collars, and the defect characterized. Other drillstem components should receive similar inspection. Often, it is beneficial to inspect drillpipe and other drillstem components before and after a well is drilled to substantiate the actual corrosion, wear, and mechanical damage that has occurred in a particular well and to avoid disputes among the operating company, the drilling contractor, the rental tool company, and the inspection company.

NDE methods successfully identify existing cracks and pits in components, but currently, no methods exist to test for fatigue damage or hydrogen embrittlement before actual crack initiation. This is important to remember because NDE tests are used extensively, and after examination, many components are pronounced defect-free and suitable for further use. Generally, under drilling conditions, approximately 80% of the fatigue life is used before cracks initiate and the remaining 20% of life is expended during crack propagation; thus, cracks can be detected only during about the last 20% of the component's life.

Destructive testing of metal samples removed from equipment exposed to H_2S, by either bend or tensile testing, can demonstrate hydrogen embrittlement caused by H_2S, however, the sample must be tested immediately after the equipment is exposed. No method exists to evaluate this nondestructively. Moreover, hydrogen accumulation in the steel from corrosion by H_2S is reversible by baking before crack initiation. Once cracks have formed by SSC, they cannot be removed.

4.5 Hydrogen Removal

Once equipment, especially drillstrings and BHA's, have been inadvertently exposed to H_2S, steps should be taken to eliminate future potential problems that may result from hydrogen absorption during this exposure. Residual hydrogen in the steel can induce cracking of the string components after they are removed from the well because the stresses and temperature on the surface are different from those in the well. In some instances, merely allowing the string components to bake in the sun for several days at temperatures >80°F [>27°C] will allow hydrogen to egress and greatly reduce the tendency for cracking. The time for sufficient natural baking is a function of the average ambient temperature, the thickness of the drilling components, and the hydrogen concentration in the steel.

For example, assume a drillstem assembly with H_2S in the mud is stuck in a well and exposed for several days. For typical drilling-component thicknesses, the following order-of-magnitude relationships can be generated with diffusion data for hydrogen in steel to determine the necessary baking time and temperature to reduce hydrogen to a relatively safe level.

Steel Thickness in. [cm]	Baking Time (Days)	
	At 77°F [25°C]	At 150°F [65°C]
2 [5.08]	19	9
1 [2.54]	5	2

These baking times and temperatures represent a simplification of the actual outgassing process and should not be used for any purposes other than this example. These data demonstrate that reduced wall thickness and increased temperature decrease the time required to remove sufficient hydrogen for safe operation. After baking, some type of NDE test should be performed to determine whether SSC has occurred.

4.6 Corrosion Protection

As discussed earlier, mud chemistry and maintaining mud density at overbalanced conditions are the primary means of combatting corrosion and cracking from H_2S. The specific mud program for a well depends on a number factors that are not within the scope of this monograph. Muds with pH in the alkaline range (pH>8) are adequate for drilling in areas where the necessary mud density is known and the expected H_2S level is low. However, if H_2S concentrations could be high, or effective control of H_2S intrusion from kicks is uncertain, then sulfide scavengers should also be used. If a low-solids mud is being used, the additional application of filming amine corrosion inhibitors or passivating inhibitors may be successful in reducing corrosion from H_2S.

For deep, hot, sour-gas wells, oil-based muds are the best alternative for controlling corrosion in the drilling environment. Again, stability of the emulsion is critical to maintain this control.

Plastic-coated internal corrosion protection for the drillstring, combined with mud control, generally is also effective. While a continuous coating of high integrity is beneficial for corrosion prevention, it should not be relied on as the only system for corrosion protection. Once the coating begins to degrade, it can actually enhance localized corrosion and reduce the effectiveness of inhibitors, thereby becoming a detriment to corrosion inhibition. Therefore, drillpipe should be cleaned and recoated when the original coating becomes significantly damaged.

4.7 Materials Selection

When drilling in potential sour-gas regions, in addition to the mud program, drilling components should be evaluated for exposure and resistance to SSC in the event the system cannot control a sudden influx of H_2S. Blowout preventers (BOP's) and other pressure-containing components (i.e., valves, manifold, chokes, and kill lines) should be resistant to SSC.

Because the shear blades of a BOP must be hard enough to shear the drillpipe tool joint, the blades are often hard enough to sulfide stress crack. Likewise, the shear rams may not be resistant to SSC. NACE *Standard MR-01-75*[17] excludes rams and ram shear blades but cautions about their susceptibility to SSC. Shear ram blades may be overlayed with a hard material such as tungsten carbide that will resist SSC. All other BOP components must be manufactured from materials that are resistant to SSC.

If there is any possibility that the choke/kill manifold will be exposed to sour gas, the components of the manifold should be resistant to SSC. In some cases, fabrication and assembly of a new manifold may be required because available equipment is unidentifiable and/or untraceable.

Rental drilling equipment, especially BOP's, manifolds, chokes, and kill lines, should be inspected and hardness tested before being used on a potential sour-gas well.

Whenever drilling in H_2S-bearing formations, it is advisable to run the lowest grade of drillpipe possible. The probability of failure decreases for the drillstring if Grade E-75 or X-95 is used. Grade G-105 is intermediate in its resistance, depending on the H_2S concentration and other factors. Grade S-135 pipe is highly susceptible to SSC and should never be run when H_2S is present.

Whenever possible, sour-service drillpipe with low-strength tool joints should be run instead of standard API tool joints. In the few instances where these lower-strength joints have been used, they have been quite successful.

Wellhead components such as casing hangers should be manufactured to resist SSC in accordance with NACE *Standard MR-01-75* if conditions where H_2S will contact these components are anticipated. Moreover, the production casing hanger should be designed especially for sour service, meeting NACE *Standard MR-01-75* requirements, because it is not uncommon for sour gas to enter the tubing/casing annulus after the well begins production.

The production casing, and sometimes an intermediate string, depending on the drilling conditions, must be designed for exposure to sour gas and resistance to SSC to ensure control of the well during drilling and in the future during gas production. The important factors involved in selecting sour-service casing are combined with the discussion on tubing in Chap. 5.

4.8 Safety on the Rig Floor

As described earlier, a sudden reduction in mud pH or a gas kick containing H_2S can lead to an abrupt release of harmful levels of H_2S on the rig floor. Safety measures must be in place before H_2S is encountered to avoid serious hazards to the health of rig personnel.

At the very least, a drilling rig must be equipped with detection equipment and fresh-air breathing devices for rig personnel. All rig and support personnel must be trained in the use of this equipment and in the early warning signs of H_2S poisoning. Furthermore, a specific plan of action that details the procedures to follow when drilling into an expected sour-gas formation, and similarly, when an unexpected sour-gas kick occurs, should be developed for each drilling operation. Some factors to address for each case are given below.

When a sour-gas formation is expected.

1. Drill overbalanced.
2. Include H_2S scavengers in the mud program.
3. Maintain a mud pit-level measurement system to detect pit gain as an early warning of a kick.
4. Know kick control procedures, including those for the kill system.
5. Verify that all equipment that may be potentially exposed to H_2S complies with NACE *Standard MR-01-75*. This includes welds for choke manifolds and kill lines, wellhead equipment, and BOP's.
6. Conduct safety training.
7. Have safety equipment.
8. Monitor H_2S on the rig floor, rig location, and mud pits.
9. Have written procedures for normal operations and emergencies (see Chap. 2).

Unexpected sour-gas kick.

1. Circulate out the kick or bullhead it back into the formation.
2. Add H_2S scavenger to the mud.
3. Perform safety actions for remainder of potential H_2S exposure.
4. Trip out drillstem assemblies for inspection and replace as necessary.
5. Inspect surface equipment for H_2S resistance or change out.
6. Train rig personnel in detection of H_2S and its consequences.

If these programs are well-thought out and good procedures are in place, the risk of drilling in sour-gas wells can be substantially reduced. By following these procedures and those detailed in Chap. 2, sour-gas wells have been successfully drilled and completed by the industry for many years with no serious consequences.

Nomenclature

K_{ISSC} = SSC threshold stress intensity, ksi $\sqrt{in.}$ [MPa$\sqrt{m}$]
p_{H_2S} = H_2S partial pressure, psi [kPa]
S_T = dissolved sulfides in solution, ppm

References

1. Goins, W.C. Jr. and Sheffield, R.: *Blowout Prevention,* second edition, Gulf Publishing Co., Houston (1983) **1.**
2. *Spec. 7, Specification for Rotary Drilling Equipment,* 37th edition, API, Dallas (Aug. 1, 1990).
3. *Spec. 5D, Specification for Drill Pipe,* third edition, API, Dallas (Aug. 1, 1992).
4. Watkins, M. and Vaughn, G.A.: "Effects of H_2S Partial Pressure on the Sulfide Stress Cracking Resistance of Steel," paper NACE 220 presented at the 1985 NACE Corrosion '85, Boston, March 25-29.
5. Bush, H.E., Barbee, R., and Simpson, J.P.: "Current Techniques for Combating Drill Pipe Corrosion," *Drill. & Prod. Prac.*, API, Dallas (1966) 59-69.
6. Person, N.L.: "Fatigue Properties of Prior-Corroded Aluminum Sheet Alloys," *Materials Performance* (1975) **14,** 22-26.
7. Craig, B.D.: *Practical Oilfield Metallurgy,* PennWell Publishing Co., Tulsa, OK (1984).
8. Greer, J.B.: "Core Drilling for Ultra-Deep Scientific Targets: An Engineering Challenge," paper presented at the 1986 Engineering Foundation Conference, Dilliard, GA, April 20-25.
9. Ohtani, S., Nishimura, T., and Moriguchi, Y.: "A Beta Type Ti-15 Mo-5Zr-3Al Alloy for Sour Well Service," *Alloys for the 80's,* American Metals Climax Inc., Ann Arbor, MI (1980) 263-67.
10. Adams, N. *et al.*: "H_2S Detection and Protection," *Pet. Eng. Intl.* (March 1980) **52,** 30-34.
11. Wendt, R.P.: "Generalized Theory of Evolution and Dispersion of H_2S From Alkaline Muds," *SPEJ* (April 1983) 365-76.
12. Garrett, R.L., Carlton, L.A., and Denekas, M.O.: "Methods for Field Monitoring of Oil-Based Drilling Fluids for Hydrogen Sulfide and Water Intrusions," *Drilling,* Reprint Series, SPE, Richardson, TX (1987) **22,** 317-28.
13. Garrett, R.L. *et al.*: "Chemical Scavengers for Sulfides in Water-Base Drilling Fluids," *Drilling,* Reprint Series, SPE, Richardson, TX (1987) **22,** 329-38.
14. Samuels, A. and Wendt, R.P.: "Proper Fluid Pretreatment To Minimize Hydrogen Sulfide Dangers," *J. Cdn. Pet. Tech.* (April-June 1981) 55-63.
15. *RP 13B, Recommended Practice for Standard Procedure for Field Testing Drilling Fluids,* 11th edition, API, Dallas (May 1985).
16. Singh, A.K., Kohli, B.S., and Wendt, R.P.: "Handling Hydrogen Sulfide in Drilling Fluids," *World Oil* (Nov. 1989) 99-103.
17. *Standard MR-01-75, Sulfide Stress Cracking Resistant Metallic Materials for Oilfield Equipment,* NACE, Houston (1988).

SI Metric Conversion Factors

bbl	× 1.589 873	E−01	=	m^3
ft	× 3.048*	E−01	=	m
°F	(°F−32)/1.8		=	°C
in.	× 2.54*	E+00	=	cm
ksi	× 6.894 757	E+00	=	MPa
lbm	× 4.535 924	E−01	=	kg
lbm/ft^2	× 4.788 026	E−02	=	kPa
mil/yr	× 2.54*	E−02	=	mm/a
psi	× 6.894 757	E+00	=	kPa

*Conversion factor is exact.

Chapter 5
Producing Sour Gas

5.1 Introduction

All aspects of producing sour gas—the design, selection, and procurement of materials and installation of equipment for a well—are critical. Historically, casing and tubing have represented the components that most frequently fail when exposed to sour-gas streams, and they always are one of the largest investments in the cost of a well. Because of these factors, a large body of research and published data exists on properties of casing and tubing in sour gas. The petroleum industry refers to casing, tubing, and line pipe as oil-country tubular goods (OCTG). This chapter reflects the greater amount of information available on performance of OCTG compared with other oilfield equipment.

5.2 Casing and Tubing Considerations

5.2.1 API Grades. The American Petroleum Inst.'s (API's) *Spec. 5CT*[1] covers the requirements of casing and tubing and gives the metallurgical requirements for each grade (**Tables 5.1 and 5.2**). These specifications are widely applied throughout the world.

Note that the API chemical composition requirements for Groups 1 and 3 casing and tubing are limited only to the impurities (sulfur and phosphorus) which allows great flexibility in the alloys manufacturers select to meet the specified mechanical properties. This flexibility, however, may create a problem for the user because the chemical composition and certain properties of the steel may vary widely from manufacturer to manufacturer for materials with the same API grade.

In general, the lower-strength grades are carbon-manganese steels with essentially no other alloying elements. As the required strength levels increase, manufacturers commonly add small amounts of chromium, molybdenum, titanium, boron, or vanadium in various combinations to achieve the desired mechanical properties.

Those grades API lists in Group 2 are restricted yield-strength grades originally designed for use in sour service. These grades have a 15,000-psi [103-MPa] yield-strength range compared with the 25,000- to 40,000-psi [172- to 276-MPa] range for the other groups. In addition, Grades L-80, C-90, and T-95 are the only ones that have a hardness limitation imposed by the specification. Note that Group 2 is the only series that includes such higher-alloy steels as 9% Cr-1% Mo and 13% Cr, although, as described later in this chapter, 9% and 13% Cr steels are not well-suited for sour service.

API *Spec. 5CT* Grade Q-125 (Group 4) is the only grade that requires impact testing and the only one for which the minimum Charpy V-notch energy required for various ranges of wall thicknesses is provided. Similar requirements for other grades are pending at this time. Fracture mechanics shows that thicker materials with the same strength require greater toughness.

5.2.2 Specialty Grades. Numerous specialty and proprietary OCTG grades developed by various steel mills around the world for specific applications are not listed in API *Spec. 5CT.* These specialty tubulars represent about 5% of the total OCTG market. Typical of these are Grades S-95, HC-95, and V-150 for high collapse strength, but these grades have poor resistance to sulfide stress cracking (SSC). Many other grades with better resistance to SSC are available. Specific steel mills offer a variety of proprietary grades for different applications. Very-high-strength steels, such as Grades 140 and 150, may fail by hydrogen stress cracking even if no H_2S is present.

5.2.3 OCTG Manufacturing. Casing and tubing made to API *Spec. 5CT* standards can be manufactured by either seamless or electric-resistance welding (ERW) processes, depending on the grade (**Table 5.3**). Although the ERW process also covers electric-flash welding, only ERW is discussed here because it is the principal means of electrically welding OCTG today.

After ERW, the weld's heat-affected zone can be extremely hard. The weld seam and the heat-affected zone usually are normalized immediately after welding to bring the weld properties back in line with those of the base metal. The term "seam annealing" is most often applied to this operation, even though the annealing term is incorrect technically. API does not require weld-seam heat treatment, which can be a significant factor in the SSC behavior of electric-resistance welded pipe. A few mills full-body normalize or quench and temper the pipe after welding rather than heat-treating only the weld seam. The various heat treatments used by different mills can produce significant differences in SSC resistance for basically the same API grades.

Seamless pipe is made by heating a round billet to an appropriate temperature and then piercing it with a mandrel. After piercing, the tube is sent through a rolling mill to produce the required wall thickness and then to reeling and sizing mills to form the specified diameters.

Failures resulting from manufacturing defects occur in both seamless and electric-resistance welded pipe. Such defects as laminations, slivers, scabs, and hard spots in the pipe body can occur in both types of pipe. In electric-resistance welded pipe, the weld is most often the location for defects that lead to failure. Such defects as cold and stitch welds, penetrators, hook cracks, hard zones, and contact marks are observed in the weld line or adjacent to it. Electric-

TABLE 5.1—CHEMICAL REQUIREMENTS (%) (AFTER API *SPEC. 5CT*[1])

			Carbon		Manganese		Molybdenum		Chromium		Nickel	Copper	Phos-phorous	Sulfur	Silicon
Group	Grade	Type	Minimum	Maximum	Minimum	Maximum	Minimum	Maximum	Minimum	Maximum	Maximum	Maximum	Maximum	Maximum	Maximum
1	H-40	—	—	—	—	—	—	—	—	—	—	—	0.030	0.030	—
	J-55	—	—	—	—	—	—	—	—	—	—	—	0.030	0.030	—
	K-55	—	—	—	—	—	—	—	—	—	—	—	0.030	0.030	—
	N-80	—	—	—	—	—	—	—	—	—	—	—	0.030	0.030	—
2	L-80	1	—	0.43*	—	1.90	—	—	—	—	0.25	0.35	0.030	0.030	0.45
	L-80	9% Cr	—	0.15	0.30	0.60	0.90	1.10	8.00	10.00	0.50	0.25	0.020	0.010	1.00
	L-80	13% Cr	0.15	0.22	0.25	1.00	—	—	12.0	14.0	0.50	0.25	0.020	0.010	1.00
	C-90	1	—	0.35	—	1.00	0.25**	0.75	—	1.20	0.99	—	0.020	0.010	—
	C-90	2	—	0.50	—	1.90	—	NL	—	NL	0.99	—	0.030	0.010	—
	C-95	—	—	0.45†	—	1.90	—	—	—	—	—	—	0.030	0.030	0.45
	T-95	1	—	0.35	—	1.20	0.25‡	0.85	0.40	1.50	0.99	—	0.020	0.010	—
	T-95	2	—	0.50	—	1.90	—	—	—	—	0.99	—	0.030	0.010	—
3	P-110	—	—	—	—	—	—	—	—	—	—	—	0.030	0.030	—
4	Q-125	1	—	0.35	—	1.00	—	0.75	—	1.20	0.99	—	0.020	0.010	—
	Q-125	2	—	0.35	—	1.00	—	NL	—	NL	0.99	—	0.020	0.020	—
	Q-125	3	—	0.50	—	1.90	—	NL	—	NL	0.99	—	0.030	0.010	—
	Q-125	4	—	0.50	—	1.90	—	NL	—	NL	0.99	—	0.030	0.020	—

*Can be increased to a maximum of 0.50% if the product is oil quenched.
**Has no minimum tolerance if the wall thickness is <0.700 in. [1.778 cm].
†Can be increased to a maximum of 0.55% if the product is oil quenched.
‡Can be decreased to a minimum of 0.15% if the wall thickness is <0.700 in. [1.778 cm].
§The phosphorous is 0.02% maximum and the sulfur is 0.010% maximum for electric-welded Grade P-110.
NL = No limit. Elements shown must be reported in product analysis.

resistance welded pipe that has not been heat-treated after welding or that is improperly heat-treated has been observed to fail by SSC adjacent to the electric-resistance weld in H_2S environments. The hardness, as determined by typical Rockwell C hardness (HRC) or Brinell hardness (HB) testing, will not indicate a problem.

5.2.4 Applications and Problems. Most casing and tubing failures are not manufacturing related, but instead, result from misapplication, operational problems, corrosion-related causes, or mechanical damage (burst, collapse, etc.) and handling damage (e.g., tong marks containing cold-worked metal at a sharp notch).

SSC is the most serious problem for tubulars exposed to H_2S. The greater concern by the industry of failure by SSC compared with corrosion from H_2S stems from the time it takes for each to occur. Corrosion often requires months or years to cause a failure, while SSC can occur in just a few minutes or several hours with no prior warning. **Figs. 5.1 and 5.2** show the specific SSC behavior of tubular materials in a standard test[2] environment as a function of H_2S concentration and temperature.[3] As discussed previously, SSC resistance decreases with increasing yield strength and increasing H_2S concentration. **Fig. 5.3** shows another example of this behavior.[4] Note that Grade P-110 casing has essentially no threshold (applied stress below which failure does not occur) and is susceptible at H_2S partial pressures below 0.05 psi [0.34 kPa] at ambient temperature. Moreover, industry experience has shown that there is probably no temperature above which Grade V-150 casing is resistant to SSC. In contrast to Figs. 5.1 and 5.2, Fig. 5.3 presents SSC resistance as a function of H_2S partial pressure rather than H_2S concentration. H_2S partial pressure is a better measure of the severity of a sour environment.

Because yield strength can be measured only with a destructive test, SSC resistance is most often related to hardness because hardness can be measured in the field and used easily for quality control. **Fig. 5.4** illustrates the SSC dependence of carbon steel on

TABLE 5.2—TENSILE AND HARDNESS REQUIREMENTS (AFTER API *SPEC. 5CT*[1])

			Yield Strength ($psi \times 10^3$)		Tensile Strength Minimum	Hardness*		Specified Wall Thickness	Allowable Hardness Variation
Group	Grade	Type	Minimum	Maximum	(ksi)	HRC	HB	(in.)	HRC
1	H-40	—	40	80	60	—	—	—	—
	J-55	—	55	80	75	—	—	—	—
	K-55	—	55	80	95	—	—	—	—
	N-80	—	80	110	100	—	—	—	—
2	L-80	1	80	95	95	23	241	—	—
	L-80	9% Cr	80	95	95	23	241	—	—
	L-80	13% Cr	80	95	95	23	241	—	—
	C-90	1.2	90	105	100	25.4	255	≤0.500	3.0
	C-90	1.2	90	105	100	25.4	255	0.501 to 0.749	4.0
	C-90	1.2	90	105	100	25.4	255	0.750 to 0.999	5.0
	C-90	1.2	90	105	100	25.4	255	≥1.000	6.0
	C-95	—	95	110	105	—	—	—	—
	T-95	1.2	95	110	105	25.4	255	≤0.500	3.0
	T-95	1.2	95	110	105	25.4	255	0.501 to 0.749	4.0
	T-95	1.2	95	110	105	25.4	255	0.750 to 0.999	5.0
3	P-110	1-4	110	140	125	—	—	—	—
4	Q-125	1-4	125	150	135	—	—	≤0.500	3.0
	Q-125	1-4	125	150	135	—	—	0.501 to 0.749	4.0
	Q-125	1-4	125	150	135	—	—	≥0.750	5.0

*In case of dispute, laboratory HRC tests are used as the referee method.

TABLE 5.3—MANUFACTURING PROCESS AND HEAT TREATMENT (AFTER API *SPEC. 5CT*[1])

Group	Grade	Type	Manufacturing Process	Heat Treatment	Minimum Tempering Temperature (°F)
1	H-40	—	S or EW	None	—
	J-55	—	S or EW	None*	—
	K-55	—	S or EW	None*	—
	N-80	—	S or EW	None*	—
2	L-80	1	S or EW	Q&T	1,050
	L-80	9% Cr	S	Q&T**	1,100
	L-80	13% Cr	S	Q&T**	1,100
	C-90	1	S	Q&T	1,150
	C-90	2	S	Q&T	1,150
	C-95	—	S or EW	Q&T	1,000
	T-95	1	S	Q&T	1,200
	T-95	2	S	Q&T	1,200
3	P-110	—	S or EW	Q&T	—
4	Q-125	1	S or EW†	Q&T	—
	Q-125	2	S or EW†	Q&T	—
	Q-125	3	S or EW†	Q&T	—
	Q-125	4	S or EW†	Q&T	—

S = seamless.
*Full length normalized, normalized and tempered, or quenched and tempered (Q&T) at the manufacturer's option or if so specified on the purchase order.
**Can be air quenched.
†Special requirements unique to EW P-110 and Q-125 casing are specified in Special Requirement 11. When EW P-110 and Q-125 casing is furnished, the provisions of SR11 are automatically in effect.

hardness and applied stress.[5] The hardness needed to cause SSC is reduced as applied stress is increased. **Fig. 5.5** shows a similar relationship among hardness, H_2S concentration, and time to failure.[5] For example, increasing the H_2S content at the same hardness level and relative stress significantly decreases the time to failure (areas above the curves in Fig. 5.5).

Several other factors are important to the resistance of steels to SSC. Cold work applied to tubulars can seriously reduce SSC resistance.[6] **Fig. 5.6** shows that steels normally resistant to SSC can crack in H_2S if cold-worked.[6] Greer and Holland[7] determined that the amount of martensite formed during the quench is important to achieving maximum resistance to SSC. **Fig. 5.7** shows that the greater the martensite content of the steel, the higher the SSC resistance.[7] Thus, for steels to achieve the greatest resistance to SSC, they must be quenched to martensite as completely as possible and tempered to as high a temperature as the material will allow and still maintain mechanical strength. API[1] requires 90% martensite in Grades C-90 and T-95. Fig. 5.7 also shows that the variation in HRC through the wall is also a good measure for quality control because it is a measure of the extent that martensite was produced by the quench. Even though a steel component is properly manufactured, mishandling of the component can result in mechanical damage (notches), and cold work may reduce the SSC behavior.[8] **Fig. 5.8** shows how severely the depth of a notch can decrease the threshold stress for SSC of Grades C-90 and L-80 steels.[8] Sharp tong and slip marks can reduce SSC resistance of such materials as Grades J-55, C-90, and L-80 tubing and casing, which normally are very resistant.

One of the difficulties in predicting the behavior of steels in H_2S environments is the lack of exact correlation between laboratory and field data. **Fig. 5.9** shows that a Grade 125 casing steel performs better in the field than expected from laboratory data.[9] Very

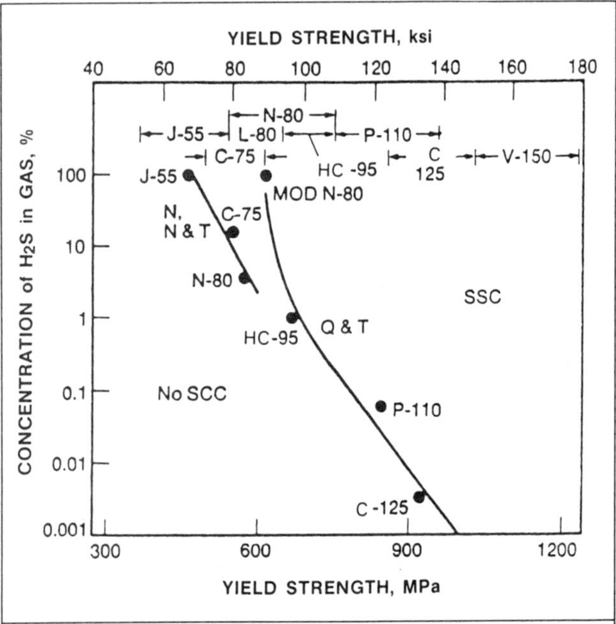

Fig. 5.1—Effect of H_2S concentration on SSC of casing and tubing steels.[3]

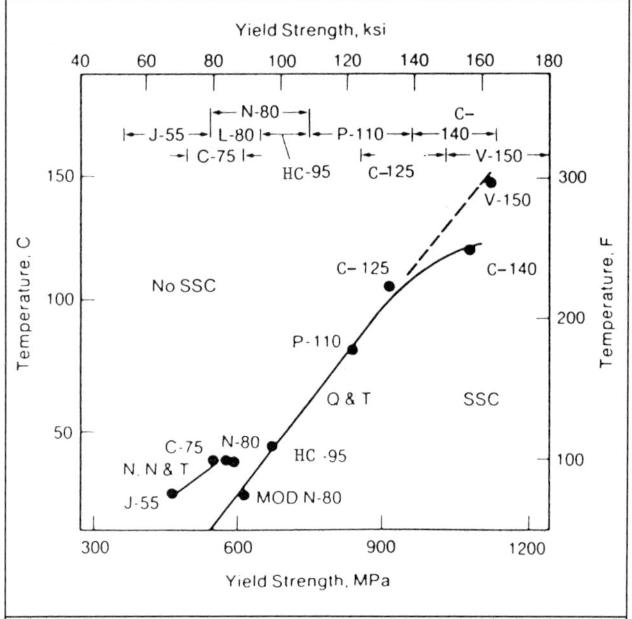

Fig. 5.2—Effect of temperature on SSC of common oilfield tubulars.[3]

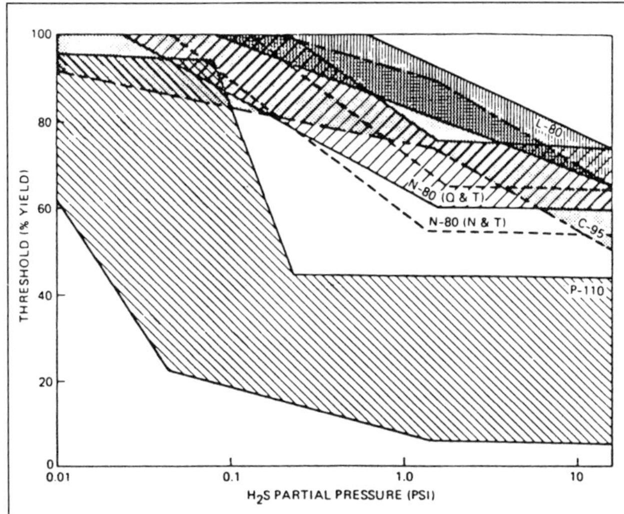

Fig. 5.3—SSC threshold of some casing steels as a function of H_2S partial pressure (©NACE, 1985).[4]

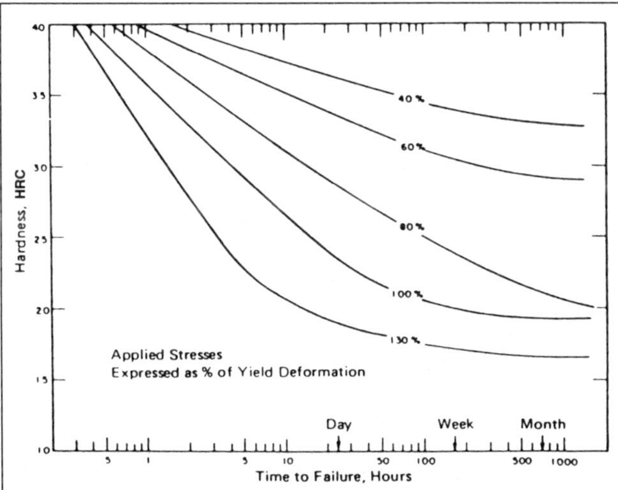

Fig. 5.4—Correlation of hardness, time to failure, and applied stress for carbon steels in an H_2S solution at ambient temperature (©NACE, 1966).[5]

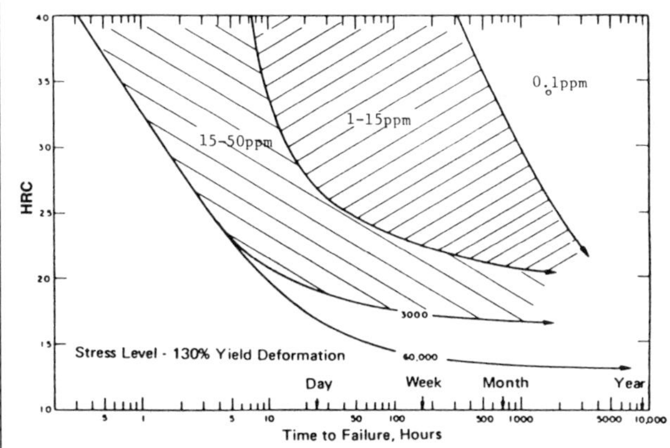

Fig. 5.5—Approximate dependence of time to failure in H_2S as a function of concentration and hardness (after Ref. 5).

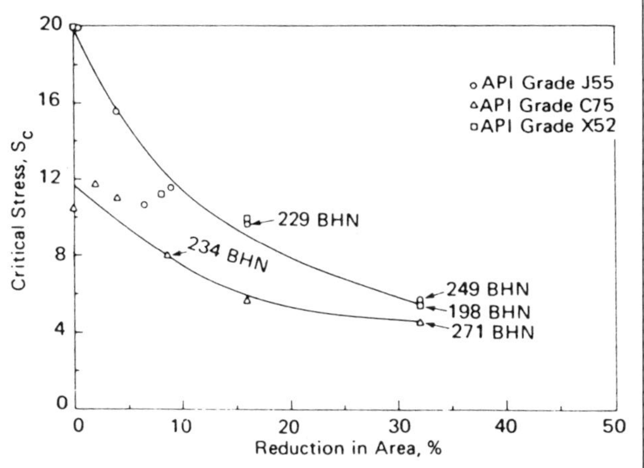

Fig. 5.6—Effect of cold work on SSC resistance of API tubulars (©NACE, 1968).[6]

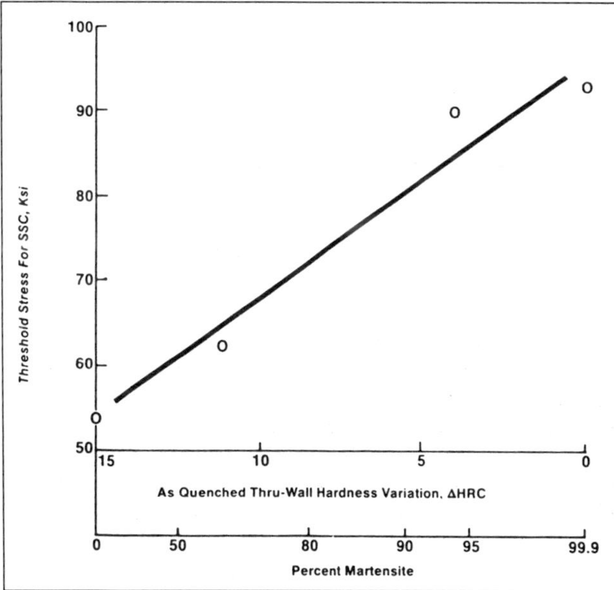

Fig. 5.7—Threshold for SSC of AISI 4130 as a function of martensite content from the quench and tempered state to HRC 25. Through-wall variation in HRC is also shown.[7]

few actual field data available on SSC failure are correlated to laboratory tests. This may be because the service stresses imposed on the equipment are complex and difficult to quantify. Laboratory results tend to be conservative partly because of the severe environment. Moreover, it is quite difficult to simulate actual dynamic field conditions and fluid compositions in the laboratory.

Grades generally accepted for OCTG use in sour service include Grades J-55, K-55, and L-80 for low-pressure sour-oil and sour-gas production and Grades C-90 and T-95 for moderate- and high-pressure sour gas. For critical service (defined by the operating company), the following minimum quality-assurance procedures should be performed on new OCTG before purchase.

1. Grades J-55 and K-55 require a flaw inspection, API *Spec. 5CT* Special Requirement 1, and a special end-area inspection.

2. Grade L-80 requires a flaw inspection with Grade N-10 notches (OD longitudinal and transverse), a special end-area inspection, and a hardness inspection (100%).

3. Grades C-90 and T-95 require a flaw inspection, including transverse and internal notches; a four-quadrant hardness-test ring of two joints from every heat-treatment lot; pipe qualified to NACE *Standard TM-01-77* with two different specimen geometries (e.g., smooth tension and double cantilever beam); prequalified nondestructive examination; 100% full-body ultrasonic inspection; surveillance of flaw inspection; hardness tests; and thread inspection.

5.2.5 Connections. Some of the highest stresses in the casing and tubing strings are at the connections. This is to be expected be-

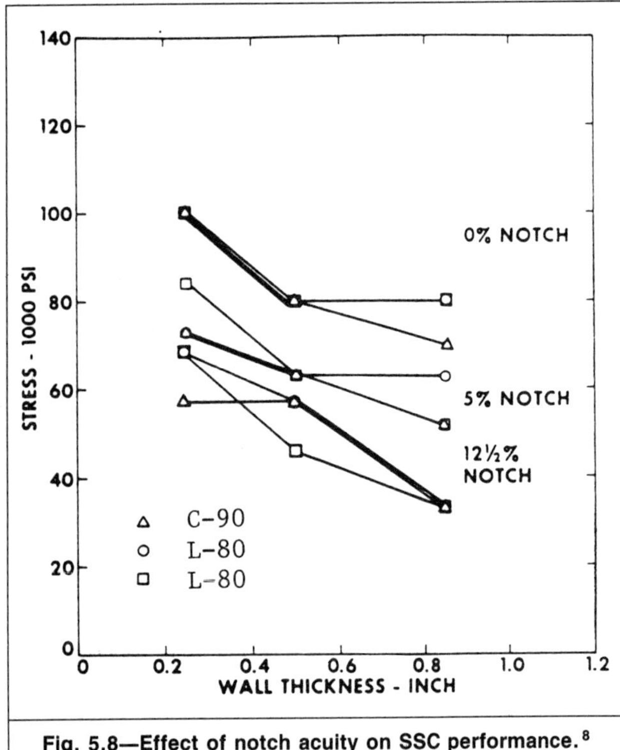

Fig. 5.8—Effect of notch acuity on SSC performance.[8]

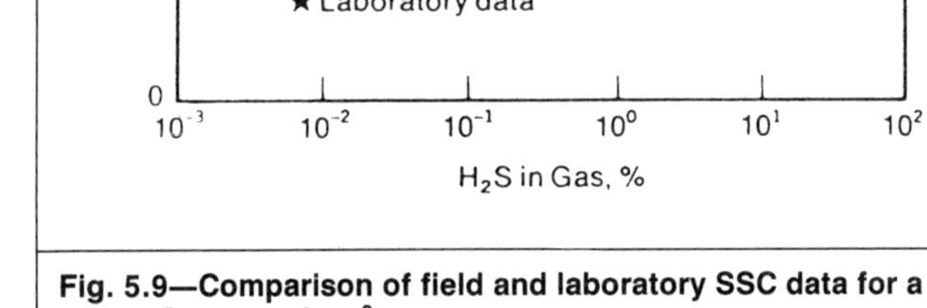

Fig. 5.9—Comparison of field and laboratory SSC data for a Grade C-125 casing.[9]

cause a primary means of maintaining the sealing in most threaded connections is by interference on the thread flanks in combination with the pipe dope.

Thread interference creates applied stresses that can exceed the local yield strength in many connections. Schneider[10] established that API connections, especially eight-round connections, often reach the yield strength when loaded. Moreover, Yazaki *et al.*[11] observed that, for buttress threads, makeup stresses on the order of the yield strength result in SSC for these connections. Along with other considerations, concern over high stresses that promote SSC susceptibility in connections has led to the development of many new connections (referred to as premium connections) designed to match the strength of the pipe body and to reduce the tensile hoop stress while maintaining a gas-tight condition. These premium connections frequently have metal-to-metal seals and torque shoulders to provide a better seal at lower stresses.

Finite-element analyses of connections have proved quite valuable in studying the behavior of connections under different loading conditions and enable comparisons of different designs, sizes, and grades without the high cost of testing each connection. **Figs. 5.10 and 5.11** show the results of finite-element-analysis calculations and stress distributions of a premium connection on 7-in., 35-lbm/ft [17.8-cm, 52-kg/m] casing after makeup and with an axial load.[12] A 90-ksi [621-MPa] yield strength was assumed. Note that with

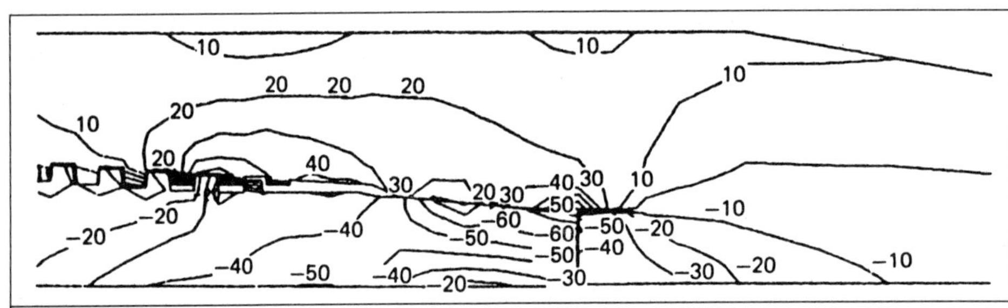

Fig. 5.10—Stress distribution for premium casing connection (7 in., 35 lbm/ft [17.8 cm, 52 kg/m]) with make-up torque of 3.25 ton-m (23,500 lbf-ft [2655 N·m]). Stress values are in kg/mm² (1.42 ksi = 1 kg/mm²).[12]

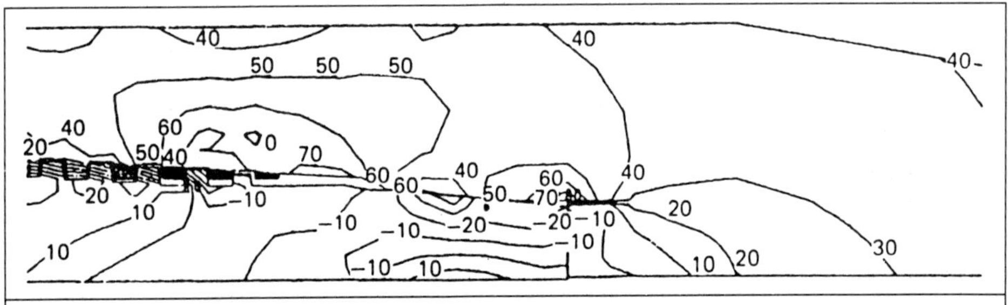

Fig. 5.11—Same as Fig. 10 but loaded in axial direction to 732,000 lbf [33×10^5 N]. Stress values are in kg/mm² (1.42 ksi = 1 kg/mm²).[12]

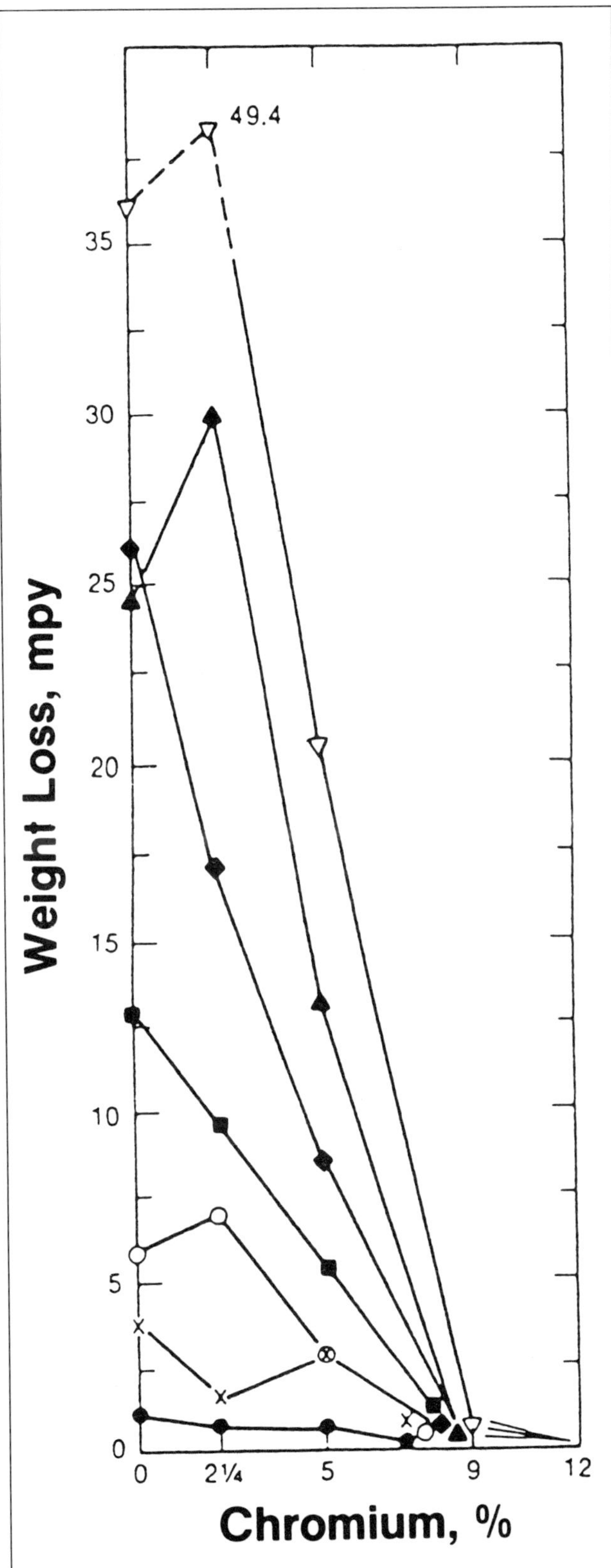

Fig. 5.12—Effect of chromium content on corrosion of steel in condensate wells containing CO_2 (©NACE, 1950).[14]

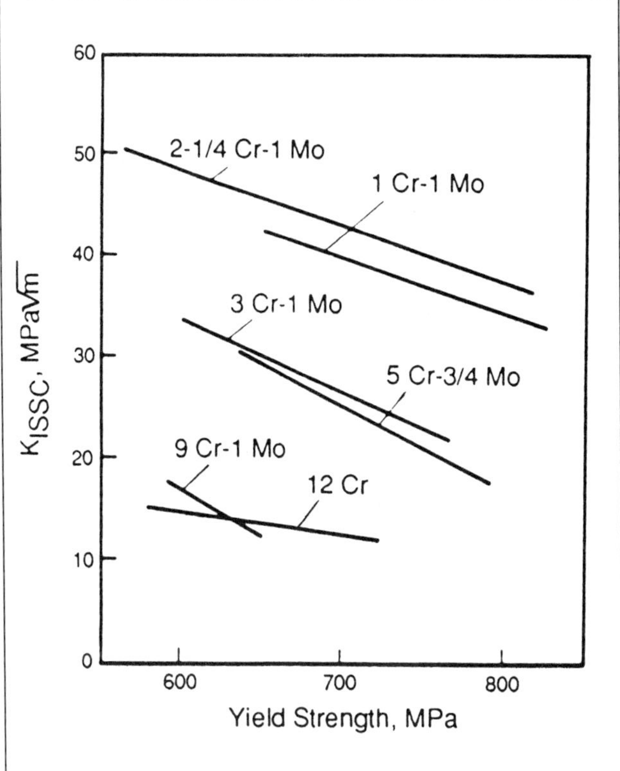

Fig. 5.13—Decrease in SSC resistance of steels with increasing chromium content (©NACE, 1983).[15]

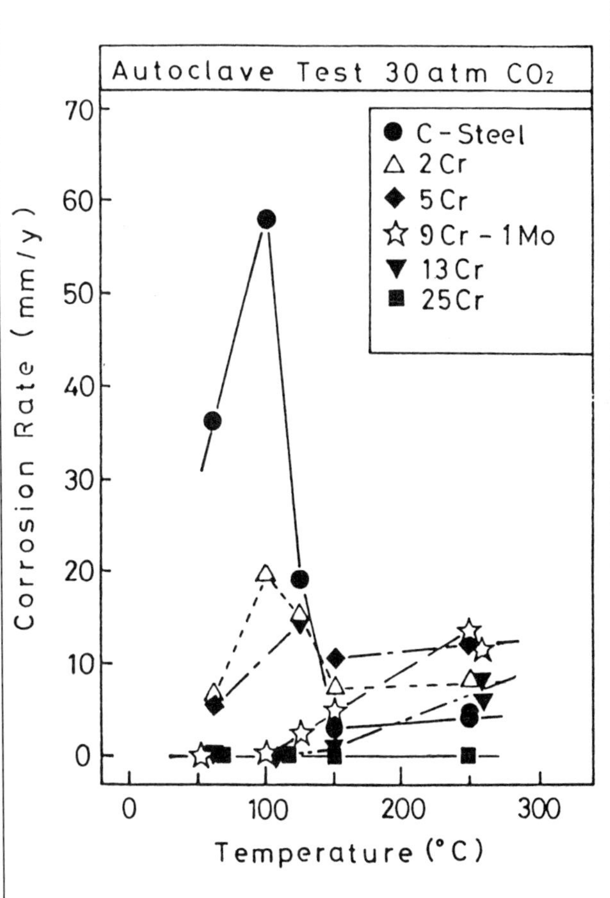

Fig. 5.14—Effects of chromium content and temperature on CO_2 corrosion of steel.[18]

an axial tensile load of 732,000 lbf [33×10^5 N], the local stress on the pin nose increases to a maximum of 100,000 psi [690 MPa] or 111% of the yield strength.

Despite the increase in connection evaluations and concerns over connection stresses, little full-scale connection testing in H_2S has been performed. Noerager and Greer[13] studied the SSC resistance of modified Grade N-80 (essentially Grade L-80) API tubing with a buttress connection made up to various torques. They exposed

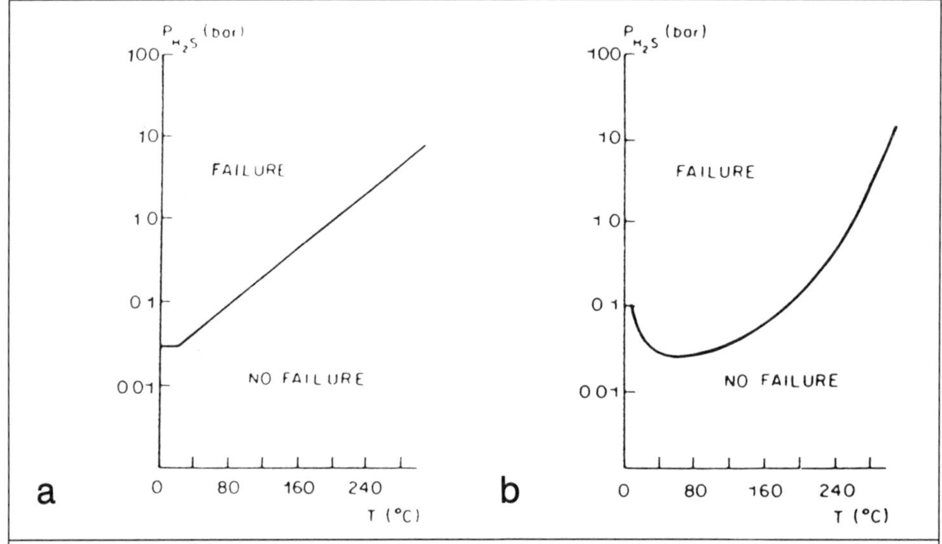

Fig. 5.15—Failure/nonfailure data of cold-worked duplex stainless-steel alloys at a stress level of 100% of the specified minimum yield strength (constant load tests).[20]

the internal and external surfaces of the connection to pressurized sour fluid and found no effect from the H_2S; failure resulted from ductile overload. Yazaki *et al.*,[11] however, observed SSC in Grade L-80 with a buttress connection and SSC failure of a premium connection on Grade P-110 casing. Higher-strength tubulars (Grades Q-125, P-110, and V-150) often fail in the connection as a result of SSC. Moreover, Grades J-55 and L-80 have been observed to fail in tong marks on connections.

When considering production casing and tubing connections for sour-gas service, a basic guideline is to use a premium connection for pressures higher than 4,000 psi [276 MPa].

5.2.6 Corrosion-Resistant Alloys (CRA's). Rarely is sour gas produced without other impurities that, when combined with H_2S, create severely corrosive environments. This combination of corrodents (H_2S, CO_2, sulfur, chloride, water, etc.) and high temperatures can be beyond the corrosion resistance of carbon and low-alloy steels, even if plastic coatings and chemical inhibitors are used. Alternatively, the corrosion rates for carbon steel can be so high that its use becomes uneconomical. In fact, the best plastic coatings and inhibitors are limited to a maximum temperature of about 375°F [191°C]. Similarly, fiberglass-reinforced plastic pipe, while suitable at lower temperatures, pressures, and H_2S contents, is unsuitable for extreme conditions. Above 375°F [191°C], only alloys with sufficient levels of chromium, nickel, and molybdenum can resist corrosion, pitting from chlorides, SSC, and stress corrosion cracking (SCC) produced by these aggressive environments. These CRA materials may also be economical at lower temperatures. The three general categories of CRA's are stainless steels (e.g., austenitic, martensitic, and duplex), nickel-based alloys, and titanium alloys. Cobalt-based alloys are CRA's used for special applications.

For wells that produce CO_2 as the primary corrodent with little or no H_2S, the 13% Cr steel has been quite successful because of

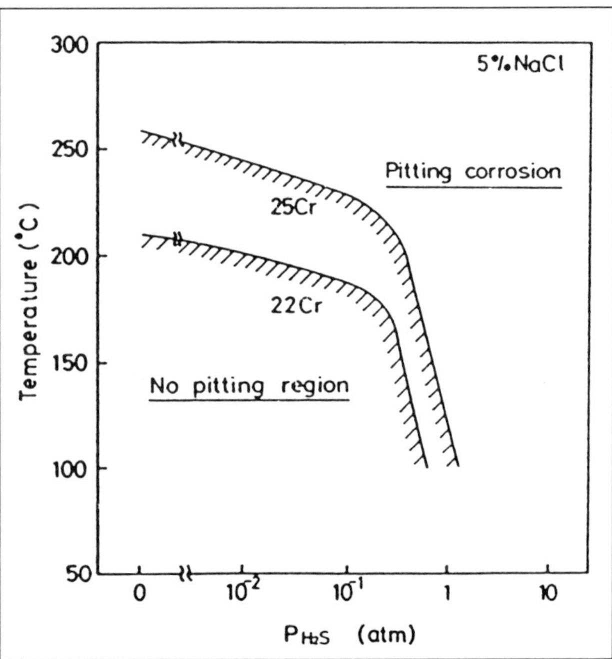

Fig. 5.16—Effects of temperature and H_2S partial pressure on pitting corrosion of two duplex stainless steels.[21]

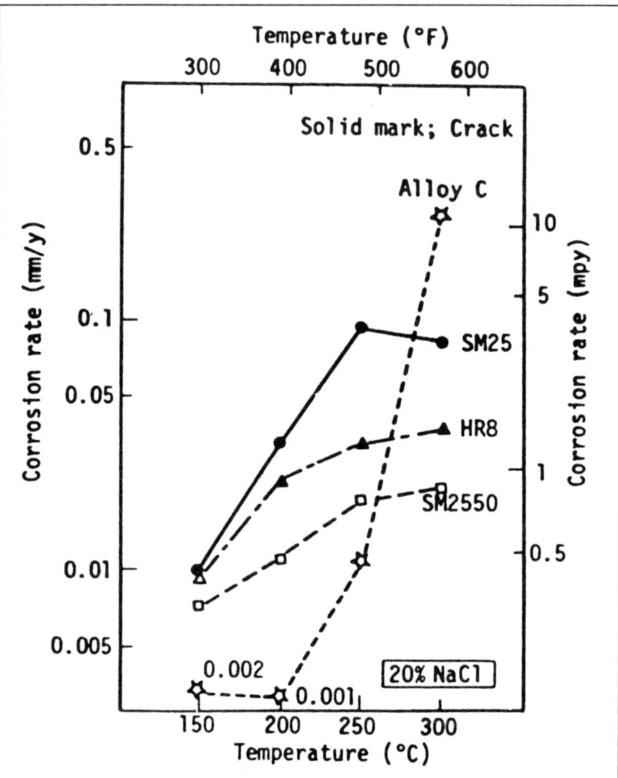

Fig. 5.17—Effect of test solution temperature on corrosion rate in 20% NaCl-10 atm H_2S-10 atm CO_2 environment.[22]

TABLE 5.4—NOMINAL COMPOSITION OF COMMON CRA's

Common Name	Unified Numbering System Number	Element (wt%) Cr	Mo	Ni	Ti	Co	Fe	Cb	Other	Strengthening Method
					Stainless Steels					
13% Cr (420)	S42000	13.0	—	0.5	—	—	Bal	—	—	HT
316	S31600	19.0	2.5	9.0	—	—	Bal	—	—	CW
DP3[a]	S31260	25.0	3.0	7.0	—	—	Bal	—	—	CW
Cr22[b]	S31803	22.0	3.0	6.0	—	—	Bal	—	—	CW
AF22[c]	S31803	22.0	3.0	6.0	—	—	Bal	—	—	CW
CD4MCu	None	25.0	2.0	5.0	—	—	Bal	—	3.0 Cu	CW
Nitronic 50[d]	S20910	21.0	2.0	12.5	—	—	Bal	—	5.0 Mn	CW
Ferralium 255[e]	S32550	25.0	3.0	5.5	—	—	Bal	—	1.0 Cu	CW
A286	S66286	15.0	1.2	25.0	2.5	—	Bal	—	—	HT
17-4PH[d]	S17400	17.0	—	4.0	—	—	Bal	—	4.0 Cu	HT
Sanicro 28[f]	N087028	27.0	3.5	31.0	—	—	Bal	—	1.0 Cu	CW
254 SMO[g]	S31254	20.0	6.1	18.0	—	—	Bal	—	0.2 N or 0.75 Cu	CW
20Cb-3[k]	N08020	20.0	3.0	35.0	—	—	Bal	—	—	CW
					Nickel-Based Alloys					
NIC 42[b]	N08825	22.0	2.9	42.0	—	—	Bal	—	—	CW
Incoloy 825[h]	N08825	20.5	3.0	42.0	—	—	Bal	—	—	CW
Incoloy 925[h]	N09925	21.0	3.0	42.0	2.1	—	Bal	—	2.0 Cu or 0.3 Al	HT
AllCorr[l]	N06110	31.0	10.0	56.0	—	—	Bal	—	2.0 W	CW
Inconel 718[h]	N07718	19.0	3.1	52.0	0.9	0.5	Bal	5.0	0.6 Al	HT
Inconel X-750[h]	N07750	15.0	—	Bal	2.5	1.0	7.0	1.0	—	HT
Inconel 625[h]	N06625	22.0	9.0	Bal	0.4	1.0	5.0	4.0	—	CW
Monel 400[h]	N04400	—	—	Bal	—	—	2.3	—	32.0 Cu	CW
Monel K-500[h]	N05500	—	—	65.0	0.5	—	1.0	—	29.5 Cu	HT
Pyromet 31[k]	N07031	23.0	2.0	56.0	2.5	—	15.0	1.0	1.5 Al	HT
SM 2550[a]	N06975	25.0	6.2	49.0	1.2	—	—	—	—	CW
NIC 52[b]	N06975	25.0	7.0	52.0	1.0	—	Bal	—	1.0 Cu	CW
Hastelloy C-276[i]	N10276	15.4	16.0	Bal	—	2.0	6.0	—	3.5 W	CW
Hastelloy G-3[i]	N06985	22.0	7.0	Bal	—	3.0	19.5	—	1.0 W	CW
Hastelloy G-50[i]	None	22.0	9.0	Bal	—	3.0	18.0	—	2.0 W	CW
					Nickel/Cobalt					
MP35N[j]	R30035	20.0	9.5	35.5	—	35.0	—	—	—	CW
MP159[j]	None	20.0	7.0	25.5	3.0	35.0	8.6	—	—	CW
					Cobalt-Based Alloys					
Haynes Alloy 25[i]	R30605	20.0	—	10.0	—	Bal	3.0	—	15.0 W	CW
Haynes Alloy 188[i]	R30188	22.0	—	22.0	—	Bal	3.0	—	14.0 W	CW
					Titanium-Based Alloys					
Ti-6Al-4V-0.05 Pd	R56400	—	—	—	Bal	—	—	—	6 Al, 4 V, or 0.05 Pd	HT
Beta C[m]	R58640	6.0	3.0	—	Bal	—	—	—	3 Al, 8 V, or 4 Zr	HT

[a]Sumitomo Metal Industries Ltd.
[b]Nippon Kokan K.K.
[c]Mannesmann
[d]Armco Steel Corp.
[e]Bonar Langley
[f]Sandvik AB
[g]Avesta Jernverks AB
[h]Huntington Alloys Inc.
[i]Haynes
[j]Standard Pressed Steel
[k]Carpenter Technology Corp.
[l]Teledyne Allvac
[m]RMI
HT = heat treatment.
CW = cold work.
Bal = balance.

its resistance to corrosion (**Fig. 5.12**).[14] As **Fig. 5.13** shows, however, the SSC resistance of 12% to 13% Cr steel is considerably less than such chromium-molybdenum (Cr-Mo) steels as API Grades C-90 and T-95 tubulars.[15] A synergistic effect of organic acid ions and H_2S on SSC showed that acetate ion concentration can significantly reduce the critical H_2S concentration to which 13% Cr steels can be exposed.[16] According to Fisher,[17] organic acids are present in gas-condensate wells. Moreover, 13% Cr steels are limited by their corrosion resistance to hot chlorides (<300°F [<149°C]) in well fluids.

Wells with high chloride contents, CO_2, and high temperatures may be completed with duplex stainless steels (22% to 25% Cr steels) because, as **Fig. 5.14** shows, resistance to high-temperature CO_2 increases by increasing the amount of chromium in the steel.[18] Duplex stainless steels have excellent resistance to corrosion in CO_2, exceeding the capabilities of 13% Cr steel, especially at higher temperatures and higher chloride contents. In addition, duplex stainless steels are much more resistant to chloride SCC than either fully ferritic or fully austenitic stainless steels.[19] However, like 13% Cr steels, duplex stainless steels are susceptible to cracking in H_2S with a limiting H_2S partial pressure between 0.1 and 5.0 psi [0.7 and 35 kPa], depending on alloy content and

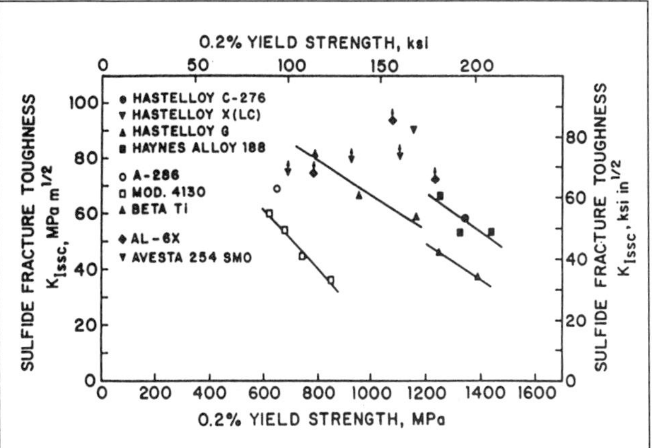

Fig. 5.18—SSC resistance of various CRA's compared with casing steel (modified AISI 4130) (reprinted with permission from *Hydrogen Effects in Metals*, "Sulfide Stress Cracking Resistance of Superalloys for Sour Gas Well Operations," by E.P. Whelan, p. 983, edited by I.M. Bernstein and A.W. Thompson, TMS, Warrendale, PA, 1981).[23]

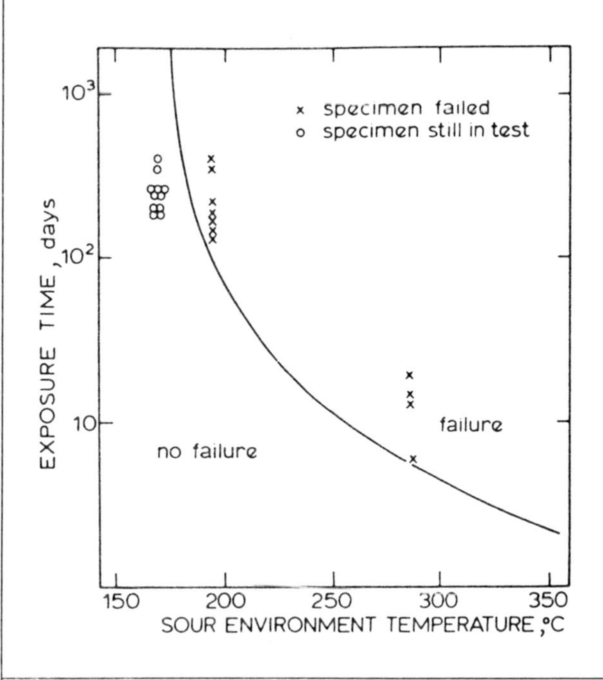

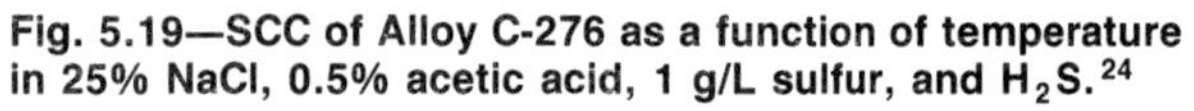
Fig. 5.19—SCC of Alloy C-276 as a function of temperature in 25% NaCl, 0.5% acetic acid, 1 g/L sulfur, and H_2S.[24]

Fig. 5.20—Effect of sulfur and molybdenum on cracking and corrosion of several nickel-based alloys (©NACE, 1988).[26]

cold work. **Fig. 5.15** shows an example of the SSC performance of solution-annealed and cold-worked duplex stainless steel.[20] This range is not universally accepted and controversy remains about the upper limit. **Fig. 5.16** shows that H_2S also increases the pitting tendency of duplex stainless steel in brines.[21] Like 13% Cr steels, albeit to a lesser degree, the increased hardness of cold-worked duplex stainless steels affect their susceptibility to cracking in H_2S. Duplex stainless steels must be cold-worked to increase strength because they are not heat-treatable. The annealed duplex stainless steels typically have a yield strength of 60,000 psi [414 MPa] for 22% Cr steel and 75,000 psi [517 MPa] for 25% Cr steel.

Because 13% Cr and duplex stainless steels have a low tolerance limit to H_2S concentration, alloys with more nickel, chromium, and molybdenum are being considered for use in wells with an H_2S partial pressure >1 psi [>7 kPa]. A specific hierarchy of CRA's does not exist.

Table 5.4 lists many alloys currently being used or considered for tubulars, downhole components, and surface equipment.

Generally, the higher the alloy content (nickel, chromium, and molybdenum) the greater the resistance of a CRA to both corrosion and environmental cracking. **Fig. 5.17** shows the corrosion resistance of several CRA's in a combined H_2S/CO_2 environment as a function of temperature.[22] Note that the most highly alloyed material (Alloy C-276) shows good resistance at low temperatures but becomes unsatisfactory at high temperatures. This reversal in corrosion resistance illustrates the importance of actually testing alloys in the expected service environment and not simply using extrapolated data. Optimizations of corrosion resistance and cost generally require laboratory testing in the expected environment. The high cost and potential savings between some alloys can warrant extensive laboratory testing.

Fig. 5.18 shows that resistance to SSC improves with increased alloy content by comparing CRA's with typical casing steels (modified American Iron & Steel Inst.'s AISI 4130).[23] The term K_{ISSC} is a measure of the resistance to crack propagation in the H_2S environment and is discussed in Chap. 3. The results in Fig. 5.18 should not be misconstrued as indicating that these alloys are totally immune to cracking in all possible sour-gas environments.

The introduction of low levels of elemental sulfur has catastrophic effects on the environmental cracking resistance of many CRA's. In many sour-gas wells, alloys such as Incoloy 825 have performed quite well. However, when elemental sulfur is included in laboratory tests, results indicate that most CRA materials considered for sour-gas service are inadequate and that only alloys like Alloy C-276 are acceptable. Moreover, as **Fig. 5.19** shows, at sufficiently

TABLE 5.5—SCC OF NICKEL- AND COBALT-BASED ALLOYS (AFTER KANE AND BOYD[25])

C-ring specimens tested in aqueous solutions containing 25% NaCl, 0.5% acetic acid, 1 g/L elemental sulfur, and H_2S.
Test duration was 150 days.
Time to failure by SCC was 100 days in some cases.

	Transverse Yield Strength at Test Temperature, °F [°C]					
	At 350 [175]		At 400 [205]		At 550 [290]	
	70%	90%	70%	90%	70%	90%
Hastelloy Alloy C-276, 37% cold-reduced	P	F	F	F	F	F
Alloy MP35N, 59% cold-reduced	F	F	F	F	F	F
Hastelloy Alloy G, 59% cold-reduced	—	—	F	F	—	—

P = passed.
F = failed.

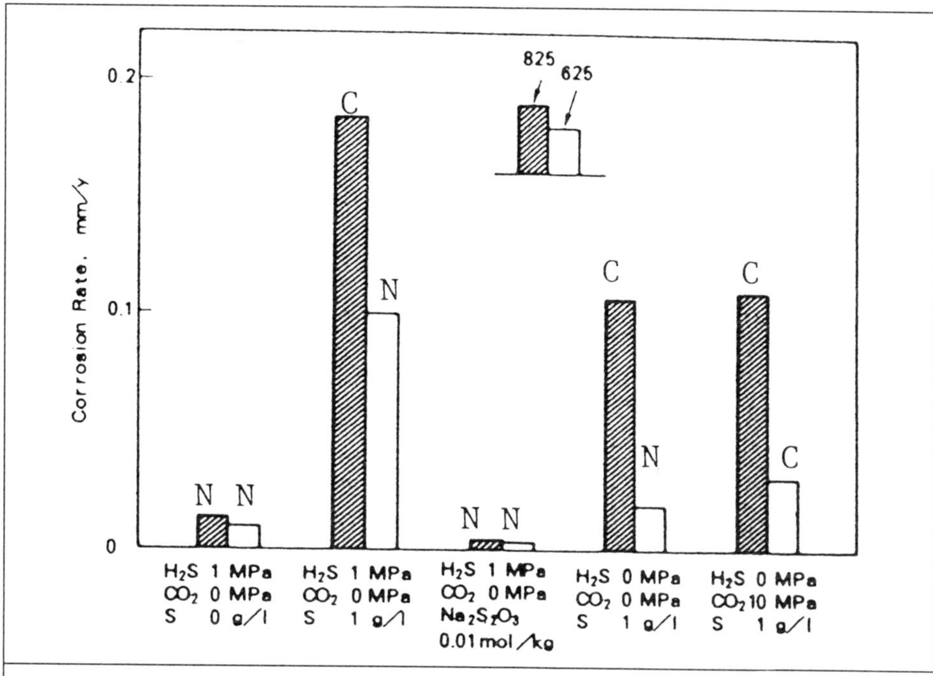

Fig. 5.21—Cracking and corrosion results on Incoloy 825 and Inconel 625 in various environments. N = no cracking; C = cracking (©NACE, 1989).[28]

high temperatures, even Alloy C-276 is susceptible to SCC.[24] **Table 5.5** shows the SCC of some normally resistant CRA's after the addition of only 1 g/L of elemental sulfur.[25] Elemental sulfur has been found in some hot-gas wells containing H_2S. Moreover, corrosion is more severe when sulfur is present as a liquid than when it is present as a solid.* Recent research[26-28] in this area has shown the beneficial influence of molybdenum content on corrosion and cracking of CRA's in sulfur-bearing solutions (**Fig. 5.20**). **Fig. 5.21** also illustrates the benefit of higher amounts of molybdenum by comparing Incoloy 825 (3% Mo) with Inconel 625 (9% Mo).[28]

Acidic conditions are important to the promotion of significant corrosion in free sulfur and so is the effect of sulfur concentration. Increasing sulfur concentration and decreasing pH significantly increase the corrosion and pitting rates of alloys. Recently, titanium alloys have been considered for these hostile environments. Titanium alloys offer several advantages over nickel-based alloys, including good corrosion resistance and the ability to be heat-treated to high strength levels. **Table 5.6** shows the results of several titanium alloys compared with Alloys 2550 and C-276 in a sour environment at different temperatures.[29] Some of the beta alloys look quite promising compared with the nickel-based alloys.

As a result of the high cost involved in the use of these CRA's, there is a growing demand and use of internally clad pipe and components. A thin layer of CRA is often sufficient to provide good corrosion resistance at a lower cost than solid CRA's.

*Personal communication with M. Milligan, Shell Canada, 1990.

TABLE 5.6—RESULTS OF SCC AUTOCLAVE TEST (AFTER REF. 29)

Four-point bent-beam specimens tested in solution of 25% NaCl + 1 g/L elemental sulfur and 10 atm H_2S + 10 atm CO_2.

	Yield Strength (ksi)	482°F	450°F			482°F
		500 hours	336 hours	500 hours	2688 hours	500 hours
Super titanium-based alloys						
Ti-6Al-4V-0.05 Pd	150	G		G		
	130	G	G	G	G	
Ti-6Al-2Sn-4Zr-6Mo-0.05 Pd	190	G				
	170	G				
Conventional alloys						
Ti-6Al-4V	150	O				C
	130	C	C	C	C	C
Bc(Ti-3Al-8V-6Cr-4Mo-4Zr)	180	O	O			O
	130	O				O
	120	C				C
Ti-6Al-2Sn-4Zr-6Mo	190	O	G			G
	170	O	G		G	G
	150	G	G			G
BIII(Ti-11.5Mo-6Zr-4.5Sn)	190	G	G			G
	170	G	G		G	G
	150	G	G			G
Nickel-based alloys						
2550 (6 Mo)	120		O			
C-276 (15 Mo)	130	G	G		C	

G = good.
O = SCC occurred.
C = severely corroded.

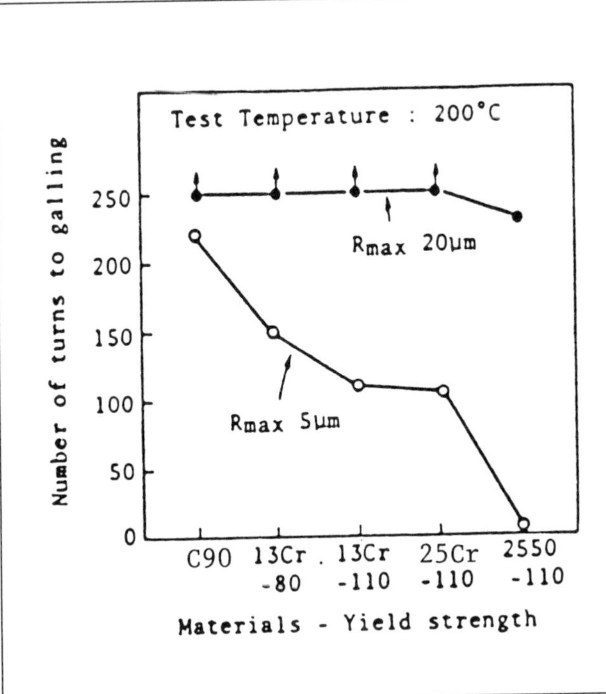

Fig. 5.22—Galling resistance of several alloys as a function of initial surface roughness.[26]

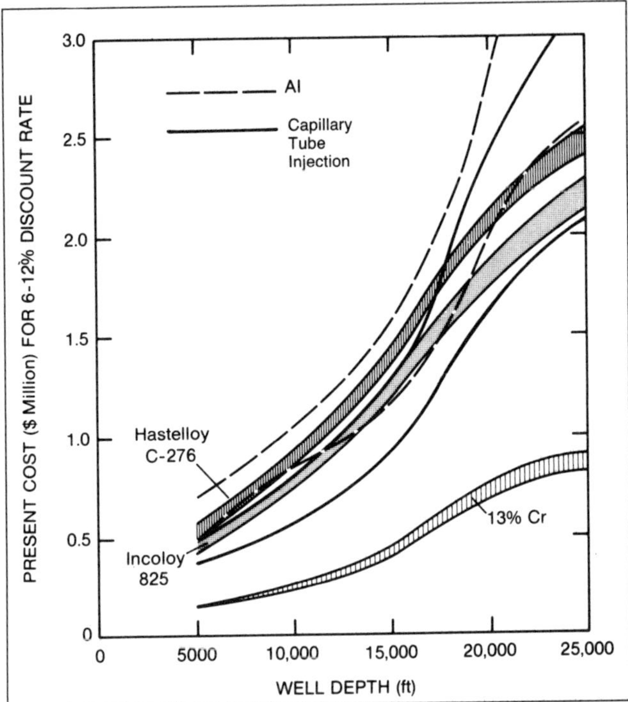

Fig. 5.23—Present cost for various completion schemes as a function of depth for discount rates of 6% to 12%.[30]

Research in this area continues, with the aim of developing alloys that are resistant to corrosion and cracking in high-H_2S and sulfur-bearing environments and that are less expensive than alloys like Alloy C-276. As more areas where deep hot wells containing H_2S (e.g., Mobile Bay, offshore Alabama, and the Madden Deep Unit in Wyoming) are produced, sulfur will continue to be a problem for CRA's. Despite these problems with CRA's, steel components have been used successfully to produce wells with a high H_2S concentration and significant elemental sulfur in western Canada and Mississippi. This largely results from the continuous injection of inhibitors and sulfur solvents. Typical sulfur solvents are dimethyl disulfide and diaryl disulfide.

With the application of CRA's for tubulars, the potential for galling of threads became a greater concern. This problem was infrequently observed with steel tubulars. Factors that affect galling are hardness, variations in hardness, inclusion content, grain size, thermal conductivity of the alloy, contact area, lubrication, crystal structure, and surface roughness. Resistance to galling decreases when (1) hardness decreases, (2) small variations in hardness exist between the two components, (3) inclusion content is low, (4) grain size is fine, (5) thermal conductivity is low, (6) contact area is high, (7) lubrication is minimal or hard to establish, and (8) surface roughness is low. All these factors are typical of CRA's compared with carbon steel. Phosphate coatings, which historically have been effective for steel pipe like Grade L-80, cannot be applied to CRA's.

Standard galling tests are unavailable currently; however, the Bowden test is frequently applied. Results of a typical galling test (**Fig. 5.22**) show that for smooth surfaces (with a root-mean-square of 5μm), increasing the alloy content significantly diminishes the number of turns to galling.[26] Surface modification is the most common technique used to overcome galling problems. This is accomplished by roughening one of the mating surfaces by sandblasting or glass-bead blasting. Another method is to plate one surface with a softer or harder material. While tin can improve the galling resistance of CRA's, its melting point is too low, and at high bottomhole temperatures (>300°F [>149°C]), solid- or liquid-metal embrittlement is possible. Therefore, because copper has a higher melting point, it is preferred and has performed well in sour-gas wells.

Another important consideration in CRA application is the ineffectiveness of ferromagnetic-related inspection techniques. Because austenitic stainless steels and nickel-based alloys are nonmagnetic, such standard industry inspection methods as magnetic particle inspection and electromagnetic inspection are applicable only for 13% Cr CRA's, because 13% Cr steel has magnetic properties similar to carbon steel. The eddy-current method can be applied to CRA's but is limited to thin sections of nonmagnetic metals. Thus, full-body ultrasonic inspection and dye penetrant are the only available methods for CRA inspection. CRA's used for sour-gas service generally have good toughness, which provides good tolerance to flaws. Therefore, nondestructive examination need not be as sensitive to small flaws as for conventional steel products.

5.2.7 Chemical Inhibition. Traditionally, sour-gas wells are completed by running carbon or low-alloy steel tubulars and, if required, batch or continuously injecting corrosion inhibitors and/or scale

TABLE 5.7—COMPARISON OF CORROSION TREATMENT METHODS (AFTER BRADBURN AND KALRA[32])

Corrosion Treatment Method	Formation Type		Production				Inhibitor Film Repair	Efficiency (%)	Frequency (days)	Formation Damage	Shut In	Hole Angle	
	Consolidated	Unconsolidated	Gas	Gas Condensate	Oil	Flow Velocity						Straight	Deviated
Batch	Yes	No	Yes	Yes	No	$<v_E$	No	60 to 80	≤30	Very Unlikely	Yes	Yes	No
Tubing Displacement	Yes	No	Yes	Yes	Yes	$<v_E$	No	80 to 90	≤30	Unlikely	Yes	Yes	Yes
Formation Squeeze	Yes	No	Yes	Yes	Yes	$>v_E$	Yes	80 to 95	>30	Possibly	Yes	Yes	Yes
Continuous	Yes	Yes	Yes	Yes	Yes	$>v_E$	Yes	95 to 100	—	None	No	Yes	Yes

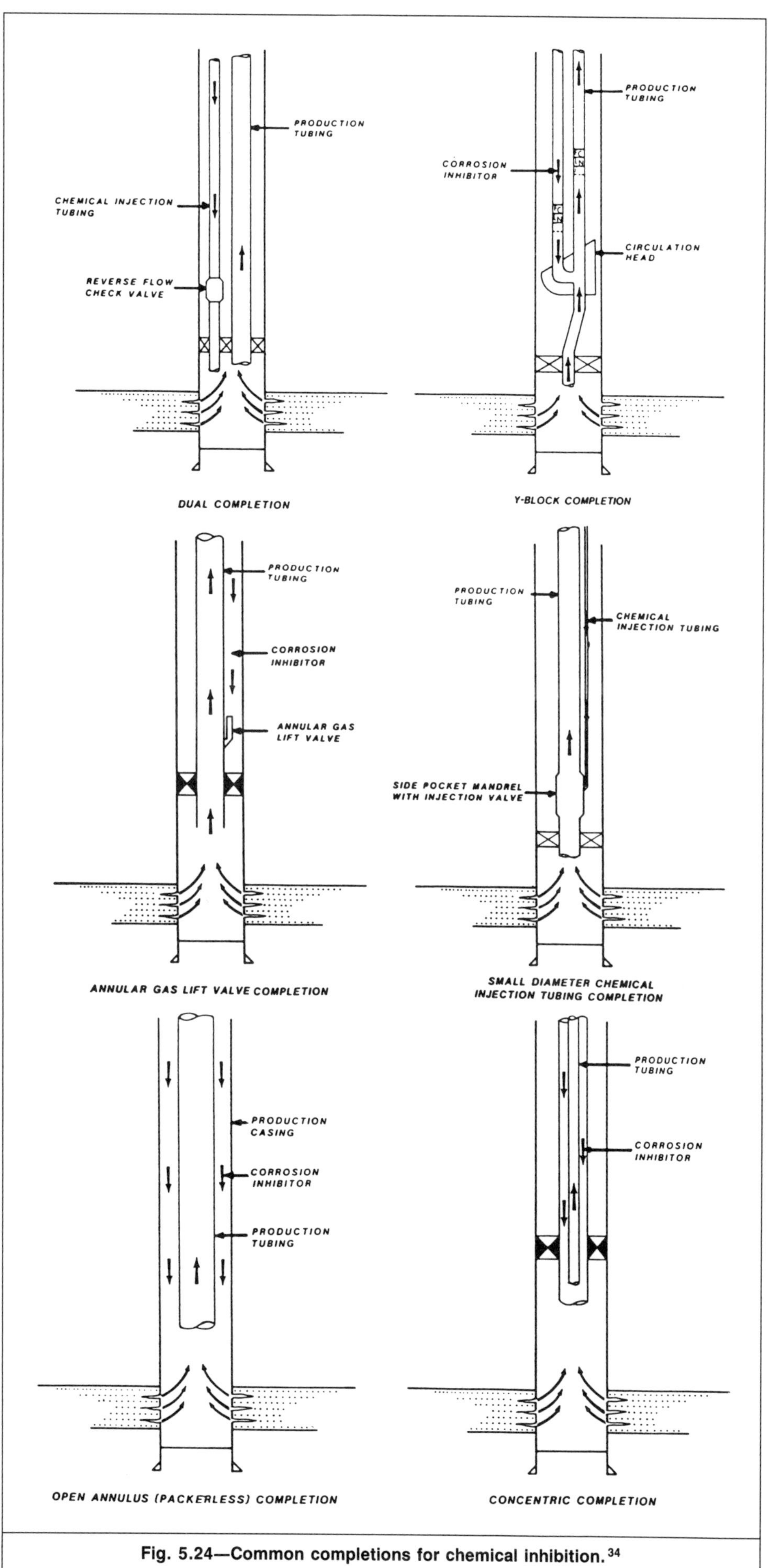

Fig. 5.24—Common completions for chemical inhibition.[34]

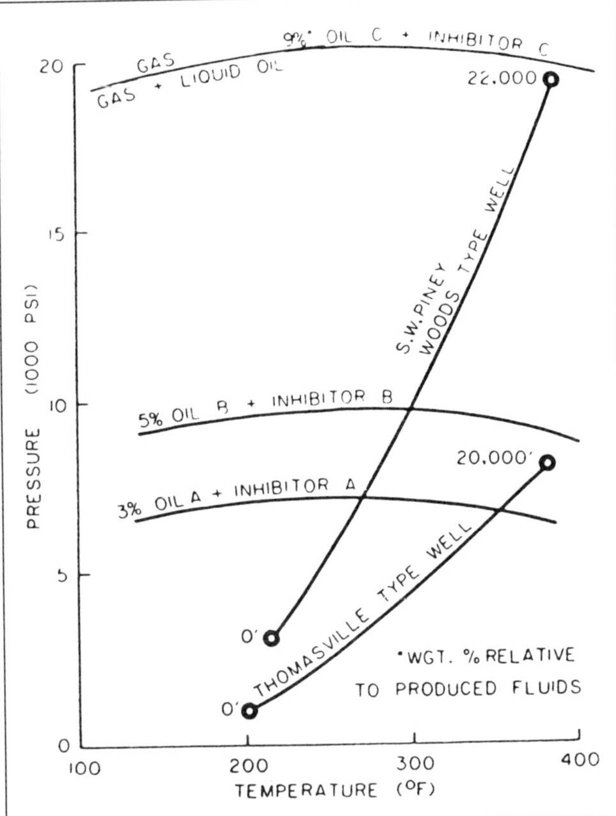

Fig. 5.25—Phase behavior of certain inhibitor oil mixtures in deep gas wells.[35]

inhibitors. For wells that contain large oil/water ratios, inhibition is not required; however, condensate does not offer the same protection. Only recently has use of CRA's become competitive with use of carbon and low-alloy steels and inhibitors. In hot (>375°F [>191°C]) wells, CRA's are necessary because of the limitations on inhibitor stability and carrier-fluid volatility at high temperatures. At shallower depths, the inhibitor system may be more economical than CRA's, depending on the factors selected for analysis (**Fig. 5.23**).[30] CRA's may also permit higher production velocities because of their higher erosion/corrosion limit.[31]

The selection and application of corrosion inhibitors to sour-gas wells is complex and specific to the particular well environment. Testing should include the actual produced fluids mixed with the candidate inhibitors and carriers. Common methods to deploy chemicals and to inhibit a well for corrosion control are discussed in this section. **Table 5.7** shows typical characteristics of various treatment methods.[32]

Batch-treatment and tubing-displacement methods are used frequently when corrosion is not a serious problem and when treatments are required only every 2 to 4 weeks. Formation squeeze is effective only in certain formations, and one must be careful not to damage the formation. Generally, continuous inhibitor injection is most effective for controlling corrosion in very corrosive hot-gas wells. A successful continuous inhibitor system incorporates proper phase behavior, has a predictable uniform quality and a low-vapor-pressure, is nonscaling and easy to handle and maintain, can be dehydrated, and mitigates corrosion.[33] **Fig. 5.24** shows the most common chemical delivery methods.[34] Each delivery system has advantages and disadvantages, and use of one over another must be evaluated on a case-by-case basis. Most recently, the method of capillary tube injection (CTI) has gained wide use, especially for high-CO_2 gas wells.

Inhibitor selection is crucial to the success of CTI for corrosion control. Because corrosion inhibitors are specific for each application, a comprehensive laboratory testing program should be conducted to select one or more chemical candidates for field testing. As the temperature increases, many inhibitors and/or their carrier (diluent) become unstable and may vaporize into the gas phase or polymerize (solidify) into a highly viscous material that offers no corrosion protection and plugs the tubing. **Fig. 5.25** illustrates the phase behavior encountered in typical deep, hot, sour-gas wells and the performance of different inhibitors and diluents.[35] Note that different inhibitors and carrier oils were needed because the phase behavior in the two wells differed.

Besides corrosion inhibitors, a solvent sometimes must be injected to prevent precipitation and bridging by elemental sulfur. In addition to the sulfur solvent, the carrier oil must be designed to enhance sulfur solubility.[33] Some sulfur solvents are based on ethylamine, dimethyl disulfide, diaryl disulfide, and carbon disulfide because sulfur is highly soluble in these compounds. Carbon disulfide, however, is not commonly used because it is quite toxic and highly flammable. Similarly, other chemicals can be injected to reduce scaling, hydrate formation, and paraffin deposition. Evaluation of the compatability of all additions and diluents with each other and the well environment is essential.

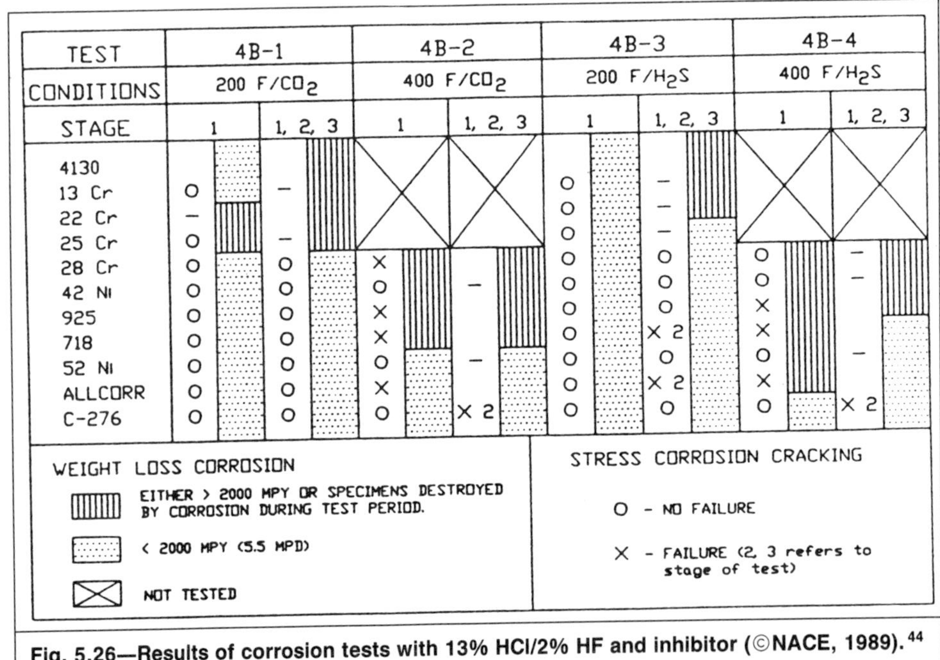

Fig. 5.26—Results of corrosion tests with 13% HCl/2% HF and inhibitor (©NACE, 1989).[44]

TABLE 5.8—COMMON ELASTOMERS

Designation	Elastomer
FKM-B (C)	Viton B
FKM (P)	Peroxide-cured conventional fluoroelastomer (vinylidene fluoride/hexafluoropropylene type)
FKM (B)	Bisphenol-cured conventional fluoroelastomer
FFKM	Perfluorinated rubber
EPDM	Ethylene-propylene-diene
EPDM/FKM	EPDM/FKM blend
NBR (P)	Peroxide-cured nitrile
NBR (S)	Sulfur-cured nitrile
XNBR (P)	Peroxide-cured carboxylated nitrile
XNBR (S)	Sulfur-cured carboxylated nitrile
HNBR	Hydrogenated nitrile
ECO	Epichlorohydrin
TFE/P	Tetrafluoroethylene-propylene
Kalrez®	DuPont's totally fluorinated FFKM elastomer
AFLAS®	Asahi Glass' half-fluorinated FKM elastomer

The decision to use chemical inhibition or CRA's requires considerable evaluation of the well environment, type of completion, safety environments, economics, and risk analysis. Each factor must be weighed carefully. For example, economics may favor chemical inhibition for corrosion control of an offshore well, but reliability of the injection system and the risk involved may shift the advantage to CRA's. Some of the most important advantages of using CRA's vs. a carbon steel/inhibitor system are listed below.

1. No corrosion chemical-delivery system is needed.
2. Because of higher strength and thinner walls, CRA's can have a larger ID for the same OD and thus be more productive.
3. The tubing life is the same as the well life.
4. CRA's have a high degree of reliability during service.
5. The quality of CRA's is often higher than that of low-alloy-steel tubes.
6. CRA's reduce or eliminate the need for corrosion monitoring.
7. CRA's have no continuous-inhibitor-supply problem (e.g., for use in remote and offshore locations).

However, use of CRA's also has disadvantages.

1. CRA's require ultrasonic inspection rather than electromagnetic inspection.
2. Connection galling can occur.
3. Galvanic coupling can occur with the casing.
4. Corrosion attacks are localized; i.e., corrosion is not uniform.
5. Corrosion is difficult to monitor.
6. CRA's have no inherent means to counter scale or sulfur precipitation.
7. Acidizing problems can occur.
8. CRA's are susceptible to pitting in oxygenated brine completion fluids.
9. CRA's require a high capital investment vs. the operating cost.

5.2.8 Packer Fluids. The main functions of packer fluids are to provide safety (for pressure control), formation protection, and long-term corrosion control. Various types of chemicals are added to fluids to achieve the desired packer fluid criteria, especially for low corrosion rates. Corrosion rates of less than 5 mil/yr [0.02 mm/a] and an average packer fluid life of 10 to 15 years are expected, with periodic adjustments during workovers. Some of the more common packer fluids are oil-based drilling mud; conditioned crude- or refined-oil packer fluids; water-based drilling mud; and clear-water or low-solids brines (e.g., fresh water; produced brines; and synthetic brines consisting of calcium chloride, sodium chloride, zinc chloride, calcium chloride-calcium bromide, calcium chloride-potassium chloride, and various other salts).

A properly conditioned oil-based drilling fluid has minimal corrosive properties and is inactive biologically. However, if water eventually segregates from the emulsion, these factors may change dramatically and reduce the benefits of this fluid.

When crude or diesel oil is used as a packer fluid, it often contains enough water to warrant treatment with a corrosion inhibitor. The corrosion inhibitors should inhibit both the liquid and the vapor phases of oil packer fluids.

Water-based muds have been used for many years as packer fluids because of their low cost and convenience. In general, however, they are not good packer fluids. Water-based fluids are limited to

TABLE 5.9—TEMPERATURE RATINGS OF ELASTOMERS FOR SOUR-GAS APPLICATIONS (©NACE AFTER ENDER[36])

	Resistance Rating To Problem At Temperature (°F [°C])		
Seal Material	Oil-Based Packer Fluid	Sour Gas	Extrusion
ECD-006*	Excellent (400 [204])	Good (400 [204])	Very Poor (300 [149])
EPDM (Nordel)**	Poor (300 [149])	Excellent (300 [149])	Poor (300 [149])
Nitrile rubber	Excellent (230 [110])	Poor (230 [110])	Good (300 [149])
Viton	Excellent (230 [110])	Poor (230 [110])	No test
Teflon™ TFE	Excellent (400 [204])	Excellent (400 [204])	Good (400 [204])
Teflon PFA†	Excellent (500 [260])	Excellent (500 [260])	Good (500 [260])

*DuPont's perfluoro elastomer.
**DuPont's ethylene-propylene elastomer.
†DuPont's perfluoroalkoxy fluorocarbon.

TABLE 5.10—PERFORMANCE SUMMARY FOR HARD-SEAL VULCANIZATES (90-95 DUROMETER SHORE A) 3 DAYS/302°F [150°C] (©NACE AFTER PUGH[37])

	Nitrile 922	FKM-A (C) 82	FKM-B (C) 285	FKM-GF (P) 81
Crude oil	Good	Good	No data	Okay
Sour oil	Brittle*	Very good	Good	Good
Sour oil + NACE B	Brittle*	Fair	Fair	Fair
Sour gas	Brittle*	Okay	Good	Okay
Water + mud + NACE A	Good	No data	Okay	Fair
Oil + mud	No data	Okay	Fair	Okay
Completion fluid				
Basic	Okay	Very good	No data	Very good
Acidic	Brittle*	Very good	Very good	Very good

*Same result at 212°F [100°C].

TABLE 5.11—EFFECT OF CORROSION INHIBITORS ON AVERAGE ELASTOMER PROPERTIES AT 212°F [100°C] (AFTER WATKINS[39])

Effect on Average Nitrile Properties								
Inhibitor*	A	A	B	B	B	C**	C**	D†
Concentration, %	1	1	1	1	5	1	5	1
Exposure, hours	70	168	70	168	70	70	70	70
Hardness, points change	−5	−5	−8	−4	−13	−1	0	−6
Tensile strength, % change	−7	−31	−24	−26	−31	−14	−17	−19
Elongation, % change	+1	−9	−3	−16	0	−14	+19	−14
Volume swelling, %	+8	NA	+10	NA	+15	+4	+7	+8

Effect on Average Fluoroelastomer‡ Properties									
Inhibitor	A	A	A	B	B	B	C*	C*	D**
Concentration, %	1	1	5	1	1	5	1	5	1
Exposure, hours	70	168	168	70	168	168	70	70	70
Hardness, points change	−2	−6	−9	−2	−5	−6	−2	−1	−2
Tensile strength, % change	−20	−27	−30	−22	−36	−45	−13	−20	−19
Elongation, % change	−12	−4	−8	−10	+1	−13	−2	−7	−14
Volume swelling, %	+4	NA	NA	+3	NA	+6	+10	+3	+8

*Identified in Ref. 39.
**Commercial water-borne inhibitors.
†Commercial oil-soluble inhibitors.
‡Vinylidene fluoride/hexafluoropropylene copolymers.
NA = Data not available.

use in relatively shallow wells, where high temperatures are not encountered, because these fluids tend to have poor temperature stability. The high temperature may cause solids (i.e., barite) to precipitate from the mud, both in oil- and water-based muds, resulting in stuck tubing and packers and/or thermal degradation of the mud additives. Such thermal degradation may generate H_2S and/or CO_2, resulting in corrosion failures. Also, sulfate-reducing bacteria may become active in the packer fluid, leading to corrosion from the H_2S they generate.

Clear-water or low-solids brine packer fluids solve some of the inherent problems listed. If clear-water packer fluids are selected properly and treated for control of corrosion and bacteria, they will continue to provide a long service life. Recommendations for treating clear-water packer fluids vary greatly depending on the exact chemical composition of the packer fluid to be treated. A common recommendation used today is to raise the pH of the fluid to between 11 and 12 and to treat the fluid with a biocide and a corrosion inhibitor. Many of the heavy clear-brine fluids, however, are not stable at a higher pH because of hydroxide precipitation of calcium and zinc.

Two drawbacks of clear-brine packer fluids are the potential for galvanic attack when CRA tubing is used and the lack of protection from a highly corrosive fluid when H_2S and/or CO_2 enter the packer fluid from packer and tubing leaks. High-density brines containing zinc bromide are especially corrosive to steel casing.

In effect, a large "battery" (galvanic cell) is set up between the CRA tubing, which is connected through the wellhead, and the packer to the casing, causing the steel casing to become anodic relative to the CRA tubing. The casing (anode) could experience accelerated corrosion, while the tubing (cathode) would be charged with hydrogen, possibly inducing a hydrogen-embrittlement failure. This is the reason CRA's are tested while they are connected to steel. Even without the galvanic effect and H_2S or CO_2 leaks into the packer fluid, hot temperatures could lead to SCC of the CRA from the brine. Thus, for CRA completions, nonconductive packer fluids, such as diesel or oil-based mud, are strongly recommended and are used more often than water-based fluids.

One last caution: lignosulfonate drilling muds that are circulated back as packer fluids have been found to degrade above about 350°F [177°C], releasing H_2S and causing SSC of Grade P-110 or higher-strength production casing in the cooler parts of the well.

5.2.9 Elastomers. Deeper, hotter gas wells have taxed the capabilities of many compounds used for elastomers in both downhole and surface equipment. **Table 5.8** lists some of the more common elastomers. While numerous elastomers are available, those listed in Table 5.8 represent the best ones to consider for sour-gas service. With increasing temperature, H_2S and CO_2 can severely limit the applicability of many elastomers to sour-gas service. **Table 5.9** presents ratings of several elastomers and plastics that were tested at different temperatures; the sour gas was composed of 34% H_2S, 10% CO_2, and 56% methane.[36] The fluorocarbons (TFE and PFA), which are used extensively in sour-gas service, performed best. **Table 5.10** shows more recent data for nitrile and three different Viton compounds (FKM's).[37] The resistance of Viton to sour gas shown in Table 5.10 conflicts with that shown in Table 5.9, a common difficulty in testing elastomers for sour service. The Natl. Assn. of Corrosion Engineers (NACE), however, recently established a method[38] for testing elastomers in H_2S with the aim of standardizing elastomer and seal testing.

The detrimental effects that corrosion inhibitors have on elastomeric materials also have been recognized recently. Many of the mechanical properties of elastomers can be affected by exposure to the H_2S/inhibitor environment. Loss in tensile strength, hardness, and elongation are common. Swelling is another problem that affects seal performance in the presence of inhibitors. **Table 5.11** compares the effects of various corrosion inhibitors on several of these properties for a nitrile and fluoroelastomer (Viton AHV).[39]

TABLE 5.12—TEMPERATURE LIMITS FOR ELASTOMERS ACCEPTABLE FOR USE IN SYSTEMS WITH H_2S, CO_2, AND AMINE INHIBITORS

	Temperature Limit °F [°C]				
Environment	Nitrile (Buna-N)	Viton (FKM)	Teflon (PTFE)	Aflas	Kalrez (FFKM)
H_2S	200 [93]	250 [121]	300 [149]	400 [204]	500 [260]
CO_2	NR	250 [121]	300 [149]	400 [204]	500 [260]
Amine inhibitors	200 [93]	200 [93]	NR	400 [204]	500 [260]

NR = Not recommended.

TABLE 5.13—ACCEPTABLE CORROSION RATES FOR STEEL DURING ACIDIZING (AFTER GILL AND DEMOTT[42])

Temperature (°F [°C])	Test Period* (hours)	Acid Concentration (%)	Corrosion Rate (lbm/ft^2 [kg/m^2] Test Period)
200 [93]	6 to 16	15	0.02 [0.1]
	6	28	0.02 [0.1]
	16	28	0.05 [0.24]
300 [149]	4	15	0.05 [0.24]
	4	28	0.075 [0.37]
400 [204]	1	15	0.095 [0.46]

*Time at temperature.

TABLE 5.14—EFFECT OF H_2S ON CORROSION RATE OF STEEL TUBULARS DURING ACIDIZING IN 15% HCl AT 200°F [93°C] AFTER 6 HOURS OF EXPOSURE (AFTER GILL AND DEMOTT[42])

	Concentration (%)	Corrosion Rate H_2S+HCl (mil/yr [mm/a])	HCl (lbm/ft^2 [kg/m^2])	Relative Rate* H_2S+HCl	Relative Rate* HCl
Grade N-80 Tubing					
Inhibitor A	0.3	0.026 [0.0006]	0.016 [0.781]	1.30	0.80
	0.5	0.015 [0.0038]		0.75	
Inhibitor B	0.3	0.051 [0.0013]	0.014 [0.068]	2.55	0.70
	0.5	0.021 [0.0053]		1.05	
Inhibitor C	0.3	0.035 [0.0009]	0.013 [0.063]	1.75	0.65
	0.5	0.030 [0.0008]			
Grade J-55 Tubing					
Inhibitor A	0.3	0.137 [0.0035]	0.018 [0.088]	6.35	0.90
	0.5	0.040 [0.0010]		2.00	
Inhibitor B	0.3	0.751 [0.0191]	0.008 [0.039]	37.60	0.40
	0.5	0.044 [0.0011]			
Inhibitor C	0.3	0.058 [0.0015]	0.019 [0.093]	2.90	0.95
	0.5	0.032 [0.0008]		1.60	

*Based on acceptable rate of 0.02 lbm/ft^2 [0.1 kg/m^2] per test period.

TABLE 5.15—EFFECT OF DIFFERENT GASES ON CORROSION RESISTANCE OF ALLOYS IN INHIBITED (0.2 vol%) HCl SOLUTION AT 350°F [177°C] (AFTER KOLTS AND COREY[43])

Alloy	15% HCl+5% NaCl, mil/yr [mm/a] N_2	CO_2	CO_2+H_2S	H_2S
825	1,270 [32.26]	1,400 [35.56]	>4,800 [>121.92]*	>6,200 [>15.75]*
G-3	480 [12.19]	600 [15.24]	2,900 [73.66]	>5,200 [>13.21]*
C-276	850 [21.59]	860 [21.84]	1,100 [27.94]	1,150 [29.21]
B-2	19 [0.48]	43 [1.09]	85 [2.16]	2 [0.05]

*Sample dissolved.

At temperatures above 200°F [93°C], the propylene tetrafluoroethylene copolymer Aflas® is more resistant to amine-based corrosion inhibitors than Viton or nitrile; however, all three are equally resistant below this temperature.[40] Note that simply immersing elastomers into a test solution may not be sufficient to determine their resistance to a well environment. Elastomers and coatings may fail as a result of explosive decompression if they are subjected to rapid depressurization. Therefore, testing under simulated conditions is recommended.

Amine inhibitors may degrade seal material chemically and, in the case of fluoroelastomers, may also serve as catalysts in the dehydrofluorination of these materials. Viton is not recommended for use in sour environments with amine-type corrosion inhibitors, but Aflas and perfluorocarbon elastomers (e.g., Kalrez®) show good resistance up to 400 and 500°F [204 and 260°C], respectively. **Table 5.12** shows typical temperature limits for elastomers that are acceptable in systems containing H_2S, CO_2, and amine inhibitors. The limits given are only general guidelines and not strict requirements.

Because of these problems with seals and elastomers in sour service, much equipment is now designed with metal-to-metal seals to eliminate the need for elastomers whenever possible. In fact, in some equipment, complete sealing integrity could be attained only with metal-to-metal seals.[41]

5.2.10 Acidizing Wells. Acidizing wells with hydrochloric (HCl) acid and hydrochloric/hydrofluoric (HCl/HF) acid generally is accomplished over short times using acetylenic alcohols as inhibitors. One reason for short-duration acidization is the tendency of the inhibitors to break down early, leading to rapid corrosion of equipment in the presence of these acids. **Table 5.13** gives acceptable corrosion rates for steel in HCl acid.[42] As shown, the loss of 0.02 lbm/ft^2 [0.1 kg/m^2] over an 8-hour acid treatment is a frequently accepted maximum.

The presence of H_2S during acidizing significantly increases corrosion rates, especially with increasing temperature. **Table 5.14** shows the effect of H_2S on the corrosion rate in 15% HCl at 200°F [93°C] after 6 hours of exposure with either 0.3 or 0.5 vol% corrosion inhibitor added.[42] For both Grades N-80 and J-55 tubing, the corrosion rates increase in the presence of H_2S and HCl compared with exposure to HCl only.

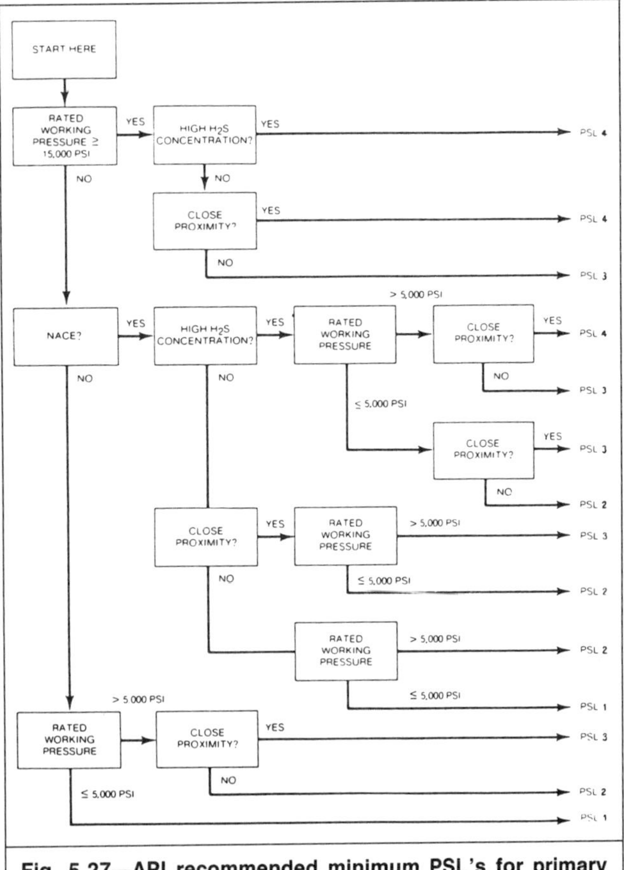

Fig. 5.27—API recommended minimum PSL's for primary parts of wellheads and Christmas trees. [46]

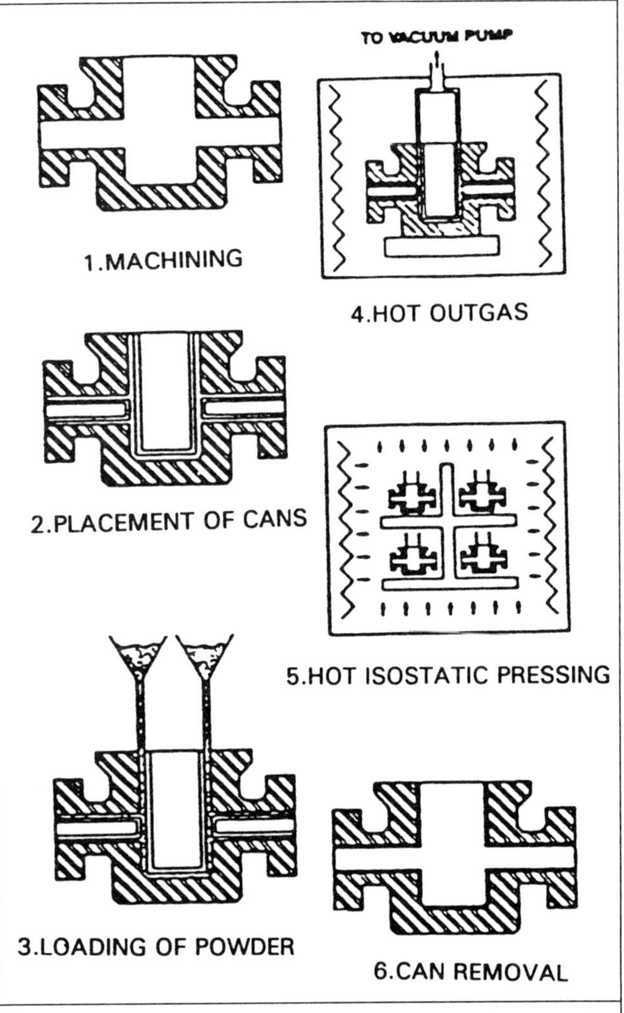

Fig. 5.28—HIP process for CRA-clad valves (©NACE, 1984). [47]

Somewhat surprisingly, recent work[43] has shown that CRA's are severely attacked in HCl-acidizing environments, even after very short exposures. Furthermore, effective inhibitors for carbon steel tubulars often are inadequate in protecting CRA's. **Table 5.15** shows the effect of different gases (H_2S, CO_2, and N_2) on corrosion rates of nickel alloys in inhibited HCl environments at 350°F [177°C].[43] The highest corrosion rates are observed in H_2S for alloys with the least general corrosion resistance. Duplex stainless steels and 13% Cr steels are attacked even more severely than the alloys presented in Table 5.15 under similar conditions.

Simulated environment testing has demonstrated that the most critical aspect of acidizing comes during the return of spent acid. **Fig. 5.26** shows results of acidizing with 13% HCl/2% HF with an unspecified inhibitor.[44] Test Stages 1 through 3 refer to exposure to concentrated acid with inhibitor, followed by exposure to spent acid plus inhibitor, and finally, dilute spent acid with no inhibitor. Thus, at 400°F [204°C], in the presence of CO_2, most of the CRA's failed by SCC as did those exposed at 400°F [204°C] to H_2S in solution. Corrosion rates were extremely high for lower-alloy materials.

While special inhibitors for acids exist for use with CRA's, some operators prefer to use organic acids (e.g., formic or acetic acid) to reduce the potential damage to the CRA's. Other operators strictly prohibit acid jobs through their CRA's, preferring to use an expendable, conventional steel workstring.

5.3 Wellhead Equipment

In the presence of H_2S, wellhead and Christmas tree components (e.g., hangers, valves, crosses, and chokes) must, at a minimum, meet the requirements of NACE *Standard MR-01-75*[45] to resist SSC. API *Spec. 6A*[46] provides a decision tree for determination of the recommended product specification level (PSL) to achieve reliable service in environments of varying severity (**Fig. 5.27**). Factors used to determine the PSL are rated working pressure; sour production, as defined by NACE[45]; H_2S concentration; and well proximity to public roads, buildings, houses, etc. These factors are defined in API *Spec. 6A*. The H_2S concentration and the proximity are defined by radius-of-exposure calculations that were presented in Chap. 2 of this monograph. These requirements generally are used for, but not limited to, the primary parts of the wellhead and Christmas tree that are specifically defined by API *Spec. 6A* as the tubing head, the tubing hanger, the tubing-head adapter, and the lower master valve. In addition to resisting SSC, wellheads and Christmas trees also must be resistant to corrosion from chlorides, CO_2, and H_2S. Moreover, with high surface temperatures, the possibility of SCC exists for CRA components.

In mildly corrosive environments, internal valve parts in contact with the producing environment may be supplied with such CRA's as AISI 410 or 316 or Alloy 17-4 PH stainless steels. These alloys are used especially for seats and gates and other trim components, but they are not particularly resistant to SSC. These alloy trims in valves are adequate for mildly corrosive production but, in the event of more severe corrosion, solid stainless steel or alloy valves may be required. Moreover, if the fluids are sour, the trim and body must meet the requirements of NACE *Standard MR-01-75.* Solid stainless-steel Christmas tree equipment has been used successfully in corrosive environments containing high amounts of CO_2 and moderate amounts of H_2S. Solid AISI 410 stainless-steel type equipment has been used extensively. The cast equivalent of AISI 410 is Grade CA15 and a common modification (4.5% Ni) is Grade CA6NM. The forged version of this latter alloy (Grade F6NM) is widely used in Christmas tree and wellhead equipment. A few solid duplex stainless-steel trees have been supplied for corrosive fields, including the sour Lacq Supérieur field in France and, on one occasion, solid Incoloy 925 (a nickel alloy) Christmas trees were supplied to India for sour service.

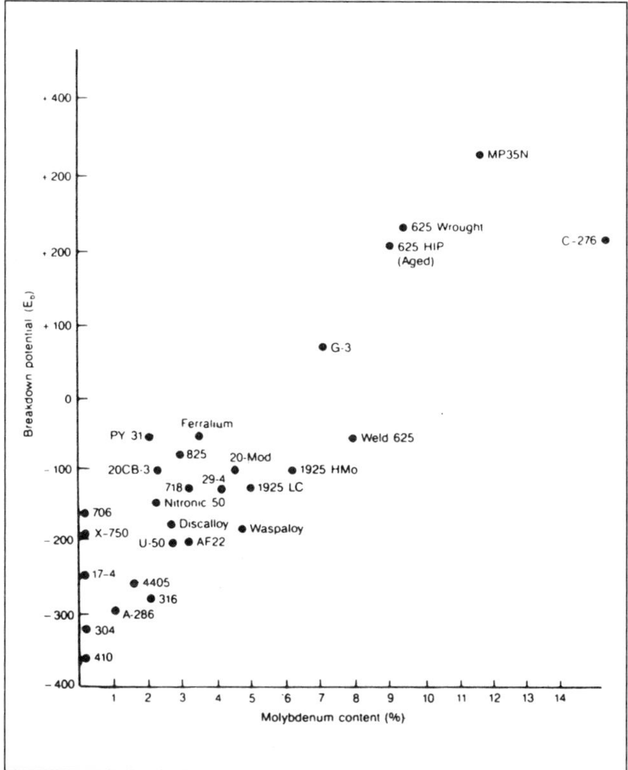

Fig. 5.29—Relative pitting resistance of CRA's in a simulated oilfield environment as a function of molybdenum content. [48]

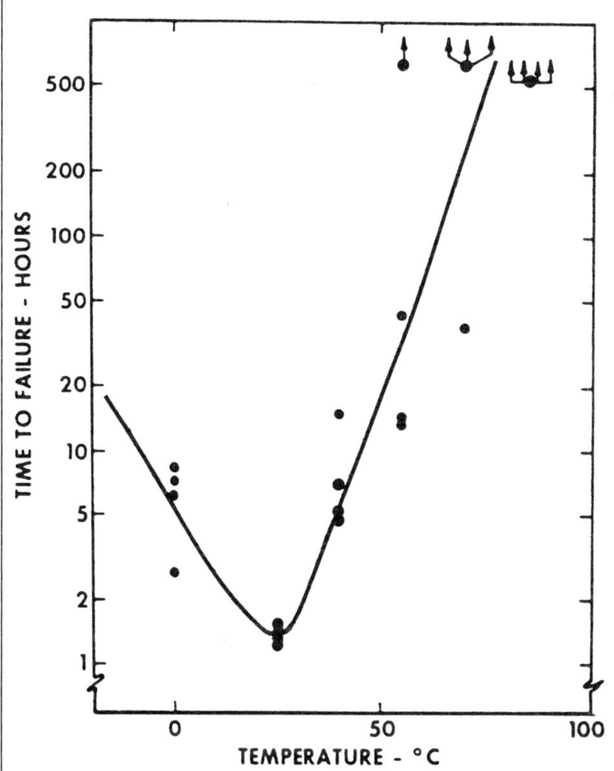

Fig. 5.30—Temperature dependence for SSC of high-strength steel wires (©NACE, 1972). [50]

The cost and availability of highly alloyed (nickel-based or high-nickel-content ferrous alloys) solid valves can become prohibitive, so the valve industry offers two alternatives for internally cladding valves with CRA: weld overlay and hot isostatically pressed (HIP) clad valves. The former involves overlaying low-alloy steel components with CRA filler metal to produce a thin ($\approx$0.125 in. [3.2 mm] minimum) high-alloy surface that is resistant to corrosion attack.

Cladding oilfield valves is also performed with the HIP technique (**Fig. 5.28**).[47] The valve body is machined to allow insertion of gas-tight liners that provide spacers for the alloy powder metal. Under high pressure and temperature, the alloy powder becomes bonded to the low-alloy base metal, producing a homogenous high-alloy structure. Essentially any material, including titanium alloys and ceramics, can be HIP clad to low-alloy steel components. In practice, both weld overlay and HIP methods are referred to as cladding and have provided excellent service in extremely corrosive wells. Usually, Inconel 625 is used as the cladding. The result is a corrosion- and SCC-resistant valve or other component at lower cost compared with the cost for comparable solid high-alloy equipment.

Many alloys used for CRA tubulars also are used for components in wellheads and Christmas trees. As **Fig. 5.29** shows, the resistance to pitting in a chloride environment increases with the alloy's molybdenum content.[48] An empirical relationship—the pitting index (PI)—relates the pitting resistance in oxidizing chloride environments to the chromium, molybdenum, and nitrogen content: PI=wt% Cr+3.3 (wt% Mo)+16.6 (wt% N).

The PI is useful in comparing resistance to chloride pitting of alloy's with different chemical compositions. The greater the PI, the greater the pitting resistance of the alloy. However, the values in themselves are meaningless. Moreover, it is important to remember that pitting in the presence of H_2S occurs at lower chloride contents and lower temperatures than when no H_2S is present. Moreover, elemental sulfur leads to severe pitting, especially on CRA's. The PI does not account for either of these effects.

5.4 Wirelines

Wirelines (braided wire rope and single-strand slicklines) are used for servicing downhole equipment, setting downhole valves, and running measurement tools such as calipers and logging tools. Wirelines are covered by API *Spec. 9A*, Secs. 8 and 9.[49] The strength of these steels may exceed 250,000 psi [1724 MPa]. Traditional steel wirelines are galvanized. In use, these cables are also treated with a corrosion-inhibitor compound that is effective in many environments. This type of treatment, as well as wellsite chemical inhibition, however, is not totally effective against corrosion, and environmental cracking can occur, especially in H_2S-containing environments. Because of the high strength of these steels, SSC can occur rapidly (**Fig. 5.30**).[50] A common misconception is that when the wireline in the well is above about 200°F [93°C], no SSC will occur. This is generally true, but if hydrogen enters the wire from corrosion by H_2S downhole at high temperature, once the wireline is returned to surface, SSC will occur rapidly if sufficient hydrogen concentration is trapped in the steel. Because the diameter of slicklines is between 0.066 and 0.108 in. [0.17 and 0.27 cm], a small reduction of a few thousandths in cross section caused by corrosion can produce failure. Similarly, the wire diameter in multistrand electric-line armor is 0.014 to 0.059 in. [0.036 to 0.15 cm].

Monel K500 wirelines have been run successfully in Canada, but corrosion can be significant in areas of high H_2S concentration and high temperatures. Moreover, in high-stress, high-H_2S environments, Monel K500 is susceptible to SSC.

AISI 410 stainless steel has been used, but because of the high strength required and the stresses on the wireline, it too fails by SSC in H_2S-bearing environments. The austenitic stainless steels are susceptible to chloride SCC as well as SSC when cold-worked as wireline; thus, they are not good candidates for sour service. Because nearly all oil and gas wells contain water with chlorides, the use of chloride-cracking-sensitive materials should be excluded from wireline service. Wirelines made of austenitic stainless steels have failed by chloride SCC. Moreover, duplex stainless-steel wirelines have also exhibited SCC.

Because of the very high tensile strengths required for wireline wire, few alloys are suitable for service in the presence of high temperatures, chlorides, and H_2S. This is evident by the data[51] presented in **Fig. 5.31**. The tensile strength of all the alloys tested was approximately 220,000 psi [1517 MPa]. Under severe laboratory conditions, the only alloy resistant to environmental cracking was Alloy MP35N. This behavior explains why Alloy MP35N currently is being used for wirelines and slicklines in extremely severe H_2S service and why, to date, no failures of Alloy MP35N wirelines have been reported. Recent laboratory data[52] suggest that Alloy C-276 may be even more resistant than Alloy MP35N to cracking in well fluids containing free sulfur. Therefore, either of these alloys should give excellent service.

5.5 Quality Assurance

Safe, uninterrupted production of sour-gas wells requires careful attention to the procurement, handling, and installation of high-quality equipment. The more aggressive the well environment, the more attention must be paid to quality assurance and quality control of equipment to be used on the well. This often means that more restrictive specifications are required or that the current specification must be supplemented. This increasing level of quality assurance for wellhead equipment used in increasingly severe environments is reflected in Fig. 5.27. Each successive PSL calls for a higher degree of inspection, testing, traceability, and documentation. One must always remember, however, that API standards represent the minimum requirements a manufacturer must meet to be in compliance with a particular API specification. Therefore, an operating company may need to supplement API specifications to achieve the desired level of confidence necessary to meet the demands of a critical well or field. Many API specifications contain supplementary requirements that may be invoked by the purchaser to increase the level of inspection or testing on certain components, especially when unusually severe conditions (e.g., Arctic service) are expected. Additionally, some equipment used in a well (CRA's, premium connections, liner hangers, polished bore receptacles, packers, etc.) are not covered by API specifications, and an operating company must be alert to the quality-assurance needs of these items.

An operating company must develop a quality-assurance plan that includes, but is not limited to, the following.

1. Determination of critical wells.
2. Components required for critical wells.
3. Identities of people responsible for planning, procurement, specifications, inspection, approval of deviations from specifications during manufacturing, and recordkeeping.
4. Special packaging and transportation requirements.
5. Special handling or running requirements in the field.

The level of inspection, testing, and third-party surveillance needed on equipment for sour wells is a matter of much discussion in the industry. The decision is based on a company's particular philosophy and requires the input of many disciplines and judgment in the areas of risk analysis, economics, environmental concerns, and legal requirements for the location.

5.6 Safety Valves

Surface or subsurface safety valves are considered necessary for the safe production of sour gas. Subsurface safety valves are recommended in addition to double master valves in the event the wellhead is damaged. Offshore operation requires the use of surface-controlled subsurface safety valves (SCSSV's) as mandated by U.S. Outer Continental Shelf regulations. However, SCSSV's require a hydraulic control line to the valve from the surface that must be considered during design of the well. SCSSV's are typically set at least 100 ft [30.5 m] below the surface or mudline and are either tubing- or wireline-retrievable. Tubing-retrievable valves are used more often because of their higher reliability.

In Canada, regulations of the Alberta Energy Resources Conservation Board stipulate that, as a minimum, SCSSV's be installed in any well producing >5% H_2S that is within 5 miles [8 km] of a city, town, or village and that has the potential for producing >5 MMscf/D [$>1.42\times10^5 m^3/d$]. However, Canadian operators usually install SCSSV's in all wells where the risk of wellhead damage exists, especially in sour wells and remote locations.

In cases where the H_2S concentration is low and the proximity of the well to populated areas is remote, conventional steel surface safety valves may be adequate. In wells that are extremely corrosive or where the H_2S concentration is high or pressures are very high, the dependability of the safety valve must be unquestionable. Thus, in severe environments, safety valves are often made from CRA's such as Inconel 718, Inconel 625, Hastelloy C-276, Alloy MP35N, or titanium alloys. In addition, routine leak testing of the SCSSV's is essential to ensure functionality.

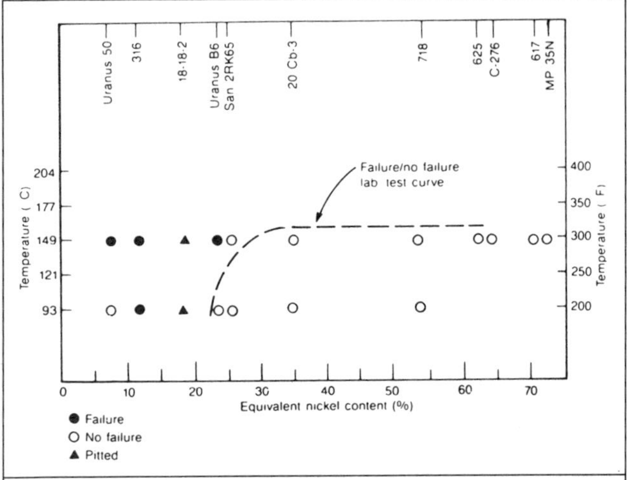

Fig. 5.31—Effect of alloy content on SCC of CRA-wireline materials in a field environment (©NACE, 1982).[51]

One means to monitor for a potential hazardous release of H_2S is to equip the casing/tubing annulus with a high/low pressure switch to detect a pressure increase/drop from a preset casing pressure. Typically, an increase in pressure activates an alarm of some type either locally or at a remote station so that proper steps can be taken to identify the problem and to shut in the well, if necessary.

In some systems, the casing pressure monitor is tied directly into the safety-valve system, and automatic shut-in occurs when a predetermined pressure differential exists.

In the event other systems fail or a total shut-in of the well is necessary, a kill system should be an integral part of the high-pressure sour-gas well design. A kill system should have enough redundancy that, if a portion of the system fails, the kill can still be made because this is usually the last measure available to bring the well under control. The kill system often is controlled remotely through electropneumatic solenoid-operated valves that supply power to activate gate valves on the wellhead.

A good kill pumping system should include adequate mud-storage capacity and mud-conditioning systems, high-pressure injection lines to the tubing and annulus outlets at the wellhead, and the ability to monitor pressure, temperature, and flow rate remotely.

A diverter system also should be incorporated with a manifold that can divert gas to the flare and return mud to the mud-storage and -conditioning plant.

The advent of computer-controlled operations has allowed the realization of central facilities in a sour-gas field where computers can constantly monitor wellhead and production information to evaluate the status of each well. Appropriate alarms and predetermined actions can be put in place to activate safety measures in the event of an H_2S release.

Nomenclature

K_{ISSC} = SSC threshold stress intensity, ksi/$\sqrt{in.}$ [MPa/$\sqrt{m}$]
p_{H_2S} = H_2S partial pressure, psi [MPa]
R_{max} = maximum root-mean-square of surface roughness, μm
T = temperature, °F [°C]
v_E = critical erosion velocity, ft/sec

References

1. *Spec. 5CT, Specification for Casing and Tubing,* fourth edition, API, Dallas (1992).
2. *Standard TM-01-77, Test Method for Laboratory Testing of Metals for Resistance to Sulfide Stress Cracking in H_2S Environments,* NACE, Houston (1989).

3. Kane, R.D. and Greer, J.B.: "Sulfide Stress Cracking of High-Strength Steels in Laboratory and Oilfield Environments," *JPT* (Nov. 1977) 1483–88; *Trans.*, AIME, **263**.
4. Watkins, M.J. and Vaughn, G.A.: "Effects of H_2S Partial Pressure on the Sulfide Stress Cracking Resistance of Steel," paper 220 presented at the 1985 NACE Corrosion/85, Boston, March 25–29.
5. Hudgins, C.M. *et al.*: "Hydrogen Sulfide Cracking of Carbon and Alloy Steels," *Corrosion* (1966) **22**, 238–51.
6. Treseder, R.S. and Swanson, T.M.: "Factors in Sulfide Corrosion Cracking of High Strength Steels," *Corrosion* (1968) **24**, 31–37.
7. Greer, J.B. and Holland, W.E.: "High-Strength Heavy-Wall Casing for Deep, Sour Gas Wells," *JPT* (Dec. 1981) 2389–98.
8. Greer, J.B.: "Effects of Metal Thickness and Temperature on Casing and Tubing Design for Deep, Sour Wells," *JPT* (April 1973) 499–510; *Trans.*, AIME, **255**.
9. Wilhelm, S.M. and Kane, R.D.: "Selection of Materials for Sour Service in Petroleum Production," *JPT* (Oct. 1986) 1051–61.
10. Schneider, W.P.: "Casing and Tubing Connection Stresses," *JPT* (Aug. 1982) 1851–62.
11. Yazaki, Y. *et al.*: "Anti-SSC Properties of Full Size Premium Joint," Technical Report No. 30, Nippon Steel, Tokyo (July 1986) 59–66.
12. "Finite Element Analysis of NK3SB Tubing," Technical Bull. No. 243-175, Nippon Kokan K.K., Tokyo (1986).
13. Noerager, J.A. and Greer, J.B.: "An Investigation of Coupled Tubing Joints for Sour Service," *Materials Performance* (1977) **16**, 37–41.
14. "Report on Field Testing of 32 Alloys in the Flow Stream of Seven Condensate Wells," Publication No. 1C150, NACE, Houston (July 1950).
15. Yoshino, Y.: "Metallurgical Influences on the Hydrogen Uptake by Steel in H_2S Environment," *Corrosion* (1983) **39**, 435–44.
16. Ciaraldi, S.W.: "Some Limitations on the Use of 13Cr Alloys for Corrosive Oil, Corrosive Gas and Oil Production," paper 71 presented at the 1990 NACE Corrosion/90, Las Vegas, April 23–27.
17. Fisher, J.B: *Acta Geochemica* (Sept. 1987) **51**, No. 9.
18. Ikeda, A., Ueda, M., and Mukai, S.: "CO_2 Corrosion Behavior and Mechanism of Carbon Steel and Alloy Steel," paper 45 presented at the 1983 NACE Corrosion/83, Anaheim, April 18–22.
19. Nagano, H. *et al.*: "Highly Corrosion Resistant Duplex Stainless Steel," paper presented at the 1980 Intl. Colloquium on Stainless Steels, Saint-Etienne, France, May.
20. van Gelder, K. *et al.*: "The Stress Corrosion Cracking of Duplex Stainless Steel in $H_2S/CO_2/Cl^-$ Environments," *Corrosion Science* (1987) **27**, 1271–79.
21. Kudo, T. *et al.*: "Localized Corrosion of Duplex Stainless Steel in CO_2-H_2S-Cl^- Environments at Elevated Temperatures," paper 293 presented at the 1984 NACE Corrosion/84, New Orleans, April 2–6.
22. Ikeda, A. *et al.*: "Corrosion Behaviors of High Alloy Oil Country Tubular Goods for Deep Sour Gas Well," paper 206 presented at the 1984 NACE Corrosion/84, New Orleans, April 2–6.
23. Whelan, P.: "Sulfide Stress Cracking Resistance of Super Alloys for Sour Gas Well Applications," *Hydrogen Effects in Metals*, I.M. Bernstein and A.W. Thompson (eds.), Metallurgical Soc. of AIME (1980) 979–86.
24. Vaughn, G.A. and Greer, J.B.: "High-Strength Nickel-Alloy Tubulars for Deep Sour Gas Well Application," paper SPE 9240 presented at the 1980 SPE Annual Technical Conference and Exhibition, Dallas, Sept. 21–24.
25. Kane, R.D. and Boyd, W.K.: "Materials Technology for Oil and Gas Production," *Alloys for the 80's*, American Metals Climax Inc., Ann Arbor, MI (1980) 225–34.
26. Mase, T. *et al.*: "Solid Lubrication on Metal to Metal Sealed Portion of Special Joint for Oil Country Tubular Goods," *Proc.*, JSLE Intl. Tribology Conference, Tokyo (1985) 829–32.
27. Shridar, N. and Corey, S.M.: "The Effect of Elemental Sulfur on Stress Corrosion Cracking of Nickel Base Alloys," paper 12 presented at the 1989 NACE Corrosion/89, New Orleans, April 17–21.
28. Miyasaka, A., Denpo, K., and Ogawa, H.: "Environmental Aspects of SCC of High Alloys in Sour Environments," *Corrosion* (1989) **45**, 771–79.
29. *Bulletin*, Sumitomo Metal Industries, Osaka, Japan (1989).
30. Craig, B.D.: "Controlling Corrosion in Deep Hot Wells," *Pet. Eng. Intl.* (Oct. 1987) **59**, 35–40.
31. Craig, B.D.: "Equation Clarifies Critical Velocity Calculation," *Pet. Eng. Intl.* (Oct. 1990) **62**, 42.
32. Bradburn, J.B. and Kalra, S.K.: "Corrosion Mitigation—A Critical Facet of Well Completion Design," *JPT* (Sept. 1983) 1617–23.
33. Place, M.C. Jr.: "Corrosion Inhibition for Severely Corrosive Gas Wells," paper 266 presented at the 1990 NACE Corrosion/90, Las Vegas, April 23–27.
34. Place, M.C. Jr.: "Corrosion Control—Deep Sour Gas Production," paper SPE 8310 presented at the 1979 SPE Annual Technical Conference and Exhibition, Las Vegas, Sept. 23–26.
35. Hamby, T.W. Jr.: "Development of High-Pressure Sour Gas Technology," *JPT* (May 1981) 792–98.
36. Ender, D.H.: "Evaluation of Seal Material for Deep Sour Gas Wells," paper 102 presented at the 1975 NACE Corrosion/75, Toronto, April 14–18.
37. Pugh, T.L.: "Evaluation of Fluoroelastomers for Oilfield Service," *Materials Performance* (1985) **24**, 40–44.
38. *Standard TM-01-87, Test Method for Evaluating Elastomeric Materials in Sour Gas Environments,* NACE, Houston (1987).
39. Watkins, M.J.: "Watch Out for Elastomer-Inhibitor Incompatibility," *Pet. Eng. Intl.* (April 1984) **56**, 28–35.
40. Edwards, C.: "Effects of Inhibitors on Oil Patch Seals," *World Oil* (Nov. 1990) 83–88.
41. Hamby, T.W. Jr., Broussard, L.P., and Taylor, D.B.: "Producing Mississippi's Deep, High-Pressure Sour Gas," *JPT* (June 1976) 629–38.
42. Gill, D.H. and DeMott, D.N.: "Effect of Hydrogen Sulfide on the Inhibition of Oil Field Tubing in Hydrochloric Acid," paper SPE 6660 presented at the 1977 SPE Sour Gas Symposium, Tyler, TX, Nov. 14–15.
43. Kolts, J. and Corey, S.M.: "Corrosion and Stress Corrosion Cracking of High Performance Alloys in Simulated Acidizing Environments to 350°F," paper 217 presented at the 1984 NACE Corrosion/84, New Orleans, April 2–6.
44. Kane, R.D. and Wilhelm, S.M.: "Compatibility of Stainless and Nickel Base Alloys in Acidizing Environments," paper 481 presented at the 1989 NACE Corrosion/89, New Orleans, April 17–21.
45. *Standard MR-01-75, Test Method for Metallurgy of Oil Field Equipment for Resistance to Sulfide Stress Cracking,* NACE, Houston (March 1991).
46. *Spec. 6A, Specification for Wellhead and Christmas Tree Equipment,* 16th edition, API, Dallas (1989).
47. Uhl, W.K. and Pendley, M.R.: "HIP Clad Nickel Base Alloy 625 for Deep Sour Wells," *Materials Performance* (1984) **23**, 30–34.
48. Bednarowicz, T.A.: "Electrochemical Polarization To Determine the Localized Corrosion Behavior of Various Materials Used for Heavy Section Wellhead Equipment in a 121°C-3.5 MPa Environment," paper 178 presented at the 1982 NACE Corrosion/82, Houston, March 22–26.
49. *Spec. 9A, Specification for Wire Rope,* 23rd edition, API, Dallas (May 1984) Secs. 8 and 9.
50. Townsend, H.E. Jr.: "Hydrogen Sulfide Stress Corrosion Cracking of High Strength Steel Wire," *Corrosion* (1972) **28**, 39–46.
51. Vaughn, G.A. and Chaung, H.E.: "Wireline Materials for Sour Service," *Materials Performance* (1982) **21**, 44–50.
52. Silence, W.L. and Groeneveld, K.A.: "High Strength Alloy Wirelines for Deep Oil and Gas Well Service," paper 11 presented at the 1989 NACE Corrosion/89, New Orleans, April 17–21.

SI Metric Conversion Factors

atm	× 1.013 250*	E+05	=	Pa
bar	× 1.0*	E−01	=	MPa
ft	× 3.048*	E−01	=	m
°F	(°F−32)/1.8		=	°C
in.	× 2.54*	E+00	=	cm
ksi	× 6.894 757	E+03	=	kPa
lbm	× 4.535 924	E−01	=	kg
mil/yr	× 2.54*	E−02	=	mm/a
psi	× 6.894 757	E−03	=	MPa

*Conversion factor is exact.

Chapter 6
Surface Production Facilities

6.1 Introduction

The design and operation of surface production facilities for sour oil and gas are of considerable importance. Equipment reliability cannot be overemphasized because failure can release large volumes of toxic gas in a short time. This chapter discusses some of the more important surface-facility components, such as flowlines, gathering lines, and separators.

6.2 Flowlines

Steel pipe used for flowlines and sour-gas transmission commonly is manufactured to API Specification 5L[1] or ASTM A106 Grade B.[2] For corrosion-resistant-alloy (CRA) line pipe, API *Spec. 5LC*[3] is appropriate. An API specification for clad line pipe is expected during 1992. Like the requirements for casing and tubing, API line-pipe requirements are quite general and allow for considerable variation in chemical composition and mechanical properties. Generally, the lower-strength grades are carbon-manganese steels. More sophistication is introduced in both composition and processing as the strength increases, especially for Grades X-60 and higher. The combination of reducing the carbon content of steel, microalloying with elements (e.g., molybdenum, titanium, vanadium, and niobium), and special (thermomechanical) processing can significantly increase the strength of steels while also enhancing their fracture resistance and weldability.

Good weldability is vital to the successful joining and long-term service life of line pipe. The carbon equivalent, CE, is a good indicator of the steel weldability. Several CE formulas are used to determine weldability, but the most common formula is from the Intl. Inst. of Welding:

$$CE=C+\frac{Mn}{6}+\frac{(Cr+Mo+V)}{5}+\frac{(Ni+Cu)}{15},$$

where the elemental concentrations are in weight percent. The CE indicates the potential of a steel for weld cracking as a result of hydrogen stress cracking (HSC), also referred to as cold or delayed cracking in the welding industry. The hydrogen derived here is from the welding processes and not from the service conditions.

Carbon is the most potent element contributing to the hardenability of steels, and the CE equates other elements to carbon as the common denominator. A lower CE reduces the chance of HSC occurring in the weldment. This is a function of the hardenability of the steel and thus is reflected in the final hardness, which also is important for sour service. In addition to chemical composition and thickness, the particular welding method also is important to a weld's final properties. The primary welding processes used in oilfield operations are shielded metal-arc (or stick-electrode) welding, gas/metal-arc (or metal inert gas) welding, gas/tungsten-arc (or tungsten inert gas) welding, and submerged-arc welding. Welding a base metal having a high CE can lead to hard welds that are susceptible to sulfide stress cracking (SSC) in H_2S.

Besides the susceptibility of the base metal to corrosion and cracking in H_2S, the weld filler metal also must be considered. Commonly used filler metals such as the American Welding Soc.'s (AWS) Grades E6010, E7010, and E7018 have low carbon contents and, therefore, do not cause problems.

Generally, the lower-strength (lower-CE) pipeline steels do not display SSC because of the reduced hardness of the welds; however, higher-strength grades with carbon and manganese additions have increased hardness and, therefore, are more susceptible to SSC. Welding low-strength Grade B line pipe also can produce high hardnesses and susceptible microstructures that lead to SSC if the pipe has a high CE, thick walls, and low-heat input welding.

As line-pipe steel strength increases to 80,000 psi [552 MPa] or more, the potential of the base metal for SSC increases. The way high-strength line-pipe steels react to SSC is identical to the reactions of other high-strength steels described in Chap. 3.

One of the more serious concerns facing the petroleum industry is the SSC of weldments. As expected from data presented in Chaps. 3 and 5, the harder a steel is, the more susceptible it is to SSC. **Fig. 6.1** demonstrates this behavior as a function of the H_2S level for welded steels.[4] The SSC resistance of the heat-affected zone (HAZ) of the weld decreases with increasing hardness. The data in Fig. 6.1 are derived from welded steel plates and from API line-pipe Grades B to X-65. Clearly, even small concentrations of H_2S can cause SSC if the hardness of a weld is excessive.

One of the important questions that remains unanswered is, "What is the critical size or area of a hard zone that may initiate SSC?" Contrary to base-metal properties that are relatively uniform and for which the hardness does not vary significantly, the weldment contains a variety of metallurgical phases and corresponding hardnesses. The hardness differences among regions in the HAZ, the base metal, and the weld metal can be significant on a small scale, discernible only by a microhardness test such as Knoop, yet essentially undetectable by macrohardness tests such as Brinell. The relationship among the size of the hard zone, the number of zones, and the distribution of hard zones sufficient to induce SSC remains unknown. Moreover, there is apparently no absolute hardness below which SSC does not occur in welds.

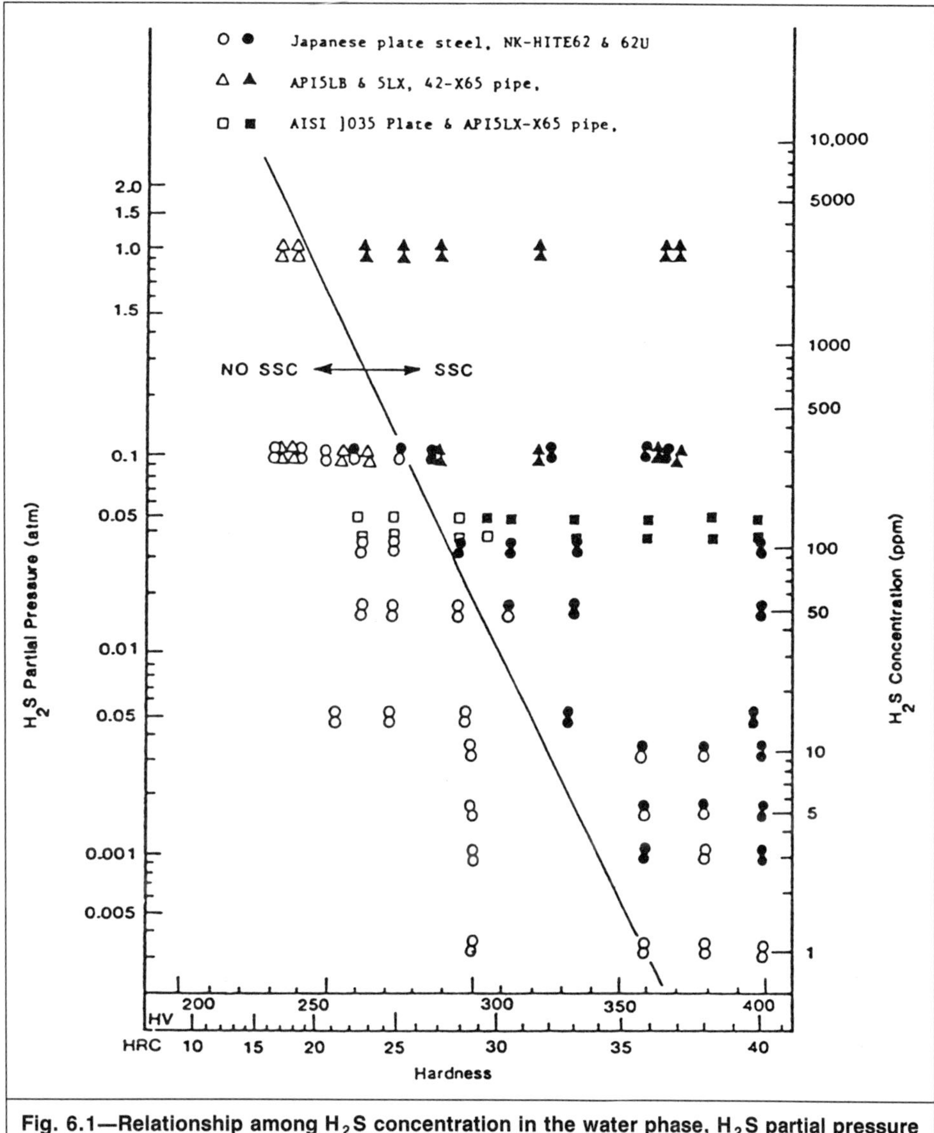

Fig. 6.1—Relationship among H_2S concentration in the water phase, H_2S partial pressure in the gas phase, hardness in the weld HAZ, and SSC.[4]

Fractures from SSC in the base metal, the HAZ, and the weld metal are not always associated with the hardest areas of the weldment. **Fig. 6.2** shows an SSC fracture of a weld with a Rockwell C hardness (HRC) of less than HRC 22 [Vickers hardness (HV) of 248].[5] Above about HV 260, there is a general correlation between SSC and hardness, but below this level, fracture is less predictable. Typically, the weld deposit is softer than the HAZ and the base metal, so cracking does not generally begin in the weld metal. However, cracking occurred in the softest part of the weld in Fig. 6.2.

The residual stresses after welding contribute to the cracking of softer steel welds. Although these stresses are difficult to measure, it has long been recognized that residual stresses after welding will locally approach the material's yield strength. The effect of residual stress on SSC has not been studied extensively, but **Fig. 6.3** demonstrates this effect.[6] Note that susceptibility to SSC increases with increasing hardness and increasing residual stress. Considerable work is being done in this area so that the SSC of welds in line-pipe steels may be better understood. When in doubt about hardness, steel composition, and weld procedures, it is considered good practice to stress-relieve welds to reduce areas of high hardness and residual stress. The cost of postweld heat treatment on flowlines and pipelines can be prohibitive. Some companies use API *Spec. 5L*[1] or ASTM *A 106*[2] Grade B pipe with AWS Grade E6010 electrodes. The resulting hardnesses in the as-welded condition are sufficiently low that SSC apparently has not been a problem, albeit residual stresses still exist. However, care must be taken to use low-CE pipe and high-heat input welding; preheat may also be needed. For small projects, postweld heat treatment of weldments provides increased resistance to SSC. For large projects, pipe with a known composition can be welded with welding-procedure specifications that have been thoroughly microhardness-tested as part of the procedure-qualification record. This requires more restrictive controls on both the welding-procedure specifications and the procedure-qualification record than the American Soc. of Mechanical Engineers[7] (ASME) or the API[8] provide. Also, the steel and fitting composition must be more restrictive than required by API *Spec. 5L*[1] and ASTM specifications.[9-11] Moreover, testing in accordance with Natl. Assn. of Corrosion Engineers (NACE) *Standards TM-02-84*[12] and *TM-01-77*[13] may be required in some critical service.

6.3 Hydrogen-Induced Damage

Even when a low-strength, low-CE, line-pipe steel is used and the welding procedures produce an SSC-resistant structure, another form of hydrogen damage may occur in the base metal. This damage is referred to variously as hydrogen-induced cracking (HIC), stepwise cracking (SWC), blister cracking, and hydrogen-assisted cracking. Unlike SSC, HIC is not strongly influenced by stress and initiates at elongated nonmetallic inclusions (often MnS) in the base metal. Cracks linking the blisters formed at inclusions may follow a stair-step pattern through the wall, thus the term SWC. **Fig. 6.4** shows this feature compared with the crack path observed for SSC.

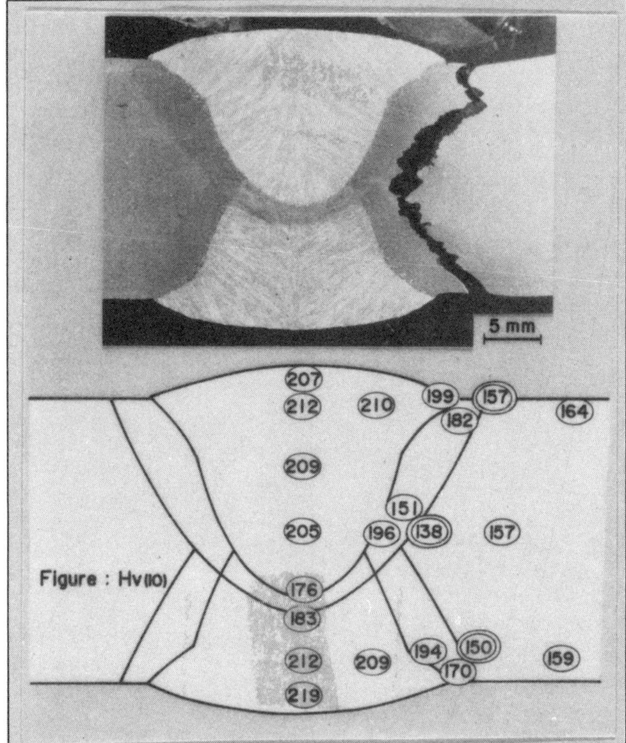

Fig. 6.2—Typical SSC at weld in ferrite-pearlite pipeline steel. Vickers hardness with a 22-lbm [10-kg] load (©NACE, 1985).[5]

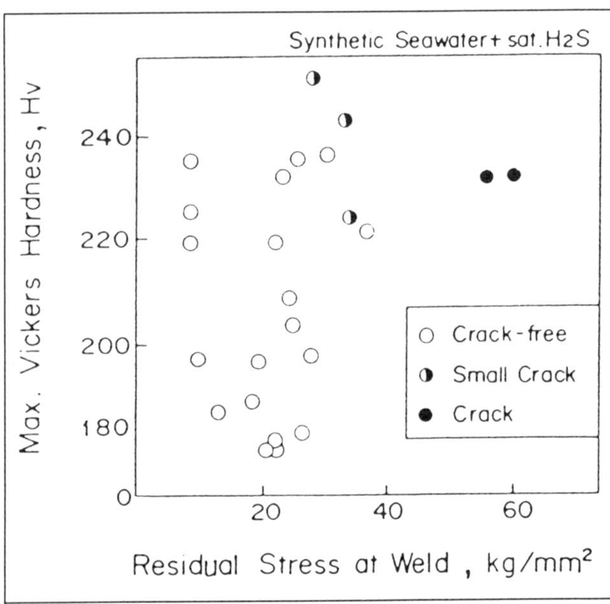

Fig. 6.3—Influence of residual stress and hardness on SSC at weld seam by full-scale pipe test.[6]

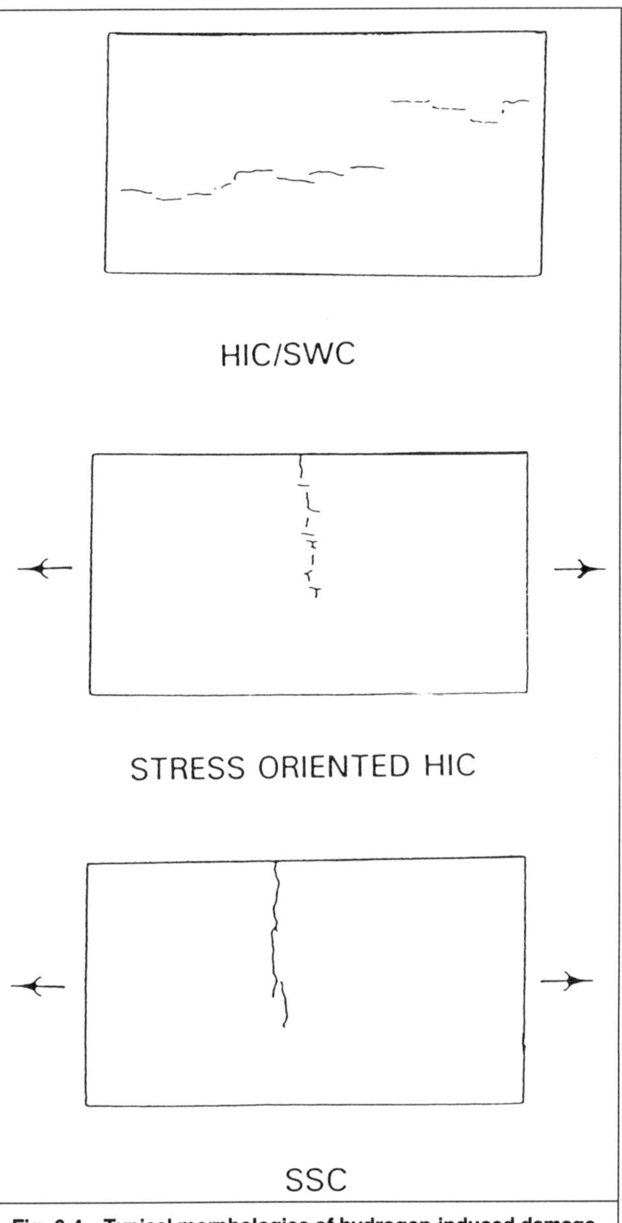

Fig. 6.4—Typical morphologies of hydrogen-induced damage.

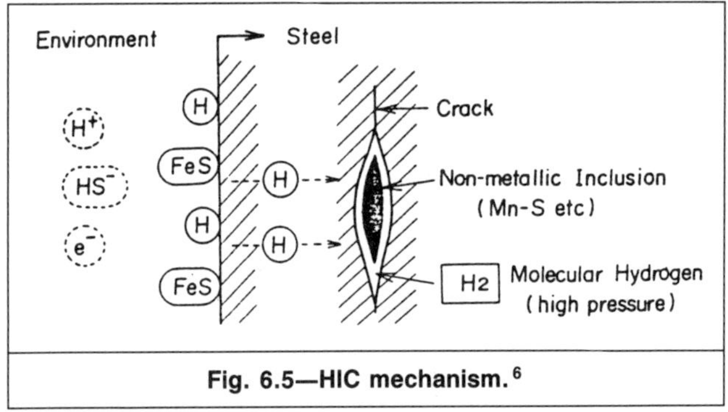

Fig. 6.5—HIC mechanism.[6]

For soft steels in which stresses are applied, the fracture morphology appears to be between HIC and SSC (Fig. 6.4) and is sometimes referred to as stress-oriented hydrogen-induced cracking (SOHIC). This is by no means a universally accepted terminology and is presented here only for information. Most cracking that occurs in environments containing hydrogen is hydrogen-induced; thus, the term HIC is not specific but is widely used in the petroleum industry to describe the cracking of soft steels in the pattern shown in Fig. 6.4. **Table 6.1** provides a sample of reported[14] HIC cases. **Fig. 6.5** illustrates the generally accepted mechanism for HIC[6]: hydrogen ions in solution are reduced to hydrogen atoms on the surface and then diffuse through the steel to nonmetallic inclusions where they collect and form molecular hydrogen. A number of factors affect HIC, including solution pH, the amount of hydrogen entering the steel, the temperature, the steel composition, and the processing and microstructure.

Fig. 6.6 shows the degree of cracking from HIC defined by NACE *Standard TM-02-84.*[12] This test procedure specifies the removal of test coupons from the pipe and the exposure of these coupons to a synthetic seawater solution saturated with H_2S. The test is run for 96 hours; then the specimen is cleaned, cross sectioned, and metallographically examined. The extent of cracking

TABLE 6.1—EXAMPLES OF FAILURE BY HIC (after Ref. 14)

Location	Plant	Steel Materials	Conditions and Environment	Operating Beginning Date	Operating Failure Discovered
U.S.	Sour refinery (crude oil) Pressure vessel (sour gas)	Mild steel (YP 28 kg/mm^2) (TS 42 kg/mm^2) C 0.24, Si 0.06, Mo 0.58, P 0.009, S 0.028, Al 0.008	Phillips Petroleum Co. more than 50 examples of blistered vessels H_2S+H_2O, low operation pressure	Unknown	Unknown
Japan	Heavy-oil desulfurization apparatus, condenser shell	Mild steel (SB42) C 0.18, Si 0.30, Mn 0.80, P<0.030, S<0.030	H_2S+H_2O, 38°C Operation pressure 48 kg/cm^2	May 1971	June 1973
Japan	Desulfurization apparatus	Mild steel (SB42) Low-alloy steel (1.25 Cr-0.5 Mo)	H_2S+H_2O, <50°C Operation pressure 32 kg/cm^2	April 1966	Aug. 1968
Japan	Desulfurization apparatus	Mild steel (SB42) C 0.17, Si 0.26, Mn 0.78, P 0.015, S 0.018, Cu 0.09	H_2S+H_2O (condensate) Operation pressure 17 to 33 kg/cm^2	April 1964	Sept. 1965
Japan	Desulfurization apparatus	Mild steel (SB42)	25 to 110°C Operation pressure 33 kg/cm^2	Nov. 1961	Aug. 1967
U.S.	Refinery vessel	Carbon steel	Shell Oil Co. H_2S, CO_2, NH_3, H_2O	—	1954
U.S.	Line pipe (Barkerdom gathering)	API 5LX-52 (24 x 0.271tSAW) cold-worked	El Paso Natural Gas Co., Ltd. Natural gas, CO_2 15%, H_2S 1%	1954	1954
Germany	Line pipe	API 5LX-42 (ERW) Annealed and straightened	H_2S max, 0.95%, CH_4, 80% to 85%, CO_2 8.7% Operation pressure 45.5 kg/cm^2	Jan. 1961	Jan. 1961
Italy	Refinery	Mild Steel C 0.12, Si 0.26, Mn 0.47, P 0.017, S 0.018	H_2S 10%, gasoline	Unknown	Unknown
Arabia (Persian Gulf)	Line pipe under sea (crude oil)	API 5LX-65 As-rolled	Crude oil (H_2S) + seawater	1972	1972
Arabia	Line pipe on land (sour gas)	API 5LS-X-42 As-rolled spiral	3.4 vol% H_2S 8.8 vol% CO_2 CH_4	1974	1974

YP = yield point
TS = tensile strength

is reported as the crack length ratio (CLR), the crack sensitivity ratio (CSR), and the crack thickness ratio (CTR).

Fig. 6.7 shows the degree of cracking (the CLR) as a function of hydrogen content; note that after a certain hydrogen threshold, C_{th}, is reached, cracking becomes significant.[15] The concentration of hydrogen in the steel is a function of the solution pH (**Fig. 6.8**).[16] Also, the partial pressure of H_2S affects both the hydrogen absorption rate and the corrosion rate of steels (**Fig. 6.9**).[17]

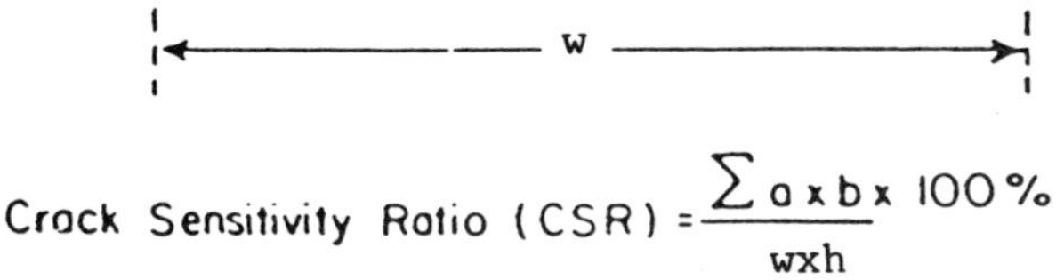

h

a_1 b_1

a_2 b_2

w

$$\text{Crack Sensitivity Ratio (CSR)} = \frac{\sum a \times b \times 100\%}{w \times h}$$

$$\text{Crack Length Ratio (CLR)} = \frac{\sum a \times 100\%}{w}$$

$$\text{Crack Thickness Ratio (CTR)} = \frac{\sum b \times 100\%}{h}$$

Fig. 6.6—NACE method for quantitative evaluation of SWC by metallography (after Ref. 12).

Other ions, such as cyanide, have a similar effect. Like the conditions for SSC, steels at ambient temperature (86°F [30°C]) appear to be the most susceptible to HIC (**Fig. 6.10**),[18] which explains why HIC is most often observed in surface facilities and not downhole.

Steel composition has a profound effect on HIC resistance. As might be expected from Fig. 6.5, a reduction in sulfur content increases resistance by reducing the number of nonmetallic inclusions that can collect hydrogen and from which HIC could initiate. This is observed to be the case in **Fig. 6.11**.[19] Furthermore, attempts to control the sulfide-inclusion shape with calcium treatments have proved beneficial (**Fig. 6.12**) in reducing the extent of HIC.[20] Calcium-treated steels generally have rounded sulfide inclusion rather than deleterious elongated inclusions (stringers).

The addition of copper decreases both the corrosion rate of steel in H_2S and the tendency to HIC (**Fig. 6.13**),[19] provided the solu-

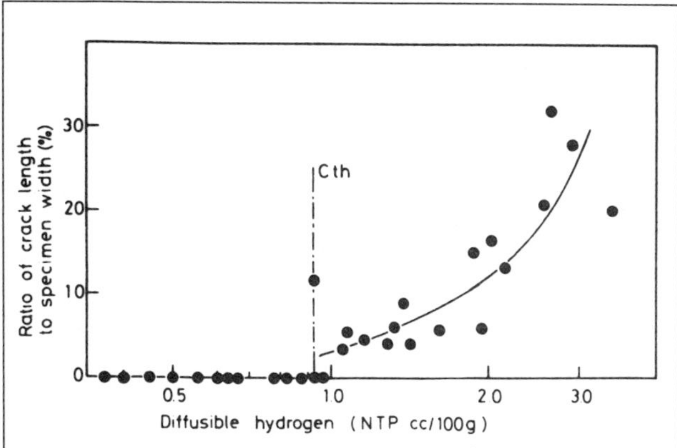

Fig. 6.7—Relationship between HIC and absorbed hydrogen.[15]

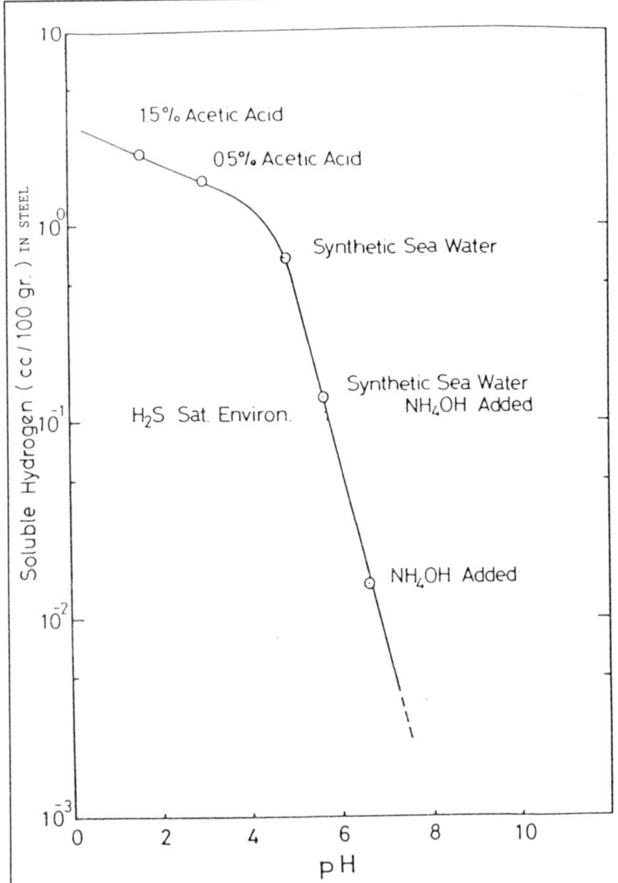

Fig. 6.8—Relation between pH of H_2S saturated and soluble hydrogen concentration in steel.[16]

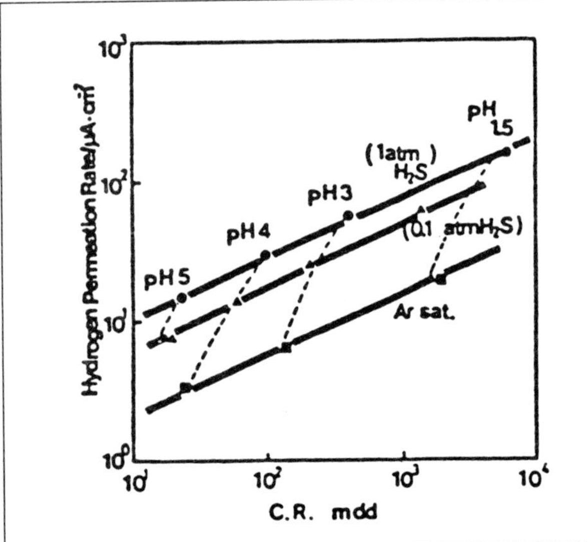

Fig. 6.9—Effect of pH and H_2S partial pressure on hydrogen-permeation rate through 0.04-in. [1-mm] -thick pure iron at 77°F [25°C] (courtesy of Nippon Steel Corp.).[17]

tion pH is greater than 5. At pH < 5, the protective iron-sulfide film no longer is present[21] and copper is not beneficial.

HIC also is dependent on steel manufacturing, heat treatment, and strength. These factors have a strong effect on the microstructure. A heavily banded (segregated) structure can reduce resistance to HIC even if all other precautions are taken. Because banding primarily is dependent on carbon and manganese contents, the amount of these elements is kept as low as possible to reduce the

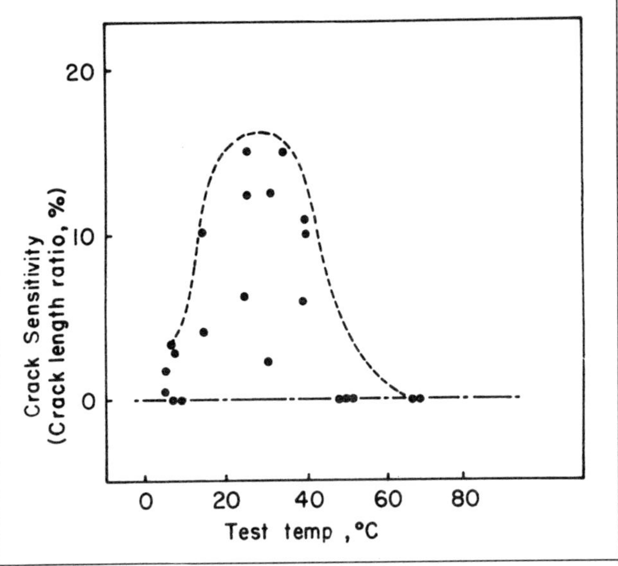

Fig. 6.10—HIC susceptibility as a function of test temperature (courtesy of Nippon Steel Corp.).[18]

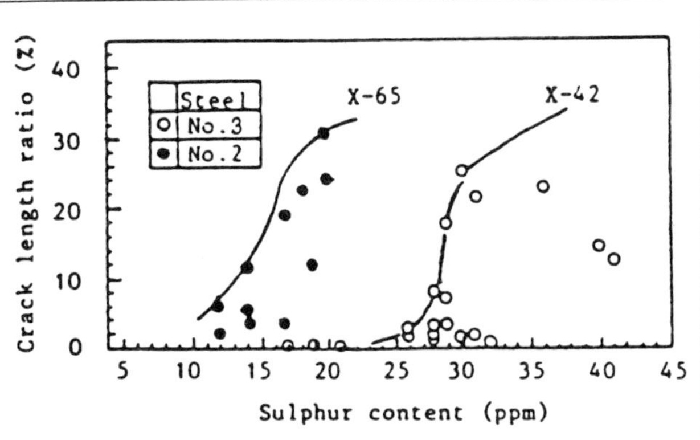

Fig. 6.11—Influence of sulfur content on CLR in NACE *Standard TM-02-84* test (courtesy of ASM Intl.).[19]

incidence of banding and the development of a highly HIC-susceptible microstructure (an anomalous structure). **Fig. 6.14** shows the effect manganese has on HIC susceptibility as measured by the CSR and the CLR.[22]

HIC must be considered when new flowlines, gathering lines, and transmission lines are constructed. If HIC is anticipated, then pipe that is resistant to this form of attack should be ordered. Generally, seamless pipe is resistant to HIC because the manufacturing processes limit the development of elongated sulfide stringers. Conversely, both electric-resistance and submerged-arc welded pipes have displayed HIC,[23,24] primarily because these types of pipe are manufactured from strip and plate that are flat-rolled, which increases the tendency to form elongated stringers. However, careful control of the factors described earlier can increase the resistance of these types of pipes to the point that they can be used satisfactorily in sour service.

Recently, a serious failure of a sour-gas line demonstrated the catastrophic aspects of SOHIC and the severity of corrosion by water with elemental sulfur produced by oxidized H_2S.[25] **Fig. 6.15** shows the kinetics of the oxidation of H_2S in the absence and presence of triethylene glycol (TEG) and monoethanolamine (MEA).[25] This figure shows that TEG and MEA catalyze the oxidation of H_2S to form sulfur and water. **Figs. 6.16 and 6.17** show the hydrogen permeation and the corrosion rate of steel as functions of the environment.[25] It is apparent that the hydrogen available for SOHIC and the corrosion rate are greatest for an environment

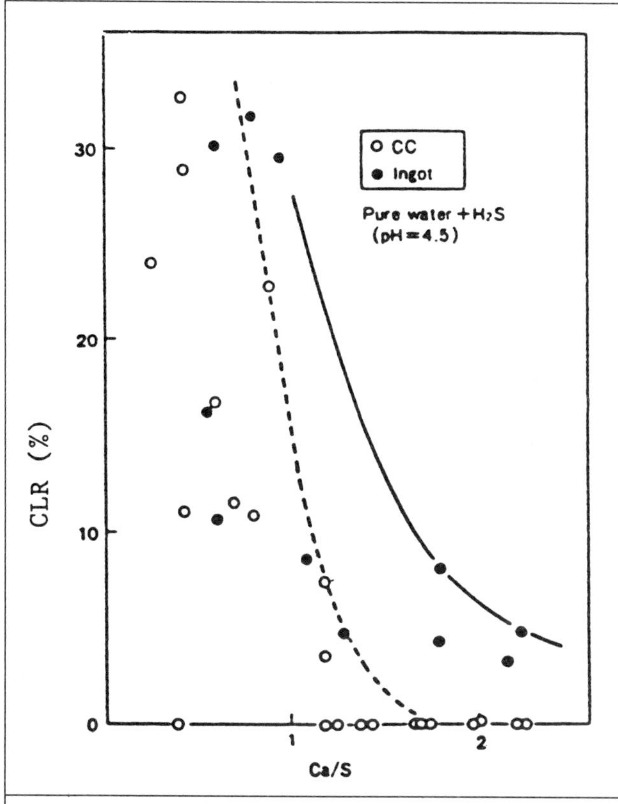

Fig. 6.12—Influence of calcium/sulfur ratio on HIC susceptibility.[20]

of H_2O+TEG+NaCl+S. These are components commonly found in most sour-gas systems that have been dehydrated.

6.4 Internal Corrosion Control

Internal corrosion of flowlines and pipelines can be controlled by different means, but the most common method is with corrosion inhibitors. In wet-gas transmission, the gas can flow in three patterns: mist, stratified, and slug flow. The flow pattern depends on the gas and liquid velocities and such other factors as pipe diameter, viscosity, and angle. This variety in flow patterns can create difficulties in chemical inhibition, particularly when water builds up in low spots. Complete inhibition is hard to achieve under all flow conditions. Because of these difficulties, frequent pigging is one of the best methods to reduce corrosion because it eliminates stagnant conditions and pushes water out of the system, especially in hilly terrain. Pipelines should be designed to minimize stagnant water phases where possible.

Some corrosion inhibitors also can reduce the hydrogen absorbed into a metal in a sour system, thereby reducing the tendency for HIC. This essentially is accomplished by reducing the corrosion rate, which reduces the amount of hydrogen generated. **Fig. 6.18** shows a dramatic drop in hydrogen absorption after an inhibitor is added.[26] Inhibition, however, is not considered a truly reliable method for controlling HIC because it is not 100% effective; occasional equipment failure will occur.

Plastic coatings, for their limited life, are beneficial for environments with low concentrations of H_2S and CO_2 at relatively low pressure. High-pressure H_2S, particularly in conjunction with CO_2, will adversely affect coatings, resulting in premature failure and often accelerated corrosion. So, while coatings may have a useful life for corrosion protection in low-pressure systems, they cannot be relied on for high-pressure systems or for SSC or HIC prevention.

Fiberglass-reinforced pipe is an alternative to plastic coatings for low-pressure sour-gas systems and has been used successfully to carry sour gas (15% H_2S) up to 400 psig [2758 kPa].*[,27]

*Personal communication, Amoco Production Co. (Sept. 1991).

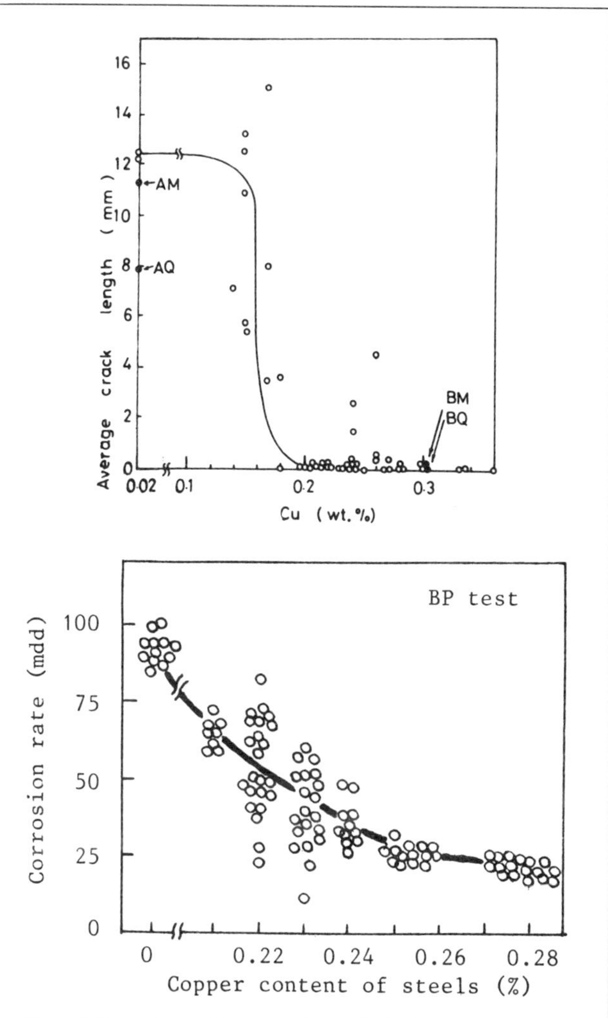

Fig. 6.13—Effect of steel's copper content on corrosion rate and HIC resistance (courtesy of ASM Intl.).[19]

Two new methods of internal corrosion control are CRA-clad and solid-CRA line pipes. Clad line pipe is manufactured with a carbon-steel base metal and various CRA-clad materials, such as the American Iron & Steel Inst.'s (AISI's) stainless steel AISI 316, duplex stainless steel, and Alloy 625 and Alloy 825. Several different methods exist for manufacturing clad pipe, but a discussion of these methods is beyond the scope of this monograph. To date, clad pipe has not been extensively applied, primarily because the necessary welding procedures do not match the rapid construction of carbon-steel pipelines thereby hampering the economics of clad pipe.[28] However, Shell Oil Co.** demonstrated in Mobile Bay that semiautomatic welding of CRA-clad line pipe is a viable method of constructing clad flowlines competitive with carbon steel.

Solid-alloy pipelines and flowlines are gaining wider acceptance, and as more lines are constructed, new techniques are increasing welding speeds. Lines laid to date, however, are primarily duplex stainless steel and are intended for high-CO_2 service in the North Sea and not for gas containing appreciable H_2S. Solid Hastelloy G flowlines were installed in Mobile Bay in 1992 to carry gas rich in CO_2 and H_2S.

Table 6.2 compares many of the important factors for line-pipe construction with different materials.

6.5 Corrosion Monitoring

Corrosion monitoring provides a means to judge the relative corrosivity of fluids or gases and hence allow corrosion-prevention measures and evaluation of the effectiveness of these measures. Monitoring may be as simple as a visual examination of compo-

**Personal communication with Glen Ducet, Shell Oil Co. (1992).

nents over a certain time interval or as complex as many of the electrochemical polarization techniques currently available in instrument form. One of the most common monitoring methods is to expose preweighed metal coupons to the fluid. These coupons can be made in any geometry (e.g., strip, disc, and rod), but the most common is a strip coupon that is installed in the system at a specific location. Coupons are exposed to the corrosive media from 30 days to 1 year, depending on the expected corrosion rate. Corrosion rates can be calculated from the coupon's weight loss, and the actual form of attack (uniform, pitting, or crevice) can be observed on the coupon surface.

Coupons have the advantages of being inexpensive and easy to install, but they also have several disadvantages. Because coupons must be placed in areas where water is present, they typically are inserted perpendicular to the flow direction, which produces different flow conditions and possibly changes the corrosion-rate behavior compared to that of the pipe wall. Coupons must be exposed long enough to produce measurable corrosion; thus, they do not give instantaneous measurements.

The use of a spool or a nipple is one monitoring technique that can overcome the problem of orienting coupons to the flowstream. Pipe spools or nipples of the same line size as the production pipe enable a more representative determination of corrosion. This technique has the advantage of measuring corrosion at all locations (top, bottom, etc.). However, if localized corrosion does occur, simple weight-loss measurements will not be accurate.

Another drawback of coupons and spools is the need to shut down the system for replacement. This, coupled with the long-term nature of monitoring with coupons, led to the development of electrical probes that allow either continuous or regular-interval monitoring of a system. Electrical probes provide an instantaneous measure of the corrosion rate and thus reduce the time needed to detect corrosion or to evaluate corrosion-prevention methods.

Many types of electrical probes are available for corrosion monitoring, but three are used extensively: the electrical-resistance probe, the linear polarization probe, and the polarization-admittance instantaneous-rate (PAIR^{SM}) probe. The electrical-resistance probe (**Fig. 6.19**) has a tubular or wire-loop sensing element[29] that forms one portion of a Wheatstone bridge. The corrosion rate is calculated by the sensing element's change in resistance, which increases because the cross section of the element becomes smaller as it corrodes. Because the probe does not rely on conductivity, it does not have to be in a continuous water phase. By measuring the resistance changes of the probe, corrosion rates can be determined at any time. The service life of the probe is limited by the thickness of the sensing element.

Although the electrical-resistance probe has numerous advantages over other monitoring techniques, it also has some disadvantages. These probes frequently are installed perpendicular to the flowstream, producing different flow circumstances from those the pipe wall experiences. In sour systems, a tenacious film of iron sulfide may form on the sensing element and essentially stifle further corrosion. Conductive iron sulfide may mask resistance changes and provide erroneously low corrosion-rate data. Pitting corrosion may cause an extremely high localized corrosion rate and soon render the probe useless.

The linear polarization probe (**Fig. 6.20**) measures the corrosion rate by the linear polarization method.[29] This technique imposes a small voltage between the two electrodes and measures the associated current flow; the resulting current is a measure of the corrosion rate. This probe is often more sensitive than those previously described and, like the electrical-resistance probe, also can be read at any time.

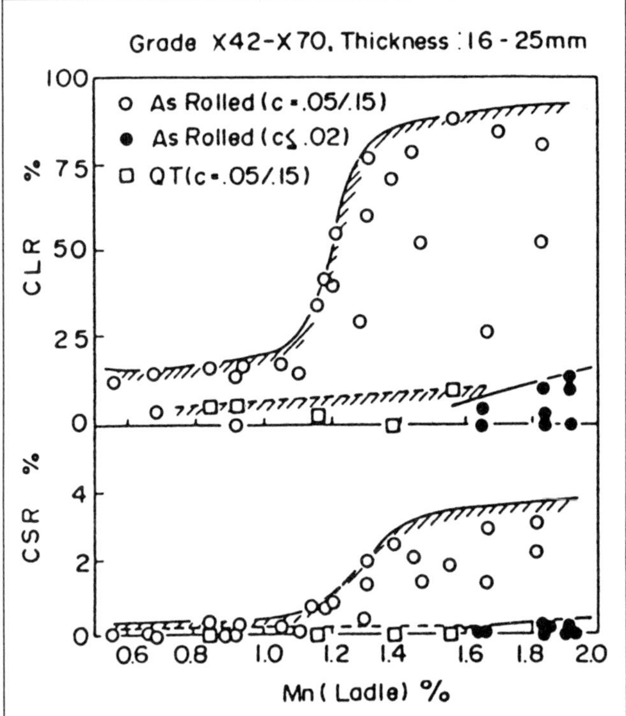

Fig. 6.14—Effect of manganese content on HIC susceptibility of pipe Grades X-42 through X-70.[22]

A serious drawback of this type of probe is the need to have a continuous high-conductivity fluid between the electrodes. This means that the linear polarization probe is ineffective in gas streams or in hydrocarbon streams where little water is present. Another problem is that, if corrosion products or solids bridge the two electrodes, erroneous readings or no readings may follow. One version of this probe allows electrodes to be installed flush with the pipe wall, which bypasses the perpendicular-orientation problem mentioned earlier; however, sufficient water must be present for the probe to work.

The PAIR probe operates like the linear polarization probe but uses three electrodes. A small current is passed between two electrodes, and the voltage difference measured between one of these electrodes and the reference electrode determines the corrosion rate. Many of the advantages and disadvantages of the linear polarization probe are inherent in the PAIR probe. The PAIR probe, how-

TABLE 6.2—COMPARISON OF VARIOUS METHODS FOR CORROSION CONTROL IN PIPE

Pipe	Corrosion Resistance	SSC/SCC Resistance	Strength	Field Welding	Manufacturing	Cost
CRA	Excellent	Good	Acceptable	Acceptable	Good	High
Clad	Excellent	Good	Excellent	Acceptable	Acceptable	High
Fiberglass	Good	Good	Acceptable	Acceptable	Good	Acceptable
Lined	Good	Acceptable	Acceptable	Poor	Acceptable	Good
Plastic-coated	Acceptable	Poor	Good	Poor	Good	Good
Carbon-steel	Poor*	Acceptable	Excellent	Excellent	Excellent	Excellent

*Poor means that some type of problem exists.

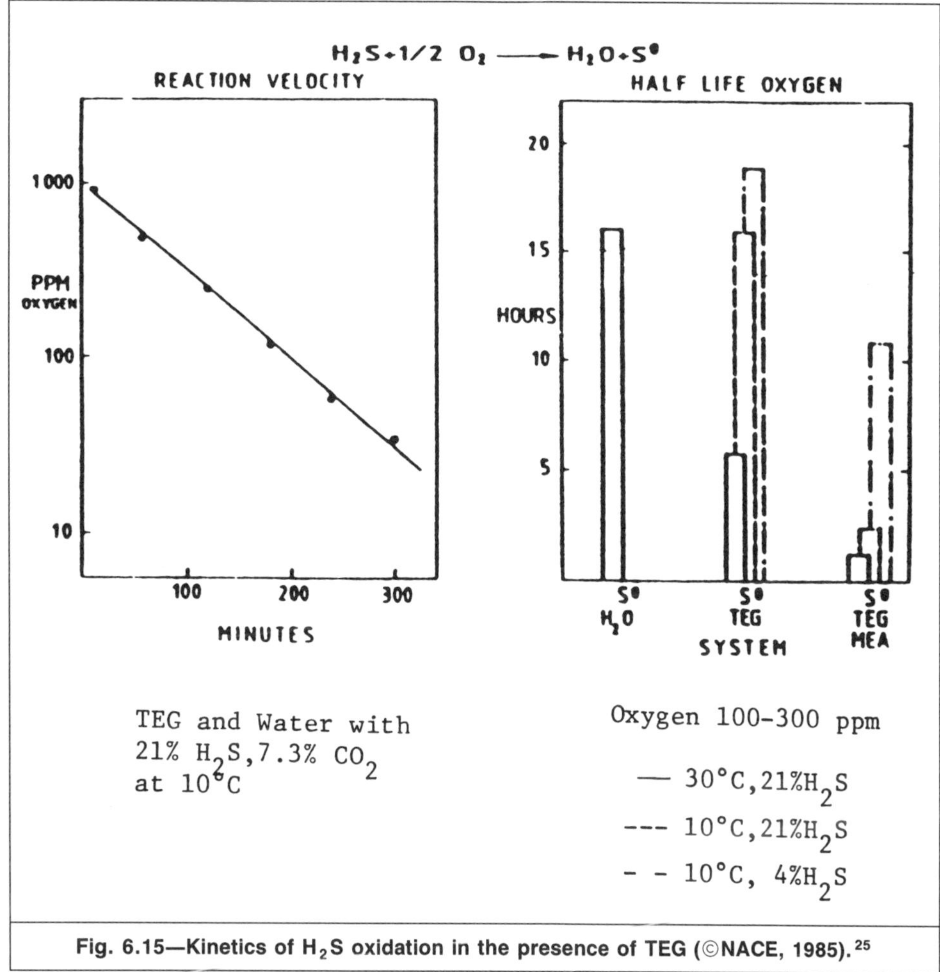

Fig. 6.15—Kinetics of H_2S oxidation in the presence of TEG (©NACE, 1985).[25]

ever, can be connected to a potentiometric device, and accurate polarization testing not available with a linear polarization system can be accomplished. Thus, laboratory and field polarization studies that reveal complex corrosion phenomena can be accomplished with PAIR probes when they are coupled to more sophisticated instruments. Cole[30] compares these corrosion-monitoring methods further.

Hydrogen probes are another monitoring method useful for obtaining comparative corrosion data in sour-gas systems. Hydrogen probes primarily are used in systems containing H_2S. The sulfide ion promotes the entry of atomic hydrogen (generated by cathodic corrosion reactions) into the steel as described in Chap. 3. After passing through the steel, the atomic hydrogen combines to form molecular hydrogen. The pressure generated by the gas within the probe is proportional to the cathodic reaction, and hence, the corrosion in the system. NACE[31] indicates that hydrogen pressure probes can detect corrosive environments containing as little as 1 ppm (0.0001 mol%) H_2S in the gas phase. Hydrogen probes are available from several manufacturers. The most common type is a pressure probe. A typical pressure-type hydrogen probe is a hollow thin-walled steel tube that is sealed at one end and has a pressure gauge and bleeder valve at the other end. The hollow tube is inserted into the corrosive system and corrosion is monitored indirectly by the rate of hydrogen pressure increase. These probes must be monitored regularly, and any hydrogen pressure must be released at specified intervals. Hydrogen probes are not precise but may provide a relative indication of corrosion.

Vacuum- and electrolytic-type hydrogen probes, sometimes referred to as patch probes, are also available. These devices are somewhat more complicated than pressure-type hydrogen probes. The vacuum and electrolytic hydrogen probes are even more sensitive than the pressure-type probes and will detect smaller amounts of hydrogen generated by corrosion reactions without H_2S or other cathodic poisons being present.

Hydrogen probes can be used to evaluate corrosion inhibitors in sour systems. Most published data[31,32] indicate that hydrogen-probe data do not necessarily correlate with coupon data (**Fig. 6.21**). In addition, oxygen may interfere with the hydrogen probe's usual sensitivity in sour systems, causing it to indicate lower corrosion rates than actually exist. Hydrogen probes should be used with other corrosion-monitoring methods and not as the only source of corrosion information.

Water analysis is another indirect means of detecting corrosion-rate changes. "Iron counts" (iron lbm/ml in the water) are the most common form of testing water to detect corrosion. Because an increase in the iron content above the natural level in the water indicates corrosion, iron counts can be used to detect a corrosion-rate increase.

Factors one should consider when using iron counts to monitor corrosion include the following.

1. Iron counts usually are not reliable in sour water. Because of the low solubility product of iron sulfide, iron may settle out of the fluid, giving misleadingly low counts at the test point.
2. Oxygen contamination of waters may cause insoluble iron oxides to precipitate.
3. Some subsurface waters contain soluble iron. This residual iron concentration should be known and considered when the iron counts of a system are evaluated.
4. The significance of a particular iron count is influenced by the type of corrosion occurring and by fluctuations in corrosive water volumes.
5. Iron counts should be substantiated or correlated with other corrosion-monitoring methods.

Manganese counts also may reflect changes in the corrosion rate, but they are used less frequently. Manganese is not typically produced from reservoirs, but most steels contain about 1%. Thus, manganese in the water indicates steel corrosion.

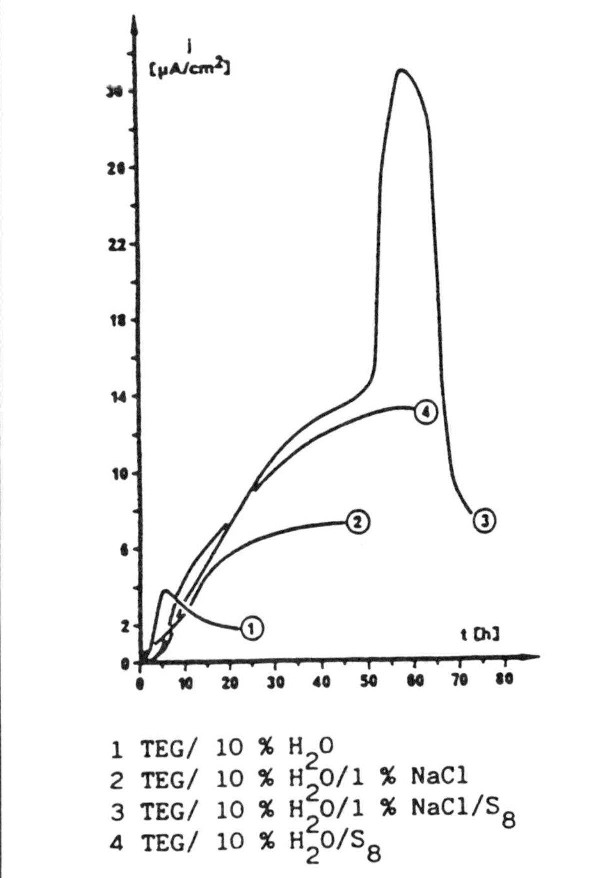

Fig. 6.16—Hydrogen permeation current vs. time in TEG solutions under 16 bar [1.6 MPa] H_2S at 77°F [25°C] (©NACE, 1985).[25]

6.6 Inspection

All the corrosion-monitoring methods discussed above do not physically measure the actual deterioration of the equipment. Because corrosion from H_2S is most often a highly localized attack like pitting, it is important to examine the actual equipment periodically. Several methods are used to determine the existing condition of equipment; three are discussed here: instrumented pigs, ultrasonics, and radiography.

The first method involves passing an instrumented pig through a pipe. As it travels, the instrumented pig induces an electromagnetic field in the pipe. Discontinuities in the pipe produce a change

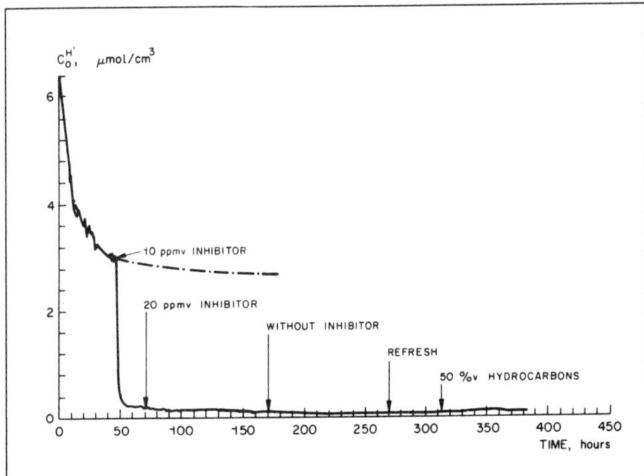

Fig. 6.18—Evaluation of inhibitor performance with respect to hydrogen absorption with the hydrogen-permeation technique (©NACE, 1986).[26]

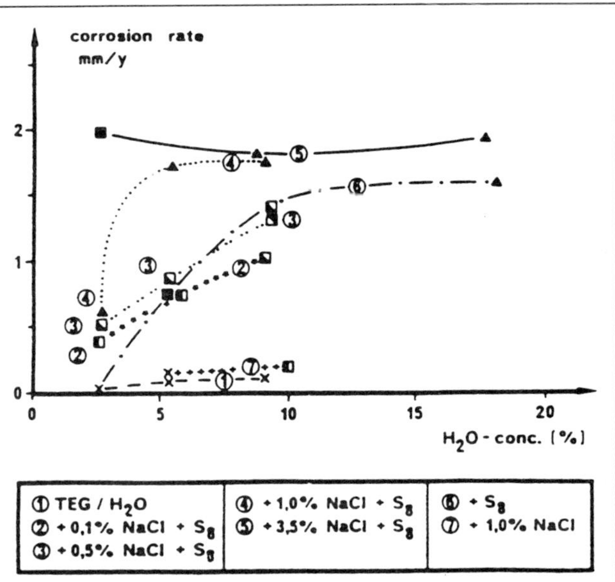

Fig. 6.17—Corrosion of steel in various TEG solutions as a function of water content at 77°F [25°C] and 16 bar [1.6 MPa] H_2S. X indicates that no hydrogen blisters or HIC occurred. All other symbols indicate that these forms of hydrogen damage were present (©NACE, 1985).[25]

in this magnetic field that the pig records. It is important to plan for pigging when designing a pipeline, especially in critical (e.g., offshore or highly populated) areas, where reliability is essential. Instrumented pigs test a larger area than the two other methods which are site-specific.

Ultrasonic testing uses the principle that sound waves travel through different media at different velocities and reflect from surfaces. Corrosion damage is determined by ultrasonically measuring the remaining wall thickness. Cracking is detected by the reflection of ultrasonic waves from the crack surfaces. Simple digital display ("D") meters that are easy to operate and interpret are available that enable rapid scanning of large areas for remaining wall thickness. The measurements then can be used to evaluate the extent and the nature of corrosion. The disadvantage of this approach is that the area to be tested must be in direct contact with the transducer head. Therefore, buried lines or downhole tubulars cannot

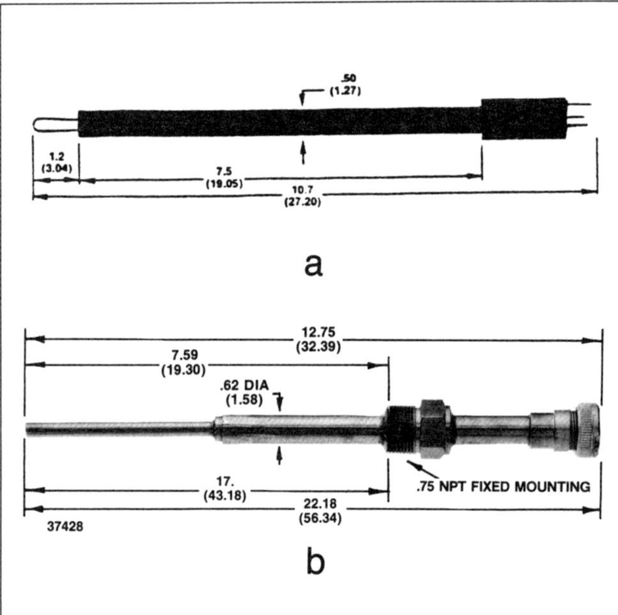

Fig. 6.19—CORROSOMETER® probes (a) wire loop and (b) tube (courtesy of Rohrback Cosasco Systems Inc.).[29]

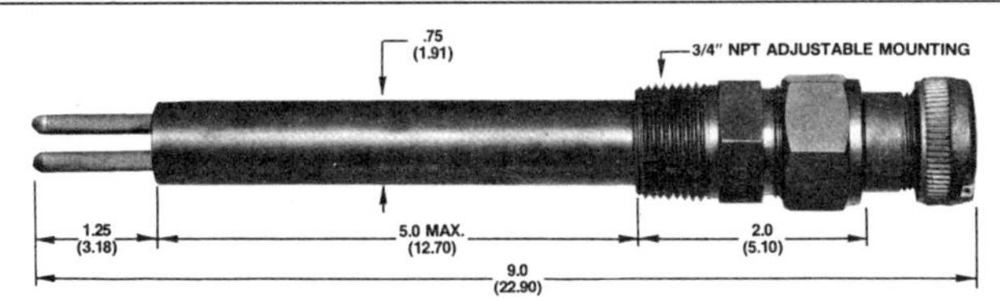

Fig. 6.20—CORRATER® probe showing two sensing electrodes (courtesy of Rorhback Cosasco Systems Inc.).[29]

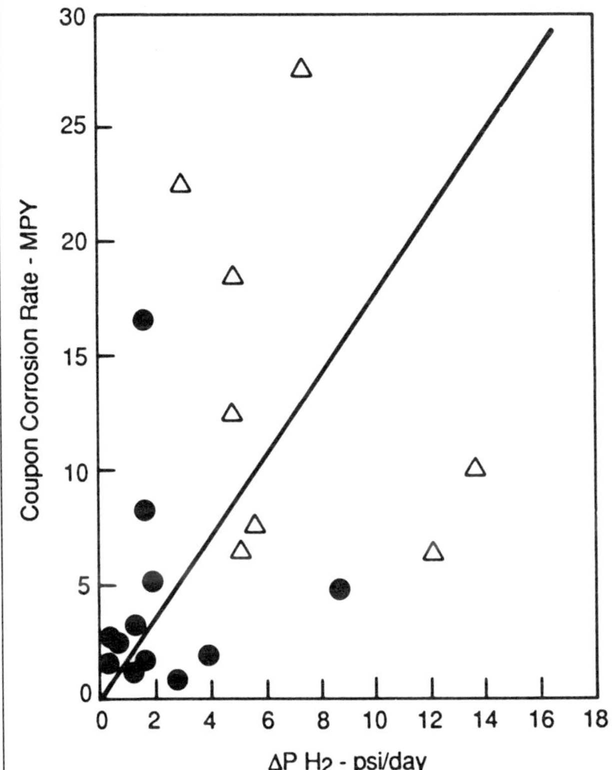

Fig. 6.21—Correlation of hydrogen probe pressure change with coupon corrosion rate for several wells (©NACE, 1976).[32]

TABLE 6.3—COMMON SPECIFICATIONS USED FOR STEEL CONSTRUCTION OF PIPING, FITTINGS, SEPARATORS, AND VESSELS*

Plates and Pipes

ASTM *A 106, Specification for Seamless Carbon Steel Pipe for High Temperature Service***
ASTM *A 515, Specification for Pressure Vessel Plates, Carbon Steel for Intermediate and High Temperature Service*†
ASTM *A 53, Specification for Pipe, Steel, Black and Hot-Dipped, Zinc Coated Welded and Seamless*
ASTM *A 285, Specification for Pressure Vessel Plates, Carbon Steel, Low and Intermediate Tensile Strength*
ASTM *A 36, Specification for Structural Steel*
ASTM *A 283, Specification for Low and Intermediate Tensile Strength Carbon Steel Plates*
ASTM *A 537, Specification for Pressure Vessel Plates, Heat-Treated, Carbon-Manganese-Silicon Steel*
ASTM *A 573, Specifications for Structural Carbon Steel Plates of Improved Toughness*

Flanges and Fittings

ASTM *A 105, Specification for Forgings, Carbon Steel, for Piping Components*
ASTM *A 234, Specification for Piping Fittings of Wrought Carbon Steel and Alloy Steel for Moderated and Elevated Temperatures*
ASTM *A 181, Specification for Forgings, Carbon Steel for General Purpose Piping*
ASTM *A 350, Specification for Forgings, Carbon and Low Alloy Steel Requiring Notch Toughness Testing*
ASTM *A 694, Specification for Forgings, Carbon and Alloy Steel, for Pipe Flanges, Fittings, Valves and Parts for High Pressure Transmission Service*
ASTM *A 707, Specification for Flanges, Forged, Carbon and Alloy Steel for Low Temperature Service*
ASTM *A 727, Specification for Forgings, Carbon Steel, for Piping Components With Inherent Notch Toughness*
ASTM *A 858, Specification for Heat Treated Carbon Steel Fittings for Low Temperature and Corrosive Service*
ASTM *A 860, Specification for High Strength Butt-Welding Fittings of Wrought High Strength Low Alloy Steel*
CSA *G40.21*‡

*Intl. Standards Organization Grades Fe42, Fe44, and Fe52 are also used.
**Grade B.
†Grades 60 and 70.
‡Grades 38W, 38T, 44W, and 50T.
ASTM specifications are available from the American Soc. for Testing & Materials, 1916 Race St., Philadelphia, PA 19103.
CSA specifications are available from the Canadian Standards Assn., 178 Rexdale Blvd., Rexdale, Ont., Canada M9W IR3.

be inspected in place by simple wall-thickness meters. Radiography suffers from the same restriction. Radiography involves exposing the test section and film to a radioactive source, similar to radiographic flaw inspection of welds. This exposure produces an image on the film that enables accurate determination of corrosion damage in one plane. Because both methods examine limited areas, they may not necessarily find the most severe corrosion or cracking.

Many other monitoring techniques are available but most are either variations on those already described or are too complex to discuss here. One important precept to keep in mind is that corrosion monitoring should never be carried out with only one method. *At least two or three different monitoring methods should be used to evaluate a system.* Relying on one method may result in an uneconomical operation or lead to catastrophic failure.

6.7 Field Vessels and Storage Tanks

Separators and vessels are designed and built to such standards as ASME's *Boiler and Pressure Vessel Code*[7] and API's *Standard 650*[33] and *Specs. 12D*[34] and *12F*.[35] **Table 6.3** lists specifications for common plates, pipes, flanges, and fittings for steel construction. Variations among the specifications above and in Table 6.3 generally deal with chemical composition, mechanical properties, and inspection requirements. The specifications are mostly for carbon or low-alloy steels with similar corrosion resistance. Corrosion is almost always found in the water phase of these vessels and separators; however, a significant vapor phase attack also may be observed, particularly in tank roofs.

The rate of corrosion depends on the temperature, the partial pressure of the H_2S gas above the water (which determines the concentration of H_2S in the water), the presence of other gases such as oxygen and CO_2, the water composition, and the relative residence time of water in the vessel. In the vapor space, water may condense, creating a phase with high solubility for acid gases, resulting in high corrosion rates.

As with pipelines, several forms of hydrogen damage can occur in vessels and tanks. Original fabrication welds for vessel construction or nozzle attachment can produce hard welds that are susceptible to SSC. In addition, high residual stresses from welding can encourage SSC even in welds with low hardness. The petroleum refining industry recognized this latter problem in the early 1970's.

The problem occurred most frequently when carbon-steel vessels, submerged-arc welded with active-bonded fluxes containing high silicon and manganese, were put in wet H_2S service in the as-welded condition. Transverse weld cracking was found to occur at hardness levels above and below the previously established Brinell hardness (HB) criterion of HB 235. Petroleum industry-sponsored research showed that welds having a hardness in excess of HB 225

(HRC 20) were susceptible to SSC because of high residual welding stresses. Welds with an overall hardness from HB 194 to 214 sometimes would crack if microscopic hard zones were present, while welds with HB 191 or less were resistant to SSC under the most severe laboratory conditions.

The results of this research were published as API *RP 942*[36] and NACE *RP-04-72*.[37] Both publications cover welds for carbon-steel refinery equipment, contain discussions of the various factors that affect weld hardness, and agree on a mandatory maximum weld hardness of HB 200. API *RP 942* places additional mandatory restrictions on weld metal chemistry. The limits for carbon, manganese, and silicon are based on the Grade P-1 chemistry limits set by ASME (see Table Q11.3 of Ref. 7), while the total maximum content of chromium, nickel, and molybdenum is set at 0.25 wt%. Note, however, that these two documents, by definition, are intended to cover carbon-steel (Grade P-1) material only and do not address such steel as Grade SA-612 that contains higher percentages of manganese and silicon and enables additional amounts of nickel and chromium for strengthening and grain refinement.

As previously stated, failures in carbon-steel vessels have been associated with high hardness and high manganese content resulting from multipass welds with active-bonded fluxes. The additive effect of the alloying fluxes results in manganese contents that often exceed 2 wt% and weld strengths, as measured by hardness, that are disproportionately high for carbon steel. With active-bonded fluxes, it is not unusual to find weld deposits having a hardness higher than HB 225 in a carbon-steel Grade SA-516-70 (70-ksi [483-MPa] tensile strength) pressure vessel.

One recent catastrophic failure illustrates the need for a comprehensive quality inspection program, especially in sour service. In mid-1984, an MEA-absorber vessel at a refinery ruptured, killing 17 people and producing extensive property damage.[38] The vessel contained propane and H_2S at 100°F [38°C] and 200 psi [1379 kPa]. A failure analysis of the vessel revealed that the submerged-arc welds in 1-in. [2.54-cm] -thick ASTM *A 516* Grade 70 (Table 6.3) steel plate had not been postweld heat-treated and that repair welds had not been preheated or postweld heat-treated. In addition, chromium-molybdenum alloy filler metal inadvertently had been used for repairs. Neither preheat nor postweld heat treatment were required by the ASME[7] for this material, but the resulting weld HAZ exhibited hardness as high as HRC 45. Failure was attributed to crack initiation by SSC in the HAZ of the hard repair weld. Crack propagation through the vessel wall was reportedly[38] a result of HIC; however, SOHIC is the more probable cause.

As a result of this incident, the petroleum industry began extensive inspection of vessels in sour service in refineries, gas plants, and liquefied-petroleum-gas (LPG) storage facilities. The industry discovered a substantial worldwide problem of cracked vessels in H_2S service. **Table 6.4** presents the results of the inspection programs of several oil companies, and **Table 6.5** lists the frequency of cracking as a function of steel composition.[39] Others[40,41] have found a high incidence of cracking in LPG storage vessels. In many cases, ASTM *A 515* (Table 6.3) Grade 70 steel microalloyed with columbium and vanadium and control-rolled, displayed a higher tendency to cracking than carbon-manganese steels. Frequently, HB testing of the welds after fabrication produced values less than HB 200. However, microhardness values were found to be greater than the equivalent of HB 248 in some cracked vessels. Note that the wet-fluorescent magnetic particle method used to find cracks is extremely sensitive. Many of the cracks discovered were thought to be original construction cracks or weld undercuts.

TABLE 6.4—INDIVIDUAL COMPANY RESULTS (After Ref. 39)

Company	Number of Vessels Inspected	Cracked Vessels Number	Cracked Vessels Percentage
A	31	14	45
B	273	118	43
C	609	259	42.5
D	65	20	31
E	79	22	28
F	10	2	20
G	101	16	16
H	344	40	11.6
I	617	80	13
J	31	2	6.5
K	203	13	6.4
L	0	0	0
Total	2,363	586	25%

(Table courtesy of *Oil & Gas J.*)

Although the preponderance of failures were in steels with tensile strengths greater than 70,000 psi [483 MPa], some lower-strength vessels also displayed cracking. In all cases involving welds that cracked in service, cracking was attributed to SSC, HIC, or a combination of the two.

Cracking of vessel steels in H_2S may be exacerbated by applied stress or areas of stress concentration. ASTM *A 515, A 516,* and *A 285* (Table 6.5) have been found to crack in the presence of notches in a stepwise fashion characteristic of HIC.[42] Even so-called HIC-resistant steels may become susceptible to cracking in the presence of applied stresses less than the yield strength,[42] (i.e., SOHIC). While SOHIC has become a common term, the proliferation of such unwarranted terminology is confusing and does not improve the understanding of hydrogen-related problems.

Merrick and Bullen[42] found that exposure of NACE *Standard TM-02-84*[12] test specimens to NACE *Standard TM-01-77*[13] solution (5% NaCl, 0.5% acetic acid, and H_2S bubbled into distilled water) produced a better screening of steels resistant to HIC in both the presence and absence of stress than did testing with the *Standard TM-02-84* solution. Moreover, a maximum permitted value of 15% for the CLR was adequate to provide SSC-resistant steels for pressure vessels in actual service.

Relatively little has been published to relate actual field experience with HIC test results. Petrie and Moore[43] reported the results of extensive HIC testing of existing pipelines and surface facilities compared with service history. Their results are presented in **Table 6.6**. In most cases, the correspondence between NACE *Standard TM-02-84* specimen cracking and in-service cracking was good. The extent of cracking, however, is not comparable between

TABLE 6.5—CRACKING EXPERIENCE vs. STEEL TYPE (After Ref. 39)

Material	Number of Vessels	Cracked Vessels Number	Cracked Vessels Percentage	Cracked > 25% Wall Number	Cracked > 25% Wall Percentage
ASTM A-212 Grade B	46	16	35	10	22
ASTM A-285 Grade C	295	116	39	35	12
ASTM A-515-70	35	22	62	16	46
ASTM A-516-60	49	4	8	1	2
ASTM A-516-65	11	2	2	1	1
ASTM A-516-70	87	31	36	9	10
ASTM A-707	24	16	67	2	8
ASTM A-106	8	3	38	0	0

(Table courtesy of *Oil & Gas J.*)

TABLE 6.6—HIC TEST RESULTS (After Ref. 43)

Facility	NSC*	Maximum Width (mm)	Maximum CLR (%)	Average CSR (%)	Service Performance
Gas/Oil/Water Separating Vessels					
Vessel 1 (7 years of service)					
8:00	0/9	0	0	0	No damage
10:00	1/9	0.1	17.5	0.01	Blisters; no cracks
12:00	1/9	0.7	13.5	0.05	Blisters; minor cracking
1:30	(5/6)	(4.2)	(104)	(4.3)	Blisters; extensive cracking
Vessel 2 (29 years of service)	0/9	0	0	0	No damage
Vessel 3 (14 years of service)					
Fifth course					
5:30	1/9	1.01	35	0.3	Extensive corrosion at 6:00; blisters with cracks in six out of nine courses
	7/9	0.96	68	1.3	
Second course					
6:00	6/9	0.85	129	8.6	
Vessel 4 (12 years of service)					
Fourth course					
5:30	3/9	0.33	46	0.3	Extensive corrosion at 6:00; blisters up to 180 × 200 mm
6:00	1/9	0.17	18	0.03	
Eighth course					
6:00	0/9	0	0	0	
Vessel 5 (7 years of service)					
6:00	6/24	1.45	62	(0.5)	Longitudinal cracks
Pipelines With Major Service Damage					
Gas Line 1a	9/9	2.4	97	19.7	Three ruptures in first month
Scraper launcher	9/9	2.01	94.6	(12.17)	Extensive cracking; replaced
Crude line (offshore)	9/9	1.58	122	(7.45)	Leaks; replaced
Crude line (onshore)	9/9	1.00	113	(3.3)	Extensive cracking; replaced
Gas Line 4	6/9	—	—	3.69	Extensive cracking; line abandoned
Pipelines With Nil to Moderate Service Damage					
Gas Line 2	0/0	0	0	0	No damage
Mixed gas and oil services	0/0	0	0	0	Blisters weep-leaked after 31 years
Gas Line 3	1/9	0.5	26	0.07	Blisters
Gas Line 5	2/9	0.44	34.8	(0.34)	Blisters; some centerline cracking
Gas plant piping	2/9	0.81	12.8	0.139	Numerous short cracks

(©NACE, 1989)
*No. Samples Cracked.

the test samples and the service equipment. Therefore, NACE *Standard TM-02-84* may be a good method for screening samples (cracking vs. no cracking) but, like many laboratory tests, may not adequately predict the extent of cracking in service. Based on their field experience, Petrie and Moore[43] suggested a revised set of graphs from NACE *Standard MR-01-75*[44] for HIC relative to the H_2S dissolved in the water phase rather than the gas phase. **Figs. 6.22 and 6.23** are not universally accepted but do provide a guideline for HIC.[43]

Note that HIC can take many years to appear or can occur in a few months. Unlike SSC, which produces catastrophic cracking in a few minutes or hours, HIC is most often a long-term problem that can be dealt with by proper steel selection, fabrication procedures, and system operation (e.g., inhibition and dehydration).

Some metallurgical factors that can reduce the incidence of HIC are (1) reducing the carbon and manganese contents of the steel as much as is reasonably possible, (2) reducing the sulfur content to less than 0.005 wt% (3) reducing the phosphorus content to less than 0.010 wt%, and (4) adding 0.20 wt% to 0.25 wt% copper. The addition of calcium also may be beneficial if sulfur contents cannot be reduced below 0.002 wt%, and microalloying with columbium or vanadium may create adverse effects if not properly controlled through welding procedures that reduce the effect of hard zones in welds.

6.8 Quality Assurance

As with any components that are designed and fabricated for sour service, piping and vessels should be purchased to specifications that outline in sufficient detail those requirements that ensure that materials are resistant to HIC and SSC (Appendix B). Moreover, it is imperative that adequate on-site inspections be performed during manufacturing and fabrication to ensure that vessels and pipelines are constructed in a manner that reduces the risk of SSC and HIC. Depending on the particular circumstances, a detailed quality-assurance plan should be developed and implemented. Such a plan provides the means to document and control the manufacture of

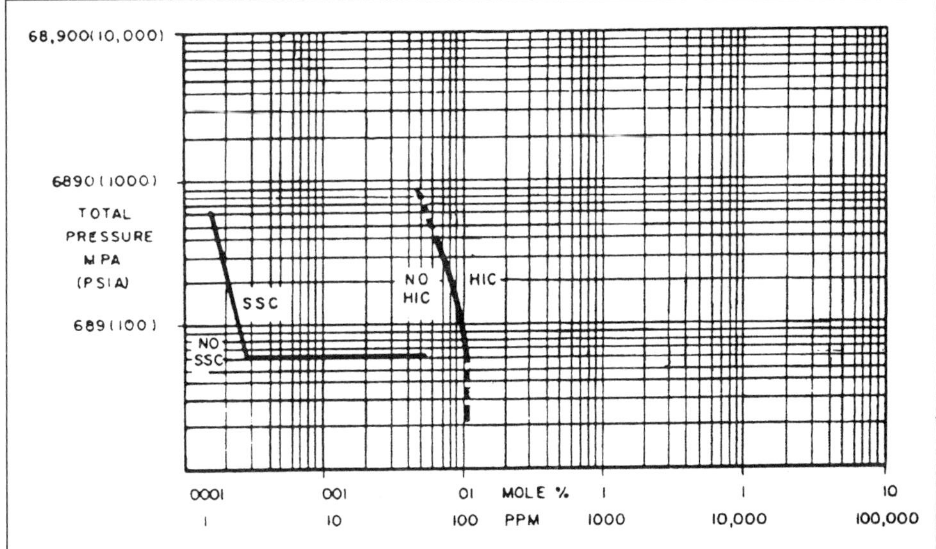

Fig. 6.22—H_2S concentration in the free-water phase of a sour-gas system and the limits for HIC and SSC (©NACE, 1989).[43]

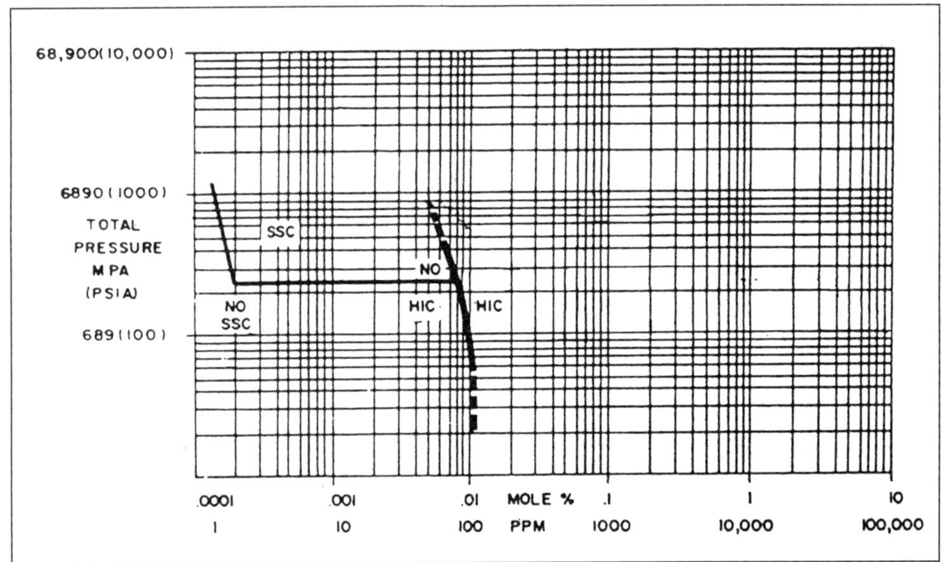

Fig. 6.23—H_2S concentration in the water phase of a sour-multiphase system and the limits for HIC and SSC (©NACE, 1989).[43]

equipment from source to final acceptance. These plans are recommended for all field, surface, pipeline, and plant facilities and may be required by law in some locations.

6.9 Safety

Safety should be the primary concern in both the design and operation of surface facilities that handle sour gas. As described in Chap. 2, radius-of-exposure calculations and plans for emergency response in the event of an H_2S release are necessary steps in designing a safe sour-gas system.

In sour-gas gathering systems, emergency shutdown valves sometimes are installed to shut the line in automatically if the pressure drops or rises outside a preset range. Some operators install online H_2S monitors on gas transmission lines that automatically close valves if the H_2S content exceeds some low preset limit.

In gas plant areas or in locations where separators and dehydrators are clustered, it is important to have an H_2S-gas detector on site and functional at all times so that personnel entering the area are immediately alerted to the presence and concentration of H_2S. Furthermore, these monitors should be incorporated into a warning system that produces an alert at a central command facility so that early action can be taken in the event of an H_2S release. Most of the safety issues discussed in Chap. 2 are pertinent to surface facilities. Finally, it is imperative that field and plant personnel be thoroughly trained in H_2S safety procedures.

Nomenclature

a = sum of crack length, in.
b = sum of crack thickness, in.
C_{th} = hydrogen concentration threshold
h = height, in.
w = width, in.

References

1. *Spec. 5L, Specification for Line Pipe,* 35th edition, API, Dallas (May 1985).
2. *A 106, Specification for Seamless Carbon Steel Pipe for High Temperature Service,* ASTM, Philadelphia.
3. *Spec. 5LC, Specification for CRA Line Pipe,* first edition, API, Dallas (June 30, 1988).
4. Omar, A.A., Kane, R.D., and Boyd, W.K.: "Factors Affecting the Sulfide Stress Cracking of Steel Weldments," paper 186 presented at the 1981 NACE Corrosion/81.

5. Ume, K. *et al.*: "Initiation and Propagation Morphology of Sulfide Stress Corrosion Cracking of Welds in Linepipe Steels," paper 240 presented at the 1985 NACE Corrosion/85.
6. Technical Bulletin 83H-001, Sumitomo Metal Industries (1983).
7. *Boiler and Pressure Vessel Code,* American Soc. of Mechanical Engineers, New York City, Secs. VIII and IX.
8. *Standard 1104, Welding of Pipelines and Related Facilities,* 17th edition, API, Dallas (Sept. 1988).
9. *A 105, Specification for Forgings, Carbon Steel, for Piping Components,* ASTM, Philadelphia.
10. *A 234, Specification for Piping Fittings and Wrought Carbon Steel and Alloy Steel for Moderate and Elevated Temperatures,* ASTM, Philadelphia.
11. *A 350, Specification for Forgings, Carbon and Low Alloy Steel Requiring Notch Toughness Testing,* ASTM, Philadelphia.
12. *Standard TM-02-84, Test Method for Evaluation of Pipeline Steels for Resistance to Stepwise Cracking,* NACE, Houston (1984).
13. *Standard TM-01-77, Test Method for Laboratory Testing of Metals for Resistance to Sulfide Stress Cracking in H_2S Environments,* NACE, Houston (1990).
14. Ikeda, A. and Kowaka, M.: "Stress Corrosion Cracking of Low and High Strength Steels in Wet Hydrogen Sulfide Environment," *Chemical Economy & Engineering Rev.* (May–June 1978) **10**, 12–22.
15. Ikeda, A., Kaneko, T., and Terasaki, F.: "Influence of Environmental Conditions and Metallurgical Factors on Hydrogen Induced Cracking of Line Pipe Steel," paper 8 presented at the 1980 NACE Corrosion/80.
16. Murata, T., Sato, E., and Hosoi, Y.: "Hydrogen Entry Process From Hydrogen Sulfide Environment and the Related Topics," paper 25 presented at the 1977 NACE Corrosion/77.
17. Sato, E., Hashimoto, M., and Murata, T.: "Corrosion of Steels in a Wet H_2S and CO_2 Environment," paper presented at the 1981 Second Asian Pacific Corrosion Control Conference, Kuala Lumpur.
18. Nakasugi, H. *et al.*: "Development of New Linepipe Steels for Sour Gas Service," *Nippon Steel Technical Report* (1979) **14**, No. 12, 66–78.
19. Yamada, K. *et al.*: "Influence of Metallurgical Factors on HIC of High Strength ERW Line Pipe for Sour Gas Service," paper 8306–032 presented at the 1983 Intl. Conference on Technology and Applications of High Strength Low Alloy (HSLA) Steels (In conjunction with 1983 Metals Congress), Philadelphia, Oct. 3–6.
20. Ikeda, A. *et al.*: "Improvement of Hydrogen Sulfide Cracking Susceptibility in Line Pipes for Sour Gas Service," *Sumitomo Search* (1981) No. 26, 91–97.
21. Craig, B.D.: "Explanation of the Effect of Copper on the Protectiveness of Iron Sulfide Films," *Corrosion* (1984) **40**, 471–76.
22. Taira, T. and Kobayashi, Y.: "Steels for Line Pipe and Pipeline Fittings," *The Metal Society*, London (1983) 170–80.
23. Hay, M.G.: "Sour Gas Linepipes—The Need for Hydrogen Induced Cracking Resistance," paper 88–39–115 presented at the 1988 Meeting of the Petroleum Soc. of CIM, Calgary.
24. Cialone, H.J. and Williams, D.N.: "Sensitivity to Sulfide Stress Cracking at Welds in Line Pipe Steels," paper presented at the 1987 ASTM Intl. Symposium on Environmentally Assisted Cracking, Bal Harbor, FL, Nov.
25. Bruckhoff, W. *et al.*: "Rupture of a Sour Gas Line Due To Stress Oriented Hydrogen Induced Cracking: Failure Analyses, Experimental Results, and Corrosion Prevention," paper 389 presented at the 1985 NACE Corrosion/85.
26. Van Gelder, K., Simon Thomas, M.J.J., and Kroese, C.J.: "Hydrogen Induced Cracking: Determination of Maximum Allowed H_2S Partial Pressures," *Corrosion* (1986) **42**, 36–43.
27. Chin, A.S. and Franco, R.J.: "FRP Line Pipe for Oil and Gas Production," *Materials Performance* (1989) **28**, 64–67.
28. Craig, B.D.: "The Economics of the Application of CRA Clad Steel Pipe Versus Carbon Steel With Inhibitors: Factors Involved and Examples," paper presented at the 1992 International Seminar on Clad Engineering, Aberdeen, England, NiDI, and I Corr, (April 8, 1992).
29. Rohrback Cosasco Systems Inc. catalog (1980).
30. Cole, E.L.: "Evaluation of Corrosion Monitoring Methods in Oilfield Systems," *Materials Performance* (1979) **18**, 16–20.
31. *Monitoring Internal Corrosion in Oil and Gas Production Operations With Hydrogen Probes,* Publication 1C184, NACE, Houston (1984).
32. Fincher, D.R., Nestle, A.C., and Marr, J.J.: "Coupon Corrosion Rates Versus Hydrogen Probe Activity," *Materials Performance* (1976) **15**, 34–37.
33. *Standard 650, Welded Steel Tanks for Oil Storage,* seventh edition, API, Dallas (1980).
34. *Spec. 12D, Specification for Field Welded Tanks for Storage of Production Liquids,* ninth edition, API, Dallas (Jan. 1982).
35. *Spec. 12F, Specification for Shop Welded Tanks for Storage of Production Liquids,* eighth edition, API, Dallas (Jan. 1982).
36. *RP 942, Recommended Practice, Controlling Weld Hardness of Carbon Steel Refinery Equipment to Prevent Environmental Cracking,* second edition, API, Dallas (Nov. 1982).
37. *RP-04-72, Methods and Controls To Prevent In-Service Cracking of Carbon Steel (P-1) Welds in Corrosive Petroleum Refining Environments,* NACE, Houston (1972).
38. McHenry, H.I., Read, D.T., and Shives, T.R.: "Failure Analysis of an Amine Absorber Pressure Vessel," *Materials Performance* (1987) **26**, 18–22.
39. Buchheim, G.M.: "Ways To Deal With Wet H_2S Cracking Revealed by Study," *Oil & Gas J.* (July 9, 1990) 92–96.
40. Cantwell, J.E.: "LPG Storage Vessel Cracking Experience," paper 157 presented at the 1988 NACE Corrosion/88, St. Louis, March 21–25.
41. Humphries, M.J., Collins, P.A., and McLaughlin, J.E.: "Cracking of LPG Storage Equipment," paper presented at the 1988 American Welding Soc. Natl. Meeting, New Orleans.
42. Merrick, R.D. and Bullen, M.L.: "Prevention of Cracking in Wet H_2S Environments," paper 269 presented at the 1989 NACE Corrosion/89, New Orleans, April 17–21.
43. Petrie, R.R. and Moore, E.M. Jr.: "Determining the Suitability of Existing Pipelines and Producing Facilities for Wet Sour Service," *Materials Performance* (1989) **28**, 59–65.
44. *Standard MR-01-75, Sulfide Stress Cracking Resistant Metallic Materials for Oilfield Equipment,* NACE, Houston (1988).

SI Metric Conversion Factors

atm	×	1.013 250*	E+05	=	Pa
bar	×	1.0*	E−01	=	MPa
°F		(°F−32)/1.8		=	°C
in.	×	2.54*	E+00	=	cm
in.^{2}	×	6.451 6*	E+00	=	cm^2
lbm	×	4.535 924	E−01	=	kg
mil/yr	×	2.54*	E−02	=	mm/a
psi	×	6.894 757	E+00	=	kPa

*Conversion factor is exact.

Appendix A
Production and Storage Facilities for Sour Gas

Introduction

As stated in Chap. 2, requirements for production and storage facilities used for sour-gas (H_2S) service generally are not included in the various specifications and standards. In Texas, however, the Railroad Commission of Texas[1] provides specifications for those conducting oil, gas, or geothermal resource operations in areas with H_2S. The Railroad Commission's Rule 36 includes information on production and storage facilities, materials, and equipment that will be used in sour service. The portion of Rule 36 that discusses production and storage facilities is reprinted here with permission.

Guidelines for Facilities and Equipment Used in H_2S Environments From Railroad Commission of Texas Rule 36

(5) Storage tank provision: Storage tanks which are utilized as a part of a production operation, and which are operated at or near atmospheric pressure, and where the vapor accumulation has a hydrogen sulfide concentration in excess of 500 ppm, shall be subject to the following.

(A) No determination of a radius of exposure shall be made for storage tanks as herein described.

(B) A warning sign shall be posted on or within 50 feet of the facility to alert the general public of the potential danger.

(C) Fencing as a security measure is required when storage tanks are located inside the limits of a townsite or city, or where conditions cause the storage tanks to be exposed to the public.

(D) The warning and marker provision, subsections (6)(A)(i),(ii), and (iv).

(E) The certificate of compliance provision, subsection (d)(1) of this section.

(6) All operators whose operations are subject to this section, and where the 100 ppm radius of exposure is in excess of 50 feet, shall be subject to the following.

(A) Warning and marker provision.

(i) For above-ground and fixed **surface facilities,** the operator shall post, where permitted by law, clearly visible warning signs on access roads or public streets, or roads which provide direct access to facilities located within the area of exposure.

(ii) In **populated areas** such as cases of townsites and cities where the use of signs is not considered to be acceptable, then an alternative warning plan may be approved by written request to the Commission.

(iii) For **buried lines** subject to this section, the operator shall comply with the following.

(I) A marker sign shall be installed at public road crossings.

(II) Marker signs shall be installed along the line, when it is located within a public area or along a public road, at intervals frequent enough in the judgment of the operator so as to provide warning to avoid the accidental rupturing of line by excavation.

(III) The marker sign shall contain sufficient information to establish the ownership and existence of the line and shall indicate by the use of the words "Poison Gas" that a potential danger exists. Markers installed in compliance with the regulations of the Federal Department of Transportation shall satisfy the requirements of this provision. Marker signs installed prior to the effective date of this section shall be acceptable provided they indicate the existence of a potential hazard.

(iv) In satisfying the **sign requirement** of clause (i) of this subparagraph, the following will be acceptable.

(I) Sign of sufficient size to be readable at a reasonable distance from the facility.

(II) New signs constructed to satisfy this section shall use the language of "Caution" and "Poison Gas" with a black and yellow color contrast. Colors shall satisfy Table I of American National Standard Institute Standard 253.1-1967. Signs installed to satisfy this section are to be compatible with the regulations of the Federal Occupational Safety and Health Administration.

(III) Existing signs installed prior to the effective date of this section will be acceptable if they indicate the existence of a potential hazard.

(B) Security provision.

(i) Unattended fixed surface facilities shall be protected from public access when located within ¼ mile of a dwelling, place of business, hospital, school, church, government building, school bus stop, public park, town, city, village, or similarly populated area. This protection shall be provided by fencing and locking, or removal of pressure gauges and plugging of valve opening, or other similar means. For the purpose of this provision, surface pipeline shall not be considered as a fixed surface facility.

(ii) For well sites, fencing as a security measure is required when a well is located inside the limits of a townsite or city, or where conditions cause the well to be exposed to the public.

(iii) The fencing provision will be considered satisfied where the fencing structure is a deterrent to public access.

(C) Materials and equipment provision.

(i) For **new construction** or modification of facilities (including materials and equipment to be used in drilling and workover operations) completed or contemplated subsequent to the effective date of this section, the metal components shall be those metals which have been selected and manufactured so as to be resistant to hydrogen sulfide stress cracking under the operating conditions for which their use is intended, provided that they satisfy the requirements described in the latest editions of NACE Standard MR-01-75 and API RP-14E, sections 1.7(c), 2.1(c), 4.7. The handling and installation of materials and equipment used in hydrogen sulfide service are to be performed in such a manner so as not to induce susceptibility to sulfide stress cracking. Other materials which are nonsusceptible to sulfide stress cracking, such as fiberglass and plastics, may be used in hydrogen sulfide service provided such materials have been manufactured and inspected in a manner which will satisfy the latest published, applicable industry standard, specifications, or recommended practices.

(ii) Other materials and equipment (including materials and equipment used in drilling and workover operations) which are not included within the provision of clause (i) of this subparagraph, may be used for hydrogen sulfide service provided:

(I) such materials and equipment are proved, as the result of advancements in technology or as the result of control and knowledge of operating conditions (such as temperature and moisture content), to be suitable for the use intended and where such usage is technologically acceptable as good engineering practice; and

(II) the Commission has approved the use of said materials and equipments for the specific uses after written application.

(iii) Existing facilities (including materials in present common usage for drilling and workover operations in hydrogen sulfide areas) which are in operation prior to the effective date of this section, and where there has been no failure of existing equipment attributed to sulfide stress cracking, shall satisfy the requirements of this section.

(iv) In the **event of a failure** of any element of an existing system as the result of hydrogen sulfide stress cracking, the compliance status of the system shall be determined by the Commission after the operator has submitted to the Commission a detailed written report on the failure.

(7) All operations subject to subsection (a) of this section shall be subject to the additional **Control and Equipment Safety Provision,** paragraph (8) of this subsection, and the **Contingency Plan Provision,** paragraph (9) of this subsection, of this section if any of the following conditions apply:

(A) the 100 ppm radius of exposure is in excess of 50 feet and includes any part of a "public area" except a public road;

(B) the 500 ppm radius of exposure is greater than 50 feet and includes any part of a public road;

(C) the 100 ppm radius of exposure is greater than 3,000 feet.

(8) Control and equipment safety provision: Operators subject to this provision shall install safety devices and maintain them in an operable condition or shall establish safety procedures designed to prevent the undetected continuing escape of hydrogen sulfide.

Reference

1. "Rule 36: Oil, Gas, or Geothermal Resource Operation in Hydrogen Sulfide Areas," *Statewide Rules for Oil, Gas and Geothermal Operations,* Oil & Gas Div., Railroad Commission of Texas, Austin (June 1991) 106–20; portion of Pages 109–12 reprinted here.

General References

Standard 253.1-1967, American Natl. Standard Inst., New York City (1967).

Standard MR-0175-92, Sulfide Stress Cracking Resistant Metallic Materials for Oilfield Equipment, NACE, Houston (1992).

RP-14E, Recommended Practice for Design and Installation of Offshore Production Platform Piping Systems, fourth edition, API, Dallas (April 1984).

SI Metric Conversion Factors

ft	× 3.048*	E−01	= m
mile	× 1.609 344*	E+00	= km

*Conversion factor is exact.

Appendix B
Guidelines for Purchase and Fabrication of Steel Components for Sulfide Stress Cracking and Hydrogen-Induced Cracking Resistance

Introduction

These guidelines are not intended to be a complete document or to represent a complete quality plan. Instead, they are meant to assist in the evaluation of important factors to consider for a sour-service project. The values for certain parameters [e.g., critical H_2S content, carbon equivalent, and crack length ratio (CLR)] given here are typical but are not universally accepted. Thus, the individual or company should determine what constitutes critical or acceptable values for these parameters.

Sour-Service Conditions

Sour-service conditions include (1) water as liquid, (2) more than 100 ppm H_2S in the water phase, (3) presence of CO_2 (although not required), (4) pH<8, and (5) temperatures ranging between 32 and 150°F [0 and 65.6°C].

Test Methods and Results

The Natl. Assn. of Corrosion Engineers (NACE) has developed test methods that specify how to conduct tests for resistance to cracking in H_2S. Some common acceptance values are given. For sour-service projects, the following test methods should be used.

1. For noncritical service, follow NACE *Standard TM-02-84*[1] with CLR ≤15%.
2. For critical service, use NACE *Standard TM-01-77*[2] solution for the *TM-02-84* test instead of the standard solution with CLR ≤15%. Use 80% of the specified minimum yield strength with smooth tensile bar for sulfide stress cracking (SSC) tests in the *TM-01-77* standard test.
3. Use ≤1.0 kgf [≤9.8 N] force with Vickers or Knoop indenters to conduct microhardness testing of welds for weld-procedure-qualification tests.

Pipeline and Plant Piping Including Fittings

Critical Service. Critical service must be defined by the individual or the company. The following guidelines should be used for critical service.

1. Conduct flaw inspection of pipe. Pipe should exceed the American Petroleum Inst.'s (API's) *Spec. 5L*[3] requirements.
2. Conduct hardness survey of welds for procedure-qualification record (PQR).
3. Postweld heat-treat plant piping but not pipelines.
4. Hardness-test a percentage of each weld type.
5. Conduct quality-assurance surveillance during materials procurement and construction.
6. Maintain quality-assurance documentation program for nondestructive examination during service.

Moderately Sour Service. Moderately sour service is defined as less severe than critical service but still requiring additional controls to ensure the risk of failure is reduced. For small projects for which available materials will be used, follow the six guidelines given under Critical Service. For large projects with no postweld heat-treated materials and for which pipe is ordered from a mill, follow the guidelines below.

1. Conduct flaw inspection of pipe. Pipe should exceed API *Spec. 5L* requirements.
2. Define material specifications with restricted carbon equivalents (CE) or P_{cm}.
3. Conduct a hardness survey on the actual materials for the PQR.

Ordinary Sour Service. Ordinary sour service is defined as marginally sour by NACE *MR-01-75.* For operations in ordinary sour service, follow the six guidelines under Critical Service, except omit postweld heat treatment for material thicknesses from 0 to 0.50 in. [0 to 1.27 cm] and allow carbon equivalents to about 0.42.

All Service. Evaluate the possibility of other forms of cracking in steel and corrosion-resistant alloys (CRA's), such as hydrogen-induced cracking (HIC) for double-submerged-arc, and electric-resistance welded pipes and chloride stress corrosion cracking (SCC) for CRA's.

Vessels

Critical Service. Critical service for vessels is defined as before for pipelines and piping. Guidelines for vessels in critical service are below.

1. Maintain clean steel for plate (e.g., maximum of 0.005% sulfur and calcium treatment for shape control).
2. Use NACE *Standard TM-02-84* with NACE *Standard TM-01-77* solution to test for HIC with a CLR≤15%.
3. Maintain a PQR that includes information on the hardness traverse; see Sec. IX of the American Soc. of Mechanical Engineer's (ASME's) *Boiler and Pressure Vessel Code.*[4]
4. Postweld heat-treat all material thicknesses; see Sec. VIII of ASME's *Boiler and Pressure Vessel Code.*
5. Conduct hardness tests following NACE *RP-04-72*[5] requirements.
6. Perform wet-fluorescent magnetic particle inspection for all internal welds.

7. Evaluate with acoustic emission for small vessels.
8. Conduct quality-assurance surveillance.
9. Develop a service inspection program that includes documentation for nondestructive examination (see API *Standard 510*[6]) and corrosion monitoring.

Moderately Sour Service With Postweld Heat Treatment. For vessels used in moderately sour service and for which postweld heat-treated materials will be used, follow the nine guidelines listed under Critical Service but use NACE *Standard TM-02-84* requirements to test for HIC.

Moderately Sour Service Without Postweld Heat Treatment. For vessels used in moderately sour service but for which no postweld heat-treated materials will be used, follow the nine guidelines listed under Critical Service and include the following.

1. Define material purchase and weld-procedure specifications that include carbon equivalent requirements for all material thicknesses.
2. Maintain a PQR on the actual materials.
3. Preheat materials as needed to develop acceptable hardness.

All Service. Evaluate the possibility of other forms of SCC and corrosion to steel and CRA's.

Tankage

The guidelines below are for tankage not covered by NACE *Standard MR-01-75*[7] but for which tanks are made to the specifications listed in API *Standard 650,* Appendix G.[8]

1. Specify a carbon equivalent for plate and fittings.
2. Specify "vertical-up" welding for cover passes and conduct hardness survey for PQR for material with carbon equivalent and thickness equal to or exceeding project material specifications.
3. For quality-assurance documentation and surveillance, identify run-off tabs for hardness survey, hardness-test a percentage of each weld type, and perform magnetic particle inspection for all attachment welds.
4. Determine corrosion protection needed for internal coatings (see API *Standard 652*[9]) and internal anodes (see API *Standard 651*[10]).
5. Develop in-service inspection program (see API *Standard 653*[11]).

References

1. *Standard TM-02-84, Evaluation of Pipeline Steels for Resistance to Stepwise Cracking,* NACE, Houston (1984).
2. *Standard TM-01-77, Test Method for Laboratory Testing of Metals for Resistance to Sulfide Stress Cracking in H_2S Environments,* NACE, Houston (1990).
3. *Spec. 5L, Specification for Line Pipe,* 35th edition, API, Dallas (May 1985).
4. *Boiler and Pressure Vessel Code,* American Soc. of Mechanical Engineers, New York City (1989) Secs. VIII and IX.
5. *RP-0472-87, Methods and Controls To Prevent In-Service Cracking of Carbon Steel (P-1) Welds in Corrosive Petroleum Refining Environments,* NACE, Houston (1987).
6. *Standard 510,* API, Dallas.
7. *Standard MR-01-75, Metallurgy of Oil Field Equipment for Resistance to Sulfide Stress Cracking,* NACE, Houston (March 1975).
8. *Standard 650, Welded Steel Tanks for Oil Storage,* seventh edition, API, Dallas (1980).
9. *Standard 652,* API, Dallas.
10. *Standard 651,* API, Dallas.
11. *Standard 653,* API, Dallas.

Author Index

Subject Index

D

E

F

G

N

O

P

Q

R

S

T